COMPREHENSIVE EDITION

TAKE CONTROL OF YOUR FUTURE!

Christopher Kuselias

© Copyright 2017

Career TEAM Education Division

CareerTEAM.com

Dear Career Seeker,

I would like to thank you personally for making the decision to participate in THE CAREER EDGE, an exciting job search training system.

If you fully dedicate yourself to this program, I am confident that the enclosed information can provide you with the competitive edge needed to succeed in today's highly specialized and competitive job markets. Remember, our business is your success!

So relax, take a deep breath, and get ready to change your life forever... for the better!

And please don't be nervous! For the duration of these exercises, I will be here to serve as your personal coach, a mentor who can help you unlock your hidden potential.

As you go on to achieve your goals, be sure to let me know so we can celebrate your success together.

So thank you again for your participation and good luck in your quest for a terrific new career. There's a lot of happiness and career opportunities out there waiting for you...

With Respect and Admiration,

Christopher J. Kuselias
CEO of Career TEAM

TABLE OF CONTENTS

Sections

GETTING TO KNOW YOURSELF

LEARNING OBJECTIVES

1. Discover what is most important to you.

2. Describe your personal and professional values.

3. Uncover what motivates your achievements and overall happiness.

4. Understand the concept of "working," justify it, and look forward to it.

"Self-education is, I firmly believe, the *only* kind of education there is."

-ISAAC ASIMOV

Did you know?

80% of working people are unhappy and unfulfilled at work while only about **20%** truly *love* their work. *No worries, you will soon be one of the 20%!* These enlightened individuals have learned the secret to greater happiness, more money and peace of mind. They know, as you soon will, that it is not luck, fate, education, race, gender or location that determines true success. It is a mindset; a proven formula and you can learn it! This book is designed to put you into this elite group, ***those who live their lives filled with passion and purpose.***

Your desire for more meaning and purpose is not unique. *Can you feel it? Change is in the air!* There is a paradigm shift occurring in this country. It has been building for a few years and is now ready to erupt! After tragic events and world events, our perspectives are always changing. More than ever before, you and I want to make a difference; we want to *matter*. We want to be inspired and no longer wish to view our career as simply a way to consume our precious time, pay our bills or purchase more material items. We want passion, purpose, and recognition! We want to find our career calling and we want it now!

SELF-EVALUATION: RATE YOUR HAPPINESS

Top performers recognize that total happiness includes mastering the following areas:

1) Financial
2) Spiritual
3) Fitness
4) Career
5) Relationships

The key to leading a happy life is to achieve balance among these five areas.

Life Area	Rating
Financial	
Spiritual	
Fitness	
Career	
Relationships	

Which areas need improvement in your life? Rate them from 1-5

Rating Key
5 – Everything is fine – no improvement needed
4 – Things are generally OK, but I could probably make 1 or 2 changes
3 – I'm coasting here. Things aren't great but they're not bad either, so I haven't made any changes lately
2 – This is an area I should really work on now before things get out of hand
1 – Wholesale remodeling necessary. My life is the pits in this area!

This self-assessment is designed to help illuminate your lack of balance you may be experiencing in your life. Being weak in one area will affect other areas in your life. This self-assessment will highlight your weaknesses you must work on.

How can you improve those areas you are not completely satisfied with?

_____

_____

_____

There has never been nor will there ever be another individual exactly like you.

You are unique and compelling. Your talents, experiences, thoughts, ideas, beliefs, desires, preferences and contributions can never be duplicated. It is time to put your self-marketing plan into action. It is time to stake your claim!

The Career EDGE is about exploring the *unique and compelling you*, the person you are today and the incredible one you have the potential to be tomorrow. It is not about directing you to "high growth" career opportunities that do not feed your passion, but rather about creating an effective game plan for realizing *your* life's work (your reason for being). It is, in essence, a system for assisting you to re-claim your passion and purpose and maximize your power, profit and peace of mind. As your personal career coach, I will introduce the process of self-exploration and how to get in touch with the real you, or as I call it, your *authentic* self.

This is not a "how to" book or one like the numerous career books you will find on the shelves of your local library or bookstore. Most of these publications, while well intentioned, miss the mark because they focus on the *mechanics* of the careering process like (finding a job, resume, dress, interviewing, etc.) with little or no attention given to the reader's mindset of the innermost wants, needs, and desires. Little has changed over the past 50 years in terms of linking one's unique contributions to a compelling vocation . . . until now!

Today we know that your mindset matters and, together, we can explore and harness the amazing power of your mind to ensure you find and obtain your unique career calling! Studies show **people only use about 10% of their brain capacity.** Together, we will explore techniques to maximize your potential.

I have dedicated my life's work to helping people obtain their career calling. I understand how central work life is to the happiness of the individual, their family, and the character of any society. If you think about it, work consumes the majority of our time, defines our values and creates our future. If time is indeed our most valuable asset, then our choice of work has a profound effect on our health, mindset, happiness, legacy, and reason for being. Those of you who have been made physically or mentally sick by an unhappy career know exactly what I am talking about.

Ten things about me

Write ten things that would help a person you don't know well get a good idea of whom you really are. What would this person need to know about your feelings, your personality, what you like, what you don't like, etc.? Be sure to include your internal feelings as well as your outward actions. You get the idea! Write them down.

1. _____

2. _____

3. _____

4. _____

5. _____

6. _____

7. _____

8. _____

9. _____

10. _____

This exercise will help you become comfortable with writing about yourself. You will quickly realize that it is difficult to write about yourself. Here are a few examples to get you started:
1. "I am a thoughtful person"
2. "I like sports"
3. "I love to exercise"

Survival to Significance:

1. *Survival:* Work is for Survival/Money: 60% of people see a job as a source of income to pay bills with financial compensation as the primary motivator

2. *Success:* Work is for Acceptance/Status: 30% percent of people see their work life not as a job but as a career where progress, promotion, advancement, and awards are the measure of success and value

3. *Significance:* Work is for Passion/Contribution: Only 10% of people see their career as an outlet for talent, where their contributions fuel their personal passions and benefit society in a measurable and meaningful way. If you find yourself in categories 1 or 2, I suggest we get busy with helping you change your perception of work so you can move to category 3! This is the ideal way!

When we are not clear on our contribution (in large part made through our work) problems occur, stress develops and we often seek relief from unhealthy sources to distract or divert our attention. The 1st step is to make a **commitment** to yourself and your loved ones that you will become a student of career success.

This commitment includes three aspects:
   1. **Possess a sincere desire to improve**
   2. **Have faith in the process**
   3. **Take decisive action**

The 21st century global economy certainly provides numerous efficiencies, but for many, this has resulted in a pace too fast to keep up with, a mentality focused on material possessions, and a culture devoid of sacrifice to attainment. Many people have lost track of their values and have chosen to follow the "*show me the money*" movement. Disturbing studies point out that college students who used to have a vision to change or improve society, now choose majors or courses of study that promise the highest initial salary, regardless of whether the actual job duties are fulfilling.

Those of us who seek to obtain their career calling are an elite force! Like the Marines, *we are the few, the proud and the brave*! By elite, I don't mean to sound condescending but rather elite in that we are willing to pay the price to seek and find answers. We don't expect handouts, we don't blame the system, and we do possess a strong moral compass. We don't need to be monitored or controlled; we know what is right and wrong. While the workplace continues to change and evolve, you will be faced with opportunities that never before existed . . . and your decisions will dictate your happiness and quality of life. ***Take comfort in knowing that within the pages of this book there is a plan!***

I promise you that each and every strategy, tip or suggestion in this program is one that I personally use to bring me closer to the balanced life I strive to live, each and every day. They say the hardest step in any journey is the first one. **By reading these words, you have begun a journey, which will activate feelings, emotions, pride, and peace of mind that you may have thought was beyond your scope or reserved for others**. Your potential is astounding and through this process, you will begin to truly realize it. Life is now in session!

The concept of corporate social responsibility is all too often absent from our nation's largest employers. Corporate scandals become everyday news as financial staff succumbs to greed and face tremendous pressure from shareholders to exceed quarterly projections or lose their jobs. Since the beginning of this century, CEO's have consistently sent over 3 million jobs overseas where labor is *cheaper* but not necessarily *better*.

WHAT IS A CAREER CALLING?

Question: *Have you ever reached a point in your life where you have lost your job or the desire to change your position and are no longer willing to tolerate an unfulfilling professional life that provides financial compensation but little else in the way of reward? It is no longer good enough to simply have a job; we want more and we want it now!*

You have heard *it* called many things. Some refer to it as your *purpose*; others refer to it as your *vision* or *mission in life*. Still others call it your *ultimate goal* or *dream*.

Whatever title you attach to it, recognizing your calling, and answering that call, is the key to experiencing **true** happiness.

If you have not found your career calling, you feel incomplete. Is there a yearning for more? Is there a hole in your soul? Is something gnawing at your gut that suggests you have not done all that you can or should? Do you worry about regret and wasted talent? When did your dream die? When was it consumed by the realities of bills, responsibilities, and deadlines? When did complacency, procrastination, and apathy creep into your life? When did you allow yourself to be consumed with daily routine and ignore the importance of taking time each day for self-awareness and personal career planning?

For me, I would define the feeling as a *restless aching*; a relentless feeling that simply cannot be suppressed or ignored. Perhaps you can relate to what I am talking about but lack a definitive plan to master this yearning to *feel significant*.

Many people lack the vocabulary to define this "restlessness" but can articulate their strong desire for a "career with more meaning." What they (you) are ultimately seeking is the key to this entire book . . . *the need to obtain happiness and peace of mind that comes from making a positive contribution to others through meaningful work.*

So the question is...

What do you really want?

Here is how many describe their ultimate career desire:

• I don't know what to call it, but I want to help other people

• I want to wake up every morning and look forward to my job

• I want to come home from work every night and know in my heart that I made a difference

• I want to be memorable and make my family proud

• I know I have a special gift; I just have not found the right outlet for it yet

• I want to be like the small percentage of people I have met who actually love their job

• I want to take pride in describing what I do for a living

• I want to know that I mattered!

Now, let me ask you a basic question: What is work? Work, which Webster's dictionary defines as "bodily or mental effort exerted to do or make something: purposeful activity" is supposed to be the outlet for our passions, personality traits and future dreams. *Can you honestly say that you are currently engaged in a "purposeful activity?"* Unfortunately, for many, work has become something much different.

Consider these common responses to the question: What is work?

- Work is a way to pay the bills
- Work is what allows me to enjoy the weekends
- Work is what keeps my (spouse or parents) off my back
- Work is what you are supposed to do to feel responsible
- Work is an alternative to boredom
- Work is what you do for 40 years so you can retire and die in peace
- Work is the opposite of play
- Work is same %#@*+, different day

Wow, if those aren't an eye opener! It seems for most, the concept of working is a dirty word often filled with negative connotations. How about *this* abbreviation

J.O.B.=Just. Over. Broke.

I have found that people, who view their occupation as a job, barely get by, while career planners like you are creating a life of abundance! Show me a person who complains about the boss, the hours or the daily grind, and I will predict they are struggling each month to pay their bills.

Be aware that there is a huge difference between a JO and a CAREER.

A career is the lifelong plan of how you will use your unique and compelling talents to contribute. A job is simply a step in the process. A useful analogy: your career is the whole ladder; a job is merely a rung on the ladder.

People who focus on **jobs** and not the careering process will find frustration and barely make ends meet. From this day forward, we focus on careers, not jobs! If you live in the western world, you can agree that we are often defined by our job . . . what we *do*. Think about when you first meet someone, one of the first questions asked is, *"So what do you do for a living?"* The words "what do you do for a living" are telling . . . Paraphrased, the question is seeking information on your quality of life based on your choice of career. I am amazed at how many people sheepishly answer the question as if they are embarrassed by their livelihood. If it is accurate that we are defined by our occupation, then far too many people are spending their lives engaged in a constant state of fear, uncertainty and doubt.

Work, for most, has become a daily grind instead of an expression of our unique and compelling skills and attributes. As of this moment, let us both agree that this is unacceptable! I wrote this book to help you identify and obtain the career of your dreams, the one that you want and the one that, more importantly, you deserve. **Why not you?**

I propose that 80% of your success will be a result of getting in touch with your authentic **self** *(understanding who you really are and what you truly want) and that the remaining 20% is simply a function of tools; teaching you how to get there by either empowering you to get off your butt and start your own venture, join a new organization, or simply improve your status with your existing employer.*

Regardless of your career goal, I am delighted that you have accepted the challenge to improve your status and I'd like to congratulate you on making the best investment you can make . . . an investment in yourself! You have now begun a process that will change the scope of your life forever, for the better. In the information to follow, *you are going to learn the formula for what separates those who have found their career calling from those that remain professionally unfulfilled.* And believe me, career success stories leave clues!

Five Reasons to Work

Everyone has his or her reasons. Of course, 'Money' comes to mind, but even if it is your first choice, it may not be the most important. Also, you have four other blanks to complete, so you will want to thoroughly analyze yourself to determine your motivations.

Some reasons people work include: for money, to maintain or improve their life style, to connect with other people, to gain respect from others, for a sense of accomplishment, for a challenge, to gain a sense of meaning in life, etc. There are many more.
What are yours?

Reason #1 _____

Why? (Include emotion) _____

_____

_____

Reason #2 _____

Why? (Include emotion) _____

_____

_____

Reason #3 _____

Why? (Include emotion) _____

_____

_____

Reason #4 _____

Why? (Include emotion) _____

_____

_____

Reason #5 _____

Why? (Include emotion) _____

_____

This exercise connects emotions to reasons. Explain your rationale of why it's important to work. Consider that emotions provide the necessary fuel to successfully complete a goal. Focus on your first reason and how important it is for you to complete this course and move on to getting a job.

If You Make Finding a Great Career a Craps Shoot . . .

. . . You Wind Up with Crap!

A famous tight rope artist was once asked the secret of successfully walking on a tightrope between two extremely tall buildings on a skinny beam, where a slip or mistake would cost him his life. He responded that the key to success on the tightrope trapeze is exactly the same as the key to life . . . One must focus on where he or she is going and look straight ahead with intense focus. Not down, not behind you, but merely where you are going without hesitation or fear. Be decisive. If you follow these instructions you will emerge victorious!

The key to finding your career calling is to focus on your values, that is, what is important to you personally and professionally. Be sure that you focus on your values and not the expectations or belief systems of others.

"Most people are trapped in an ongoing psychological wrestling contest between their own identity **(who they truly are)**, societal pressures to conform **(what society, friends or family say they should do)**, and internal limiting beliefs **(what they believe they can or cannot do)."**

—Chris Kuselias

When you find your career calling, you will know it because it your work life feeds the most important aspects of your personality. In the right career, you are making use of your best attributes and not forced to struggle with skills that don't come as naturally. You are in a flow where you are doing what comes naturally and work does not feel like work. **I would like to make it clear that there is not one ideal job to which we can all aspire, but rather, there are many different paths to many different jobs, which can match your unique and compelling personality, values, and skills.** In short, there is no magical role for everyone, but there is an ideal career for you!

Radio Station WIIFM!
(What's In It For Me?)

As crazy as it may sound, I am granting you permission to be selfish!

You will need to be if you are to experience real career progress. You must be willing to prioritize your thoughts, feelings, and emotions and find the time to dedicate yourself to uncovering your passion and purpose. This will involve changing your current routines and, in some cases, acquaintances.

Whenever you move ahead, you must leave some behaviors, habits, and people behind . . .

So far, you know that obtaining your career calling begins with a commitment to self-understanding, which is achieved through *critical reflection.*

This is a fancy term for simply taking time to explore your own wants, needs, and desires.

My 1st objective is to ignite your hidden passion and uncover your unique and compelling contributions and then provide a specific plan to show you how to make a living doing it. Once your career purpose is determined, **your job is to write it down and read it aloud every day,** which will secure this belief in your subconscious mind. This sounds deep, but it really isn't!

If you have not yet achieved what you want, I would guess it is because you have not identified exactly *what* you want. *Most people who fail to make a change have not identified a strong enough reason why.* While you may have a general idea of success and happiness, you most likely have not defined your needs, wants, and values in clear and compelling detail.

How do I know? I have dedicated my life's work to understanding the process and have created a formula based upon analyzing thousands of people who are living and working their dream. I work with individuals, corporations and governments every day who have the same challenge as yours. My conclusion: People who take the time to discover what they truly want from life usually obtain it, and people who do not spend the time and do not know exactly what they want, rarely, if ever do. You have been presented with another choice!

FRUITS + ROOTS

What to Do:

Successes are not accidents or twists of fate. They sprout from the seeds you plant. Fill in your tree of success. On each "fruit" write one of your accomplishments, successes, or achievements.

This is one of the most important exercises in this course. It is designed to a) build confidence, b) recognize achievements are not accidents c) helps you to begin a skill inventory. The accomplishments listed in the tree do not have to be huge.

FRUITS + ROOTS

What to Do:
Use each "root" as a line on which to write one of your skills, aptitudes, or good qualities used to achieve the accomplishments written in the fruits. Try to fill up all the roots.

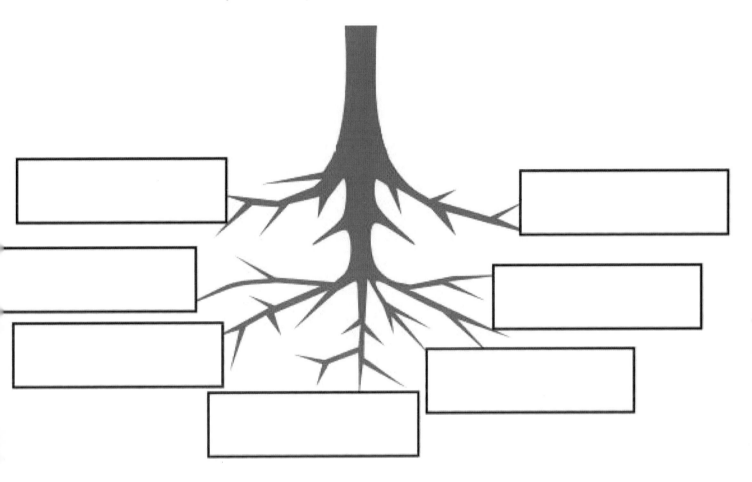

Fill in all the roots with qualities or strengths you possess. This exercise should be completed in three stages for optimum effectiveness. **Stage 1:** Identify as many skills or qualities as possible (fill the page); **Stage 2:** Select your top 5 qualities, get others opinions for what your best qualities are; **Stage 3:** Describe what your top skill is. Doing this exercise in three stages gets down to a deeper level, and helps you really discover your best skills and strengths.

One of my primary objectives is to ignite your inner flame regarding the incredible benefits of *critical reflection*. Simply defined, this means to get in touch with your *authentic* self, the real person beneath the layers of societal conditioning, kids, designer clothes, and life roles. This holistic process of reflecting is not what you might initially think; it is not like the process of burning incense, engaging in primal screaming, or chanting at the stars. I take a more practical approach.

What I profess is carving out a specific time each and every day to quietly consider your place in society, the value of your contributions and if you are on target toward fulfilling your ideal calling, in order *to truly reflect on your purpose.*

It is time to turn to station WIIFM, what's in it for me!

Anticipating the inevitable reflection that we all face, the key questions are these: *What will you remember? Will it be your relationships and those you loved and who loved you? Will you take pride in your material possessions or the inheritance you leave to your heirs? Will you recall your career achievements and relish thoughts of using your creativity and overcoming challenges? Will you have made peace with your maker? Will you experience the pleasant glow of a life fulfilled with joy, hope, risk, reward, love, and passion? Will you have regrets such as wishing you had spent more time with your children, taken more risks, traveled more, or enjoyed your work?* An increasing number of people today are making important changes in anticipation of this day and taking decisive action to ensure they live each day with zest! Their comments:

GREAT PERFORMERS START WITH THE END IN MIND!

You and I are given one chance to savor this life and extract the incredible joy available to us. And because we happen to live in the most exciting time in history, where modern day innovations and technology create incredible opportunities and more free time, you and I have more choices than ever before. The enlightened few know that the ultimate tragedy is a life filled with regret and unfulfilled potential. What will you do with these choices?

The older I become the more I realize that the day in the rocking chair is approaching faster than any of us want to admit or believe. There is no dress rehearsal or do over . . . Life is in session!

THREE IMPORTANT QUESTIONS:

1. How will others talk about you when you are gone?
2. Will you have mattered?
3. What will be your legacy?

A never-ending list of books, seminars, workshops, webinars, and coaching programs exist to remind us how to be organized, set goals, and get motivated, along with a seemingly endless array of strategies and tools to lead a more effective life. Online or in your favorite bookstore are hundreds of "How To" publications about getting a job, writing a resume, interviewing, etc. Most are well intentioned but don't produce the results you seek. With the speed of technology and rush of life, I find most people have trouble getting through the day, much less taking the time to design their life or find their career calling. Without a solid game plan, that is, uncovering your unique and compelling contribution, obtaining a great career is stressful, especially if you are unemployed, have been laid off, feel burned out, are worried about the economy, and have financial responsibilities. This is not a "How to" book, rather more of a "Why" book. The solution to career happiness is between your ears and in your heart and soul. You are unique and there will never be another human being exactly like you, with your vision, ideas, creativity, talents and mindset.

By now you may be thinking, *"OK, I get it! I need to determine who I am, what I want, and why I want it!"* But how do I do this and find my unique career calling? By applying the *Master Career Success Formula*, you can enjoy a life filled with zest and vigor, and love what you do . . . any day and every day! What is this Magical Process? *I call it ...*

THE 5 P'S TO SUCCESS

- **P**assion
- **P**urpose
- **P**ower
- **P**rofit
- **P**eace of mind

In chronological order,
the 5 P's formula includes:

1. Discovering your **Passion**, leads to . . .
2. Finding your **Purpose**, which assists you in . . .
3. Expanding your **Power**, which accelerates . . .
4. Gaining your **Profit**, which results in . . .
5. Achieving **Peace of mind**, which equals happiness, the ultimate goal!

Think of this *Master Career Formula* as a blueprint, which if followed, will lead to your unique career calling. The formula works because outcomes are in accordance with your *true* identity, that is, what is in your heart, mind and soul. It is a formula for helping you discover the *real* you and the contribution *you* were born to make!

When you really think about it, the challenge for each of us is that we enter this lifelong project without the benefit of an instruction manual. Certainly, many profound authors or consultants have attempted to provide solutions to the pursuit of passion and purpose. Few, however, have succeeded in creating a universal approach to the eternal question regarding our search for career purpose or meaning.

Regardless of gender, race, religion, education level, work experience or personality type, **we are all unique and compelling creatures with individual belief systems**. There are several versions of what constitutes happiness, the obvious outcome of achieving one's career calling. Happiness is a personal feeling within the people who consistently achieve this state of mind, and the actions they take leave clues.

There is one distinct difference between a highly successful person and one who is not, and that is that highly successful people develop good habits and make choices that others do not like to make. By having the courage to exercise their right to choose, **they achieve greatness.**

You have made the choice to pursue career greatness. Let us begin your journey to career success and happiness with a review of the *Master Career Formula* . . .

1ST "P" — FINDING YOUR PASSION

"Now, here is my secret, a very simple secret. It is only with the heart that one can see rightly: what is essential is ***invisible*** to the eye."

—**Antoine De Saint-Exupery,**
The Little Prince

Your first choice if you truly seek to be highly successful is to identify and pursue *your* passion. Not mine, not your parents', not your significant other but yours! *In order for you to achieve your potential, you must make a firm decision to restructure your life around your passion.*

Finding your passion involves getting in touch with your heart and identifying your dreams. The process has to start here, because only your heart will reveal what really matters to you and what truly brings you happiness. What is it that you crave, and what fills you with energy and excitement? What is that one thing that gets you up in the morning, and keeps you awake at night? When you answer these questions, you will ha found your passion.

Passion is not a privilege of the fortunate few; it is a right and a power that you possess. If you get in touch with the passion that defines you, I promise you will have an amazing life. In your quest to find your passion, there are a few areas you can explore that will assist you on the road to discovery, *such as:*

1. Brainstorm and identify what you daydream about, what gets you excited, what you consider fun, what you like to do, or what you would get a kick out of doing.

2. Peer into your childhood and think about anything that you may have had an affinity for growing up. Is there something that you were good at as a child that you would like to do again?

3. Evaluate your talents and skills. Take a piece of paper and write down the things that you do well or that come naturally to you, without any effort on your part. These talents should be viewed as your unique and compelling gifts . . . special gifts that have been passed on to you genetically.

4. Test yourself and your passion. One way to validate your passion is to put it to the test, and you can accomplish this by revisiting your feelings 2 or 3 weeks after you have identified it. Do you still get that fire in your belly when you think about it? Are you willing to sacrifice everything to fulfill it, or take risks for it? Your responses will separate your true passion from mere interest.

26

Once you begin to experience passion in your life's work, your passion will create a personal intensity, which will uplift and inspire you. It will heighten your performance and enable you to achieve things that you may never have dreamed possible. Finding passion is the key to happiness in your career, and in every other area of your life.

If you have uncovered your passion, but are finding it difficult to take the next step, you may need to **break down the barriers** that are preventing you from turning your passion into reality. When you make decisions based on your heart's desires, and not on what society dictates, you open up an assortment of challenges, and will have to allow yourself to move beyond the fear or paralysis that grips you and, perhaps, is preventing you from answering your calling.

"FIND YOUR PASSION AND FOLLOW IT. THAT IS ALL THE CAREER ADVICE YOU WILL EVER NEED."

— JOHN C. MAXWELL

Barriers to Living Your Passion:

1. *Fear:* Passion is a mystery, and often you do not know exactly where it will lead you. You may wonder what life would be like if you followed your heart and decided to change careers. If fear creeps in, your thoughts may become distorted and create elaborate scenarios of failure. There is no greater barrier to fulfilling your passion than fear of the unknown.

2. *Self-doubt:* Self-doubt is an extension of your fear, and focuses on your perceived personal inadequacies. This self-doubt causes you to question your own abilities and potential, and can lead you to imagining yourself as a failure, rather than a success.

3. *Paralysis or numbness:* When faced with confusion or uncertainty, you may find yourself locked into an emotional paralysis. While you may want to change your life and career, you are unable to harness the power to do so. You may become so accustomed to the demands and stresses of life that you move beyond paralysis into numbness. You may not even realize that you are unhappy and unfulfilled, and that you have become emotionally disconnected.

4. *Limited scope:* When you identify yourself by stereotype (that is, white-collar or blue-collar, baby-boomer, etc.), you limit your potential. Labeling yourself this way causes you to accept an identity that probably has nothing to do with who you really are or what your passion is.

5. *Procrastination:* "One day, some day . . . " is an excuse for putting off what could be the most important step in your life. Your passion will never become a reality as long as you keep putting off pursuit of it.

6. *Caution:* Your fears may prevent you from acting on faith and belief. You may pursue your dreams in a very controlled and calculated manner, leaving little room for your passion to take over.

While you may never know failure, you may also never know the success that comes from unleashing your passion.

MY PASSION

Here are three questions to uncover your passion . . .

    1. I am happiest when I am:

_____

    2. I feel energized when I am:

_____

    3. I would work for free doing:

_____

Moving forward, **trust your heart** and listen to your inner voice. Acknowledge your passion and nurture it. Incorporate it into your existence, and your life will become an accurate reflection of your true identity and who you aspire to become. Once accomplished, you will graduate to the next step: Acquiring a sense of **purpose**!

2ND "P"— *PURPOSE* IS OBTAINED FROM THE FUEL OF PASSION

Hans Selye, the pioneer in the understanding of human stress, often asked the following question: What is the most stressful condition a person can face? His unexpected response

. . . *"Not having something to believe in."*

What do you believe in? Why are you here? What contribution were you born to make? Were you meant to sit in a cubicle day after day without a clue as to whether you were impacting your company? Maybe yes, but most likely no!

After you have found your passion, by answering your calling you will begin to answer these questions and acquire a *sense of purpose*. Purpose springs from belief and the fact that you are doing what you love and desire. Your dreams and hopes are becoming a reality, and you have moved outside of the norm. You are engaged in tasks and activities that feel like play; working is a labor of love.

You have fought off conventional wisdom to work for the money or prestige. You are empowered and committed to continue on this path. You believe whole-heartedly in your cause. Your sense of purpose is evident in everything you do—the way you act, speak, look and think. You are contagious! This sense of purpose will continue to flourish as you completely immerse yourself in pursuing your passion.

Determining your higher purpose starts with defining the word success, because that is the paradigm with which most people identify. Later on, we will discuss this further but for now:

1. Which direction are you moving and where is your passion and purpose leading you?

2. Are you prospering toward the next achievement by building new mentors and learning from your missteps, or are you trying to avoid the prospect of failure by not competing for your career calling at all?

3. Which direction are you moving and where is your passion and purpose leading you?

4. Are you prospering toward the next achievement by building new mentors and learning from your missteps, or are you trying to avoid the prospect of failure by not competing for your career calling at all?

At this stage, the key question is: *What is important to me about being successful?*

Success is a deeply personal issue. One needs more than persistence, ambition or motivation. You need to be inspired to the very core of your being. If you cannot verbalize your contribution, it will not last.

Your true purpose is: *Your sincere, deepest desire and motivation for action!*
When you discover your true purpose, you will feel yourself gaining confidence and power.

Without a true purpose you will:

1. Experience more stress
2. Be prone to suffer burnout
3. Often feel overwhelmed
4. Have difficulty making decisions
5. Feel anxious and restless

MY PURPOSE

**Here are three questions to help
you realize your *purpose* . . .**

1. I was meant to:

_____

2. My place in this world is as a:

_____

3. I feel most meaningful when I:

_____

3ᴿᴰ "P"—*POWER* & CONFIDENCE ARE REALIZED WHEN PURPOSE IS ALLOWED TO FLOW

"Being powerful is like being a lady; if you have to tell
people you are . . . you aren't."

— *Margaret Thatcher*

It makes sense that once you acquire a sense of purpose you become more powerful. By taking the steps that lead to fulfilling your passion, you begin to feel as though you are in control of your life and your destiny. You are on a path that provides the greatest rewards one can experience. You are not working by others standards; you are working because it is what you *choose* to do. You are in command!

Like your sense of purpose, *gaining* **power** in your life evidences itself through every orifice of your being. You experience more energy and you walk with an air of confidence. This newly obtained power is also a result of confronting your fears and increasing your level of courage and confidence. Another contributor to your feeling of power is your attitude. Your positive attitude makes you happier, more productive, and more successful, which, in turn, makes you more powerful. Other people will gravitate toward your energy, which will become infectious. Those who are trapped in the fog of apathy, lethargy and even depression will crave your newfound enthusiasm and confidence. They will want to associate with you because you project an image of congruence, a trait that we all admire and aspire to obtain.

You are positively *contagious!*

MY POWER

Here are three questions to realize your power . . .

1. People recognize me for my expertise in:

_____

2. I know more than most on the subject:

_____

3. I can best assist others by:

_____

4ᵀᴴ "P"—*PROFIT* INEVITABLY FOLLOWS THOSE WHO CONTRIBUTE

If nothing else, you are already gaining *wealth* by the benefits you are enjoying up to this point (finding your passion, acquiring a sense of purpose, and gaining power).

Not only is your profit centered on financial gain, **but also on your emotional, spiritual, physical, interpersonal, and professional experiences**.

In working with numerous highly compensated executives, who often experience severe depression when laid off, it is apparent to me that many people fill voids in their emotional lives by basing their self-worth on money and material possessions. When you take away their "toys" as I like to call them, very often there is an emotional void and a lack of true identity.

How sad!
When you have found your passion, purpose, and power, interestingly, you become the center of attention, and people begin to seek you out. They want to know what you have that they do not and why you feel so good.

Hiring authorities are willing to compensate you for your knowledge. **You become in demand because**

you had the courage to pursue your passion

You are a leader!

We can all agree that leaders in any organization are typically recipients of the highest praise and most lucrative compensation. At my company, Career TEAM, we have a saying about our leaders, which is, "If the light ain't on at the top, it is dim all the way down." In my experience, society ultimately rewards those who find their unique contribution and exhibit these qualities. This is how big money is made. I know very few people, if any, who are wildly wealthy and aren't passionate about their work.

In your career, if you master the first 3 P's **(passion, purpose, and power)**, enhanced compensation (profit) will inevitably follow. Advancement opportunity and increased salary become more readily available due to your changed attitude and level of energy. People will gravitate to your knowledge and begin feeding off your passion. Having followers will increase your responsibility, which inevitably increases your earnings.

MY ECONOMIC SUCCESS

Here are three statements to help you maximize profit...

I define professional success as _____

_____

With more money I would _____

_____

What I want that I don't have now is _____

_____

5TH "P"—*PEACE OF MIND* IS ACHIEVED
WHEN WE HAVE FOUND OUR TRUE CALLING

The 5th P is the most precious asset
—*peace of mind.* This state of mind comes
from the realization that you are contributing to others
in a passionate and purposeful way. When we are contributing,
that is, truly helping others through our work, we feel a tremendous
sense of internal joy and happiness. We adopt the belief system that
we matter. We develop a legacy that outlives our physical body. People all over
the world would give their last dollar to experience true peace of mind, and for
many of them, the lack thereof, is the direct result of living their lives according to
someone else's standard.

To avoid societal conditioning and to forge your own path requires a great deal
of courage and honesty. We must be true to ourselves, live in sync with our
established identity and be congruent in our internal belief systems. Peace of
mind comes from learning the skill to become your *authentic self.*

Like you, I have always craved peace of mind but was often restless. Today, I
understand that until I lived my life in accordance with these 5P's; and spent my
time engaged in activities consistent with my identity; I would never be truly
content. Stress was my enemy and relaxation was a skill I had not mastered.

I have become a believer in meditation, not the unfavorable view of a
person in some bizarre robe with mushroom-scented incense, but rather a
more personalized experience where one shuts out the problems and
distractions of the world and contemplates their authentic self and true
aspirations. The process should provide critical benefits and that is, to learn,
recognize and *listen* to the sound of your inner voice, what I call your higher
self.

For me, this process creates a mindset that has allowed my most outstanding ideas and visions to penetrate the confusion and distractions of my hectic life. It challenged me to ask myself life's most pressing questions, those that cannot be addressed or answered with the television playing, music blasting, children crying or business looming.

Take 10 minutes and just sit quietly and reflect on what you really want, what you are great at, and what brings you joy.

MY SERENITY

Here are three questions to help you find peace of mind . . .

1. I want to look back on my life and feel:

_____

2. When people think of my life, they will think:

_____

3. I will feel my life was worth living if:

_____

THE END RESULT

By mastering the 5 P's, you will begin to understand what it truly means to be content, at peace, and happy. Having applied this *Master Career Formula* in your life, you will promote balance in what I view as the five areas that dictate the balance: career, financial, health and fitness, relationships, and spiritual enlightenment. Top performers, such as you, recognize that total happiness in life can only occur by mastering these five key areas.

When you get to this final stage of development, you will experience success on your own terms, and you will enjoy life. Your existence will be validated, and you will matter! Your life will be in harmony with your being, and you will feel whole and complete. You will bask in the glow of looking into your innermost desires and contribute your unique and compelling gifts to others in the form of your career calling. This is the essence of becoming happy and self-actualized!

"THE BEST WAY TO PREDICT YOUR FUTURE IS TO CREATE IT." -Stephen Covey

An Overview of the 21st Century Workplace

We can all agree that, more than ever in our history, the future is filled with so many unanswered questions regarding what employment will look like. Industries are being consolidated and in some cases even eliminated, seemingly overnight. International competition and the new global economy have made the world a much smaller place when it comes to marketing or producing goods and services. With so much uncertainty, you may be looking for a set of guiding principles to help you navigate through these uncertain workplace waters. Many feel like they have been thrown into the rapids without a paddle, life jacket, map, or the proper equipment! This is our collective challenge as strategies and techniques that may have worked in the past are now as obsolete as a VHS player.

Today, You Are What You Do . . .

The 21st century workplace promises more change and dramatic industry fluctuations. In my experience, there are very few things as challenging as changing careers, and few life experiences as demoralizing as the loss of one's job. Here is why. Many people *define* themselves by their job title or job description. Their job is their *identity*.

Some people identify so strongly with their job title that if they are laid off or lose their job, they feel as if their identity has been surgically removed from their body.

Clearly, your career is more than just a way to pay the bills.

So what is the solution to competing and winning in the 21st century workplace? To begin, I am an advocate that while understanding the global landscape is important and necessary, *your chosen career path should be based on your passions and internal beliefs rather than on availability or what jobs pay the most at any given moment.*

I am not naive to practical concerns or being pragmatic when it comes to formulating a decision, but I strongly believe that before falling prey to the trappings of a job and lifestyle that does not provide passion and purpose, one should explore their goals and objectives in detail. The good news is that you are living in an exciting era with incredible advances and innovations. America remains the greatest nation on Earth; we simply have more opportunities and better resources. Next time you find yourself complaining, consider this to help gain some perspective . . .

Becoming "**Me, Inc.**" Is a Must!

Avoid the single-minded danger that Abraham Maslow observed:

"He that is good with the hammer tends to think everything is a nail."

It is time to expand your horizons and take the blinders off. The 21st century global economy has created a paradigm shift where borders no longer exist and the perception of one's career identity must shift from the finite title on a business card to that of a *solutions oriented resource. You are a problem solver or you are obsolete!* Although the world is more complex, simple is still powerful.

Here is a profound message as to how you should perceive your career from this day forward . . . **ME, INC.** You are your own personal services corporation responsible for your own research, marketing, human resources, financial and quality control. There is no employer or company looking out for your best interests; this is ultimately your job.

It is time to broaden your horizons and adopt a single-minded approach to your livelihood. There is an ocean of opportunity created by this new global economy. Those who decide to put away the trappings of conformity and pursue their unique destiny are creating fortunes every day. A sample:

> • *Billionaire media mogul Oprah was only 19 when she started her career as a news anchor at Nashville's WTVF-TV; her show is now seen in over 100 countries by an estimated 46 million weekly viewers.*

> • *Billionaire Michael Dell founded Dell Computer at 19 with $1,000 from his dorm room at the University of Texas; by age 27 he was the youngest CEO ever to earn a ranking on the Fortune 500.*

> • *At 40, Harland "Colonel" Sanders began cooking chicken for his customers from his service station and sold his Kentucky Fried Chicken Company in 1964 with over 600 outlets nationwide.*

> • *At 52, Ray Kroc stopped selling milk shakes, purchased a restaurant and turned it into the planet's most successful fast food enterprise, McDonald's.*

Is there an exciting idea or two in you? Maybe you are reading this book because you have recently faced a life-altering event like a layoff or illness, or maybe you are simply tired of living an uninspired existence. Often, the will is there but the knowledge of specific strategies and techniques to realize this new ambition is lacking.

BE CAREFUL OF OTHERS' PERCEPTIONS

Far too few individuals I counsel recall a parent walking in the door grateful and exuberant for their unique contribution with positive family dialogue about the virtues of having found their calling. More likely, they presented the ingrained thoughts from an early age of "being lucky to have a job," which often extinguishes any hope or thought of finding a position they might actually enjoy.

Like you, I am challenged on a daily basis to maintain balance in my individual, married, and professional life. With three children, numerous family obligations, and a thriving business, finding time for reflection, fitness, career planning, and social activities is no easy task! Life issues like responsibility and aging often cloud the pursuit of your career calling and become an easy excuse for accepting professional mediocrity. Many people are in this vicious cycle of wanting to plan but having no time. In the past, many people looking for jobs sought a secure profession. People stayed at a company until they retired and received a gold watch or some reward for 30 years of loyal service. No matter what level of disenchantment or unhappiness, they stayed in the same occupation with the same employer.

Today, the average job tenure is only 3–4 years (the average person will hold over 15 jobs in their life!) and people are forced to take a more proactive role in how they will sustain their livelihood. We call this development a *paradigm shift*, which has led to the necessity of mastering your ability to transition between jobs and often between industries.

You should be aware that most of us identify with one or both of our parents regarding our career. Simply put, we act and behave in accordance with *their* belief systems. These may be handed down from generation to generation and seem like "tradition" but can be extremely damaging. Their belief systems, while comfortable, may not be in sync with your own.
your own.

MANAGING CHANGE & YOUR ATTITUDE

LEARNING OBJECTIVES

1. Recognize the power of a positive attitude and firm affirmations.

2. Overcome limiting beliefs and negative thoughts.

3. Understand how commitment to change influences your future.

"IF A 100-FOOT OAK TREE HAD THE MIND OF A HUMAN, IT WOULD ONLY GROW TO BE 10 FEET TALL!"
—T. Harv Eker

Your mind is like a giant super computer.

Information that enters your mind is labeled and stored in files for easy retrieval. What makes us unique is *where* we file, *how* we access and *when* we access stored information. You make choices as to what your "customized" mental database looks like, what is retained, and in what situations you choose to access it. When fear occurs, what file is accessed? When conflict arises, where do you go looking?

When ambition is needed, what file dictates your programmed response? Be aware of what books, magazines, articles, television and other stimuli you install into your supercomputer mind. Like a computer, the saying, "garbage in, garbage out" applies.

I want to help you edit and "install" some new files, which may open up a world of possibility for you. These include examples, stories, quotes, and guidance. Chapter by chapter, we are re-programming your "career files" with successful strategies. By adding these new files, we are creating new options for you, new choices to accelerate your career. From this, you will develop new habits, beliefs, and attitudes, which are the genesis of greatness. Going forward you will observe greater success simply by having better files.

FAST FACT

If your subconscious thermostat is not "set" for career success, there is no technique or strategy you can learn that will make a difference.

Your *career identity* is simply the mental and emotional picture you have of yourself. This includes what you believe you are worthy of, capable of, comfortable with, and how talented you are. *Why is your career identity important?*

Because… we as human beings always "self-regulate" to the person or level we are comfortable with. Being in sync with our identity is one of the strongest desires human beings have. We will always act in accordance with our identity. The secret to progress is not to try and fool yourself into being someone else, but rather, to take steps to alter your identity to be the person you are capable of being.

Resistance to this change will come in the form of habits, prior momentum and conditioning from family, teachers, friends, and media. This is why I am so cognizant of what my children are exposed to (television, violence, negative thinkers, cynics, etc.) because early exposure shapes identity and will create their *foundation* for life. It takes courage to make a change and explore why you are like you are and do what you do. It is almost like career therapy. But trust me, making these changes will give you what you ultimately seek, greater happiness and peace of mind!

Self-Evaluation: Resistance to Change

This quiz tells how open you are to change. It is a perfectly normal and natural human response to resist change, so answer truthfully. Seeing your answers will help you to overcome some of your resistance to change.

True or False? Check your response to each question.

1) In these days of rapid progress all around us, I am quick to learn new ways of doing things.
   True ___ False ___

2) I must be certain that doing something differently is worthwhile before I try it.
   True ___ False ___

3) As soon as I hear about something new, I like to try it.
   True ___ False ___

4) Too much time and energy is wasted in experimenting with new ideas before everything is known about them.
   True ___ False ___

5) I always try to keep myself up-to-date on current events.
   True ___ False ___

6) When it comes to using new methods of doing things, I prefer to be a follower rather than a leader.
   True ___ False ___

7) I am always eager to learn about new opportunities.
   True ___ False ___

8) If I like things the way they are; I see no reason for making changes.
   True ___ False ___

9) If I hear about something new, I feel restless until I try it.
   True ___ False ___

10) Making changes creates too many problems and pressures. I would rather relax and enjoy what I have.
   True ___ False ___

What do your answers tell you about yourself?

Consider lottery winners. Studies have shown that people who win the lottery eventually return to their original level of income, the amount they are comfortable with. *The amount they identify with!* We all think we need excessive amounts of money, but unless we modify our belief system (our comfort level) to feel deserving with this financial windfall, we will feel incongruous and sabotage ourselves until we return to our natural state.

Sounds crazy, but it's true!

Whether it is a golfer who double bogies the last hole to sub-consciously maintain their handicap thermostat, a salesperson "programmed" to make $50,000 annually who suddenly hits a slump in the 4th quarter to maintain this figure, or a student who gets a "C" on the final exam to maintain their B average, there are countless examples of *self-regulating behaviors* that occur unbeknownst to us. Where are you self-regulating or as some say sabotaging your own success? Can you see now why you are acting this way? It is because your identity and goals are not in sync. You want to weigh 110 pounds, but your identity says you weigh 130 pounds. Until you *identify* with 110 pounds, you will be engaged in a constant struggle with your own identity and most likely remain at 130 pounds. This is why diets result in frustration.

The secret? The minute you reprogram your mind and truly see yourself as a 110-pound person (a 110-pound identity), it will begin to happen. *The mind is indeed a powerful force!*

What do I need to Change?

What do you see when you read the letters below?

OPPORTUNITYNOWHERE

Some see the words, "opportunity nowhere". Others read the same letters but instead see, "opportunity now here". I think you will agree that there is a significant difference! Whether you realize it or not, you have been conditioned to see the good or the bad; to focus on the positive or negative. You can decide what type of outlook you want to have, how you earn a living, and how you choose to see the world.

DICTIONARY DEFINITION:

change *verb*

       a. to make different in some particular form
       b. to make radically different
       c. to give a different position, course, or direction

What specific changes both personally and professionally do you need to make and why? Try to list at least one change for your personal life and one change for your professional life.

_____

_____

_____

_____

_____

_____

_____

The Million-Dollar Question:
What Is Your Career Thermostat Set For?

Like the thermostat on your wall, you are currently set at a specific temperature. Unlike the thermostat on your wall, you are conditioned for a certain level of success. Your character and belief systems are essential parts of your ultimate career success. Certainly having superior careering strategies is important, but without taking the time to learn how your own mind and emotions work, you, like millions of others, can get a job, but not your ideal career.

So who are you? What are your habits? What do you believe in? Can you manage your fears? Are you deserving of a great career? Will you take risks? Are you programmed for career success? Observe yourself and your thoughts, fears, habits, actions, and lack of action. Study yourself . . . that is the 1st step towards changing your career identity.

Success Tip:

Your career will grow only to the extent your mind does.

Let me begin by reminding you that you have a conscious mind and a subconscious mind. You should be aware that whatever your conscious mind wants, your subconscious mind will accept. It is not capable of an argument.

If your conscious mind commands your subconscious mind that you are not deserving of a raise or promotion, your subconscious mind will work tirelessly to make it true. Conversely, if you instill a positive thought that you truly deserve, your subconscious mind will work to make that a reality.

All of your internal dialogue and self-talk should be aimed at moving you closer to the attainment of your life goals, including your career calling.

Although we have not personally met, I will make the bold prediction that what you are capable of is much more than what you have demonstrated to date. Will today be the day that you decide to make your life consistent with the quality of your spirit?

Remember these words: *I will not be denied.* You cannot be denied in your quest to find your passion, purpose, power, profit, and your peace of mind.

Establishing Your Priorities

The 21st century workforce requires constant change and adaptation. It becomes critical to invest the mental and emotional energy in pursuing your calling. By simply making slight changes, you can yield dramatic results!

And you need not be especially intelligent or gifted to realize your aspirations. You just need to be clear on your desired outcome. The most important question you can ask yourself is:

"What do you really want?"

You control your direction . . . not the economy, not the president, not the political landscape, housing market, or oil prices. You are not a victim, but rather the captain of your own ship, master, and commander! You will no longer focus on external forces because you have an internal plan that makes such considerations—while relevant—not deciding factors in your personal course of action.

REMEMBER THESE THREE KEYS:

1. The objective of careering is a contribution that makes you truly happy, referred to as your *calling*

2. Feelings and emotions are more important than material possessions or external rewards

3. You possess the power to find your calling; it is not a random event or based on luck

As the great motivator, Zig Ziglar, points out, "Most people are wandering generalities" vs. "meaningful specifics." I have found that most people spend more time analyzing what automobile to purchase (model, make, consumer reports, gas mileage, safety tests, etc.) than they spend on improving themselves! As a result, they drift through life without purpose or direction.

Self-Evaluation: Attributes of Success

How well do you know yourself? Read the following list of character traits commonly found in successful people. Rate how strong you believe you are in each category. Be honest! This is about self-discovery; there is nobody you need to impress here!

1 WEAKEST | 5 STRONGEST

Successful People Have:	Your Own Rating
1. The Ability to Communicate	1 2 3 4 5
2. Intelligence	1 2 3 4 5
3. Self- Confidence	1 2 3 4 5
4. The Ability to Accept Responsibility	1 2 3 4 5
5. Motivation	1 2 3 4 5
6. Leadership	1 2 3 4 5
7. High Energy	1 2 3 4 5
8. Imagination	1 2 3 4 5
9. Flexibility	1 2 3 4 5
10. Interpersonal Skills	1 2 3 4 5
11. Self-Knowledge	1 2 3 4 5
12. The Ability to Handle Conflict	1 2 3 4 5
13. Useful Job Skills	1 2 3 4 5
14. Specific Goals	1 2 3 4 5
15. Reliability	1 2 3 4 5

This test is designed to "peel the onion" layers of your character. It will help you to reveal your true attitude... do you need to make some adjustments?

What do you stand for? I have a close friend who is fond of saying, "If you don't stand for something, you will fall for anything." Have you recently stopped and considered the reality you are building for yourself? The combination of your thoughts, both positive and negative, comprises your reality. What is your reality?

Here is a dose of reality. *Every role model you identify as a success did not get there without adversity, obstacles, and challenges.* They simply focused on their outcome and did not allow themselves to become sidetracked with guilt or excuses. *"Ask and you shall receive, seek and you will find."* They focused on exactly what they wanted and formulated the internal belief and attitude that it was attainable. The common denominator to success and life balance is attitude.

Did you know that it takes the same amount of energy to formulate a positive thought as it does a negative one?

Positive thinking is ultimately about structuring your belief system; that is, substituting positive images for negative ones. It is the process of consciously filtering out unhealthy thoughts and cleansing the mind.

Self-Evaluation: My Self-Image

How do you see yourself? How does the world see you?

Use the following table to rate your own characteristics on a scale from 1-5. Then use the "Friend's Rating" column to indicate how you think one of your friends might rate you in that same category.

5 = always | 4 = usually | 3 = sometimes | 2 = seldom | 1 = never

	Self Rating	Friend's Rating
Ambitious	1 2 3 4 5	1 2 3 4 5
Cheerful	1 2 3 4 5	1 2 3 4 5
Confident	1 2 3 4 5	1 2 3 4 5
Cooperative	1 2 3 4 5	1 2 3 4 5
Dependable	1 2 3 4 5	1 2 3 4 5
Enthusiastic	1 2 3 4 5	1 2 3 4 5
Hard Working	1 2 3 4 5	1 2 3 4 5
Helpful	1 2 3 4 5	1 2 3 4 5
Neat	1 2 3 4 5	1 2 3 4 5
Outgoing	1 2 3 4 5	1 2 3 4 5
Patient	1 2 3 4 5	1 2 3 4 5
Respectful	1 2 3 4 5	1 2 3 4 5
Persistent	1 2 3 4 5	1 2 3 4 5
Self-Centered	1 2 3 4 5	1 2 3 4 5
Serious	1 2 3 4 5	1 2 3 4 5
Shy	1 2 3 4 5	1 2 3 4 5
Tactful	1 2 3 4 5	1 2 3 4 5

This test is very useful in helping you understand how perceptions of others are important. Sometime we are unaware of the image we portray to others. What have you learned about your image?

THE *WHY* BEHIND THE WANT

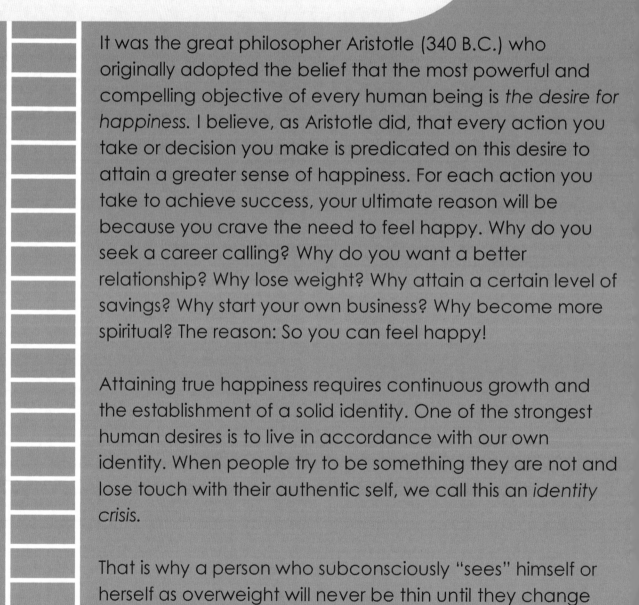

"YOU DO NOT WANT TO GET TO THE TOP OF THE LADDER AND FIND OUT YOU WERE CLIMBING THE WRONG WALL."
-ANONYMOUS

It was the great philosopher Aristotle (340 B.C.) who originally adopted the belief that the most powerful and compelling objective of every human being is *the desire for happiness*. I believe, as Aristotle did, that every action you take or decision you make is predicated on this desire to attain a greater sense of happiness. For each action you take to achieve success, your ultimate reason will be because you crave the need to feel happy. Why do you seek a career calling? Why do you want a better relationship? Why lose weight? Why attain a certain level of savings? Why start your own business? Why become more spiritual? The reason: So you can feel happy!

Attaining true happiness requires continuous growth and the establishment of a solid identity. One of the strongest human desires is to live in accordance with our own identity. When people try to be something they are not and lose touch with their authentic self, we call this an *identity crisis*.

That is why a person who subconsciously "sees" himself or herself as overweight will never be thin until they change their identity and "see" themselves as thin.

A person addicted to drugs or alcohol that "believes" (s)he is an addict, will remain one until (s)he creates a new image (and believes it at their core) of being drug or alcohol free. A person in jail often is planning his/her next crime when it comes time to being released. Why? Because this individual has developed a belief in his/her own identity as not a free person, deserving of freedoms that you and I enjoy, but rather that of a prisoner, an inmate. (S)he does not internally feel worthy of being free, so he/she sabotage his/her own freedom so that reality is consistent with identity.

We all have a tremendous desire to be congruent with whom we perceive ourselves to be, regardless of whether it is logical. Regarding your career, unless you feel worthy and deserving of a raise, promotion, or the establishment of a new venture, you will struggle and sabotage your chances.

Why? Because we all have a tremendous desire to live in accordance with our self-perception.

Finding your ultimate destination is simply a function of expanding and enhancing your internal identity and formulating a belief system that makes the attainment of this vision truly attainable. You must believe you can do it! Belief without passion *and* conviction is simply a lie. In fact, if you look carefully at the word belief, you will see something interesting. **The word** $B - E - L - I - E - F$ **actually contains the word *lie*! One of the root causes of behavioral dysfunction is an inability to connect our belief systems with our actions. We may want something, but if we do not believe with conviction, we will create an internal struggle that leads to massive stress. People can spend years in therapy trying to break through when often it is a matter of choosing goals in sync with our character and true selves vs. trying to live up to others' expectations.**

The key is not to try to change your behavior, but rather, to help you to create a new identity. My goal is to assist you to re-shape yourself to become the person needed to obtain your unique calling. Together, we will visualize you already engaged in your career calling and then provide steps to make it a reality. Research tells us that there is almost no difference in brain function when visualizing something and actually doing it! That is the incredible power of your mind!

I also know that the clearer your images and objectives, the more successful you will be in attaining them. *There is a direct correlation between low self-esteem and a lack of clarity.*

People who are successful are clear in their wants, needs and desires. Those less accomplished tend to be less focused. Avoid being vague!

The exciting news is that you and I can systematically alter our current identity to help us make the changes we need to make in order to realize our true potential. Understand that there is a direct link between what you think about yourself and your career success. If you seek a particular career calling, you must develop the proper *self-concept* needed to live into this occupation.

The fact is that you will attract into your life, the people and opportunities in sync with your most dominant thoughts. The person you decide to become is a direct correlation to how you decide to structure your values and belief systems. Character comes from what you focus on and allow into your mind, what you choose to expose your emotions to and how you react to circumstances.

The key to obtaining your calling is to create massive momentum or what I call *leverage* behind your purpose or desire. In other words, you need to build a strong emotional tie between the outcome you seek and the effort required to achieve the objective.

Said another way, you must clearly establish, *"the why behind the want."*

What was the real reason you decided to invest time and energy in finding your unique calling and learning the importance of life balance? Are you broke? Are you tired or dissatisfied with being mediocre? Are you restless for more? Do you seek peace of mind? Whatever your motivations, you need to understand your desired outcome and *why* you seek that outcome. 80% of achievement in life is in developing a strong enough *why*, the psychology behind your ambition. The other 20% is in the mechanics, the actual carrying out of your plan. If you have momentum toward a prior behavior or bad habit, your mind will resist your initial efforts to change this conditioned response.

For example, if you took 20 years to put on weight through poor eating habits, it will take a strong effort to avoid the body's conditioned response to seek a certain quantity or chemical composition of food. If the conditioned habit has been to be non-communicative (silence) during an argument with your spouse, and you want to become a good communicator (instead of using silence to express your feelings), your momentum will try to keep you from communicating by pulling you toward the familiar pattern of silence.

You must adopt a new philosophy and through positive self-talk and leverage (a strong enough justification for fighting through your natural conditioned response, for example, it will enhance the quality of your relationship), you can adopt a new conditioned response to conflict, in this case, not silence but communication!

Before you decide where you want to be, you must first determine where you are today.

Recently we purchased a new car that had one of those fancy navigation systems, which supposedly helps men like me (who hate to ask for directions) find their destination. The 1st step to using this new technology is to program your origination point, where you are now. Finding your career calling works the same way. Before you determine your ultimate destination, you must first take careful inventory of where you are today.

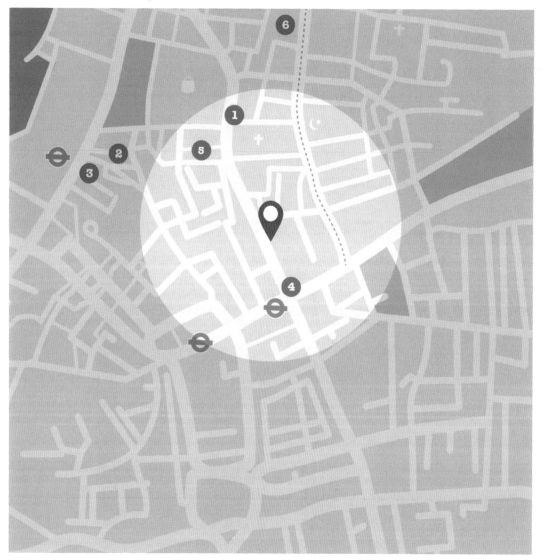

Again, we only use about 10% of our brain power. You no doubt have hidden potential that has never been identified or put into practice. Without realizing your potential and continually growing as a person, you will remain unemployed, unhappy or undervalued in the workplace.

We all have a unique gift or contribution to make, let us discover it together and put it to good use!

Self-Evaluation: My Personal Values

Knowing what you want from a job is important, and can change the entire landscape of your job search.

Rate the values listed below in the priority order for you (15 being least important and 1 being most important). Once you have rated your values, identify how each value will be of importance to you in your next job.

Rating	Value	Application on the Job
	Advancement	
	Benefits	
	Creativity	
	Flexibility	
	Free Time	
	Helping Others	
	Independence	
	Location	
	Money	
	Problem Solving	
	Stability	
	Status	
	Travel	
	Variety	
	Challenge	

This will help you to define what your needs and provide opportunities for you to correct any erroneous viewpoints you may have about one of the values listed here.

CHANGE

DEFINING

Change is modifying specific tasks or behaviors to be able to take on new or different responsibilities. The degree of difficulty involved in modifying ourselves professionally is evident when we consider all of the adjustments we make in our knowledge, attitude, individual, or group behavior.

Question:

What specific changes, both personally and professionally, do you want to make, and why?

What does change *feel* like?

Try this experiment . . .

Fold your arms across your chest normally as you would when you are relaxed. Wait one minute.
• Now try to fold the opposite way, with the opposite arm in the top position.
• How does it feel? Odd, right?
Even simple changes often feel uncomfortable . . . When it comes to careering, there are two types of change, both of which are impossible to control but important with respect to how you respond. One is called **cyclical change** and the other is called **structural change.**

Cyclical Change:

Refers to variable changes that are normal and natural.

Examples include the weather, the seasons or stock market fluctuations. We expect certain cycles where we can anticipate the change. For example, if you live in a four-season climate, you have a feel for when to put on your skis or uncover the swimming pool.

Structural Change:

Refers to changes that advance society and often make the prior way of doing things obsolete.

For example, in my company we often assist clients whose industry, employer, or job responsibilities have been replaced by technology. Examples: assembly line workers have been replaced with mechanical robots, in-store retail shopping has decreased due to online purchasing.

Changes will continue to occur and often will impact your occupation. Tracking the developments in your industry will prevent you from being blind-sided or eliminated.

Any change you make will be based on one single common reason: *the desire to gain pleasure and avoid pain!* The challenge is that each of us has adopted a different pattern to achieve these states. Some people drink alcohol, do drugs, watch TV, or read to escape boredom or pain. For those who do, these activities somehow yield pleasure. The key is to associate intense pleasure with finding work that feels like play.

Why I Resist Change

Name three reasons why you resist change.

1. _____

2. _____

3. _____

1. What actions or comments might a person display that indicate a fear of change?

_____

_____

_____

_____

2. What are some things you can do to manage your fears?

_____

_____

_____

_____

3. How do you feel when someone imposes a decision on you without your input?

_____

_____

_____

_____

Accepting change and obtaining your career calling will create a sense of internal happiness because you are making a positive contribution. In the modern, global economy, change and uncertainty are the norm and not the exception. The average job tenure is now less than four years and there is no guarantee that your career or current employer will even exist tomorrow.

Change management is no longer a "should" . . . it is a must!

So here is the question: Is the process of seeking your career calling and the changes you will be required to make, a positive for you or a negative? Change can sometimes be uncomfortable. As human beings, you and I would typically prefer to be comfortable than uncomfortable. By choosing to remain comfortable, you are in essence, making a decision to forgo your full potential and inner passion; you are settling for less than you could or should become.

Career progress requires some level of discomfort; there is no shortcut or way around it. You must learn to develop and accept the skill of being *comfortable while being uncomfortable*. Say what? What I am suggesting is that in order to accomplish a major event like a career change, you are going to have to accept the prospect of living in an uncomfortable state, where new habits, contacts and behaviors will inevitably occur. There is simply no other way to transition from your current state of affairs to a life of abundance and happiness. Changes in behavior, routine, and belief are essential ingredients.

Here is the good news: You have been successful at making major changes your entire life; a career change is simply another level of progress.

You must ultimately become the change you seek. Simply put, being out of your element is a natural and normal part of progress. Embrace this as part of the process of making change in your life. People do this every day; you can too! You must commit to persevere through the challenges and break the bad habits that have resulted in a career and lifestyle that do not meet your current standards.

Self-Evaluation: My Happiness

Are you happy with your current situation? Don't know for sure? Then take this simple test:

Check all of the statements that apply to you.

☐ I am miserable when the alarm clock rings.

☐ I am frequently tired.

☐ My days are repetitive.

☐ I have a poor attitude.

☐ I feel hostile towards others.

☐ I am very cynical.

☐ I really welcome my weekends.

☐ I frequently suffer from insomnia.

☐ I am frequently ill or under the weather.

☐ I don't consider others because I have to look out for myself.

☐ I watch too much television.

Give yourself one point for each box you checked, and read your score below.

Total: _____

Self-Evaluation: My Happiness

Now, interpret your results...

Total Points	How bored are you with your current situation?
0-1 points	**Happy Camper** You are doing what you enjoy and it shows in your happy attitude.
2-5 points	**There is More to Life Than This - Find It!** Your case is far from hopeless. Taking this class is a major step forward for you. Happier days are just ahead. Stay awake. Don't miss the turn!
6-11 points	**Emergency! Sound the Alarm** You're bored to tears. It's time to do something QUICK! Go out to eat, dance, or get some friends together and root for opposite sides in a sports broadcast. Then use your positive energy to make real changes in your life—starting with getting the most out of this class.

"As soon as you trust yourself, you will know how to live."
—Goethe

I suggest that in order to change, we must trust our decisions. You cannot fight yourself over the changes you need to make; you must truly believe they are necessary and in your best interest. So if we know we should change and it is necessary to do so to remain competitive in the 21st century workplace, why do we still resist?

The answer is simple . . .
it is *because we possess barriers to making change.*

We seek to maintain a comfort level, which often has been artificially created by our families, schooling, advertising, peer pressure, or other conformities. Some people live by the philosophy that they should not attempt to pursue their career calling because trying and failing may cause them emotional pain, so why bother? "Do nothing and worry" is the mantra of many 21st century job seekers.

Barriers are not the enemy; they are our friends! They provide a clear road map for change and help us to understand specifically what is holding us back. What are the barriers to making change and adopting a long-term career plan? In my experience, the 4-key barriers are as follows:

FOUR KEY BARRIERS TO *CHANGE*

1. *Laziness:* People find the process of exploring inner passions, finding purpose, making change and re-inventing themselves too difficult . . . so why bother?
2. *Anxiety:* Fear often prevents action while a lack of direction encourages complacency.
3. *Ignorance:* I have a job . . . for now . . . so leave me alone! I don't have to worry about finding my career calling, right? Wrong!
4. *Confusion:* Change is happening so fast, I am overwhelmed, confused and don't know where to start. So I do nothing.

"You cannot live on yesterday's standards and expect to be competitive today!"
—Chris Kuselias

If you have attended one of my speaking engagements or seminars, you know firsthand why I have the reputation as one of the most passionate and enthusiastic presenters ever to hold a microphone. Quite frankly, I get downright loud and excited! I am *that* passionate about helping others understand and achieve their career calling.

But believe it or not, at one time I was extremely nervous about speaking in public! Before I would get ready to speak I would adopt the same pattern.

First, I would start sweating, my heart would beat, I would envision a loss of confidence, picture ridicule, etc. I processed every negative emotion possible and thought about all the terrible things that could happen and psyched myself out. I would start slurring my words, lose my concentration and become consumed with fear to the point of total loss of confidence! To obtain this emotional state, I had to repeat this pattern each time!

Self-Evaluation: My Attitude

Ready to take a good look at your attitude?

Answer the following questions by putting an X next to Yes or No. Remember to be honest!

Do I try to get other people to do things for me rather than do them myself?

Yes ___ No___

Do I care about being on time? Yes ___ No___

Do I try to get by with as little work as possible? Yes ___ No___

Do I think good manners are for other people? Yes ___ No___

Am I an 8-hour worker who resents being asked to stay even for an extra few minutes? Yes ___ No___

Do I leave my personal belongings on the floor and expect someone else to pick them up? Yes ___ No___

Do I care only about "me" and forget about others? Yes ___ No___

Do I always make excuses for things I haven't done? Yes ___ No___

Do I litter when no one is looking? Yes ___ No___

Do I gossip about others, telling things I shouldn't? Yes ___ No___

Do I care only about the "glory" jobs and let everyone else do the "dirty jobs?"

Yes ___ No___

Does it seem that people are always criticizing me for something? Yes ___ No___

Do I dislike my family because they tell me what time to be in, how I should act, etc? Yes ___ No___

Do I, at times, tease and bully people just for the fun of it or to get them angry?

Yes ___ No___

Do I blame fate, "the System", or people for my current position in life? Yes ___ No___

Wow! Those were some tough questions to answer. Let's evaluate your answers...

What do your answers say about your overall attitude?

_____

_____

Do you think you have a good or bad attitude?

_____

_____

How can you change the way you see things and the way you react to different situations to become a more positive person?

_____

_____

Ideas for Problem Solving

Here are seven steps you can take when confronted with a problem. Instead of feeling overwhelmed, view the problem as a challenge or a puzzle to solve.

1. **Look at the Big Picture.** Get an overview of what is happening; look at the situation as objectively as possible. Gather relevant facts and analyze the problem. It is important to look at the situation from many different angles. Remain calm and remember to keep personal feelings and facts separate.

2. **Identify the real issue.** Sometimes there are many factors that impact a problem and make it even worse. The task is to determine the major problem that is the direct cause of the other minor problems.

3. **Brainstorm solutions.** List all the possible solutions. Do not pass any judgment on the solutions; just list them. Be creative.

4. **Select the best solution.** Consider all of the possible solutions carefully and weigh all the advantages and disadvantages. Select the solution that has the most advantages and the one that will eliminate the minor problems.

5. **Make a plan.** Develop a plan to resolve the problem by identifying the resources that can be utilized to assure that the plan will be successful. Be certain that you have a clear plan of action; otherwise the right solution will not work.

6. **Put the plan into action.** You need to be committed to follow through with the plan and put your resources to work.

7. **Check on the progress and modify the plan as needed.** The final step is to implement the plan. Don't be discouraged if it doesn't work exactly as you planned the first time. You may need to make slight modifications to the plan.

"Everything by the inch is a cinch but by the yard it's hard"

Compartmentalizing bigger items into smaller items is a suggested tip to achieve success in this process.

Section 3:

GOAL SETTING

LEARNING OBJECTIVES

1. Explain why goal setting is essential for future success.

2. Establish a clear and definite focus through goal setting.

3. Discuss the 5-Step Process for setting and achieving goals.

4. Create short and long term goals for personal development.

All Goals Must Revolve Around Your *Purpose*

How can any of us possibly expect to find genuine career happiness fueled by passion, purpose, power, profit and peace of mind (the 5P's) if our objectives are unclear?

If you do not have a plan to help you determine what you really want from your profession and cannot find or are unwilling to devote the necessary time to the process of uncovering what you truly value, you will most likely be destined to a life of regret and wasted talents.

Without a plan, you are relying on hope, and hope is *not* a strategy.

When planning your career, it is important to look at the process in three stages: **past, present, and future.** How did you get to this point, where are you now in the process and where do you want to be?

Most likely, you will not transition from your current occupation directly into your ideal career calling. There will inevitably be a progression of well-planned roles leading up to the culmination of your experience and education. Some call this a *career ladder* because with each rung of the climb you are ascending closer to the top. While there may be a series of job changes, internships, volunteer work, part time jobs, or continued education in some form, your ultimate destination needs to be defined.

The process of attaining your ideal career calling begins with the establishment of your passion and purpose. Passion and purpose are how we serve others. Once defined, you then will create your required steps to success, called *interim goals.* All of your goals should be established around your purpose, which requires critical reflection. Your purpose will not magically invade your body or fall from the sky. It must come from an exploration of what makes you unique and compelling as a human being and how you can best serve others through your talents.

Be certain to create your career plans from critical reflection (self-awareness) and not from guilt, boredom, or panic. For example, many people after a holiday season of indulgence and overeating look in the mirror at an unflattering image of themselves and set a New Year's resolution to lose weight. After two or three days of punishing themselves during an internal struggle to consume fewer calories, they regress to established habits of snacking, 2nd or 3rd helpings, or desserts every night.

There are several potential reasons for this behavior (belief systems, identity, comfort level, habit, positive or negative associations to food) but all point to one missing ingredient: if there is not a clearly defined purpose or strong enough *why,* people revert to their established comfort zone. Find a compelling reason to achieve your goal and you have a chance; without a strong enough *why,* you will fail.

Measure your career and life like a one-time opportunity and act as if there were no second chances because, in reality, there are not. There are no dress rehearsals or do-overs. Enjoy each successful experience and sensation in your development, no matter how small or insignificant.

Often, life presents us with unexpected and wonderful possibilities, which are not initially apparent. Seek the hidden treasures in a chance encounter, an email to an author who moved you, a unique opportunity to voice a new idea in your next staff meeting, or a conference where you could be inspired or meet your next new partner.

MY ACCOMPLISHMENTS

List experiences in school, in your career, or in another area of life in which you have achieved a worthwhile goal or felt excited about an accomplishment. Examples to get you thinking include: learning to drive a car, losing 10 pounds, beating a tough sales quota, settling a major family feud, etc.

Accomplishment 1: _____

I chose this because _____

_____

Accomplishment 2: _____

I chose this because _____

_____

Accomplishment 3: _____

I chose this because _____

_____

Next: Go back and think about why you were pleased or felt great.

This exercise is designed to link reasons with your goals; the "why" behind the "what." First, examine accomplishments, and ask why you chose that goal to accomplish.

Hint: The use of the word "excited" in the above text is an indicator that emotions are involved.

Effectively Forecasting Your Future

"Give me a stock clerk with a goal and I will give you a man who will make history. Give me a man with no goals, and I will give you a stock clerk."
—J.C. Penney, founder

Science has taught us that the human mind is a performance based organ. This means that whatever command you send to your subconscious mind, it will focus 24-hours a day to attain it. The more specific the request, the better results you will achieve. *How much* and *by when* are two essential aspects to any command you send to your subconscious mind. "I think I would like a career in health care" is not as powerful or effective as, "I will be a licensed practical nurse at Yale New Haven Hospital working the 2nd shift earning $45,000 annually by January 1st, of next year."

One client of mine purchased a graduation ring from the law school he wanted to graduate from the day he was admitted to their evening program. Since he was working a full time day job and going to law school at night, he needed every incentive possible to ensure he would complete his studies. He wore the ring every day and kept the ring on his night stand as a visual reminder of his dream and looked at the ring every night before bed; just so he would not quit school and would stay focused on his desired outcome.

When I decided to author this book, the first thing I did was design the book cover and place it on top of my desk so I could embed the goal into my subconscious mind to help create this work. Whether you seek to create a revolutionary exercise program, design an innovative website, become president of your class, start a new non-profit organization, host a television show, or climb Mt. Everest, I suggest you adopt the same practice.

SUCCESS TIP

I require my clients and leadership group (the highest ranking staff members of *Career* TEAM) to carry their key objectives with them at all times. You should, too!

One of my favorite examples of forecasting your future achievement comes courtesy of the actor and comedian Jim Carrey, who as a struggling young comic in Los Angeles, wrote himself a check for $10 million, dated it 5 years ahead and wrote on the check, "for services rendered." He carried the check in his wallet from that day forward until movies like *Ace Ventura: Pet Detective*, *The Mask* and *Dumb and Dumber* escalated his per movie fee to over $20 million! When Jim's beloved father died in 1994, he honored his dad and biggest fan by placing the fake check into the coffin. The lesson: *Conceive it, believe It, and you will achieve it!*

SELF-EVALUATION: MY DIRECTION

You can avoid procrastination by being focused! Answer the following to help you find your focus.

1. What are your general interests? Are they related to people, information, sports or something else?

_____

_____

2. Do you express yourself better in oral or written form? _____

3. What daily activities give you the most satisfaction? _____

_____

4. Do you like responsibility or would you rather have someone else be in charge?

_____

5. Do you have an aversion to following directions or being told what to do?

_____

6. What kind of work environment is important to you?

_____

7. Would you rather work indoors or outdoors?

_____

8. Are you more comfortable with regular routines or spur-of-the-moment projects?

_____

9. Do you enjoy new concepts and situations or are you more comfortable with the familiar?

_____

10. Would you prefer a regular salary or a commission, or a combination of both?

_____

11. Would you like to work a regular schedule (e.g., 9-5) or something more flexible?

_____

12. Are you willing to travel or would you rather stay close to home?

_____

13. Do you see yourself as a leader or a follower?

_____

14. Do you prefer to work on your own, with one other person, or as part of a team?

_____

15. Do you work well under pressure?

_____

16. Do you like excitement or danger in a job (like emergency services), or something more mundane/sedate (like office work)?

_____

17. Would you like to work in a big city or in a more rural environment?

_____

18. Do you prefer to work for a large, medium-sized, or small employer?

_____

19. Are you willing to relocate?

_____

20. What is the one thing you simply could not live without on the job?

_____

Ten Keys to Setting Effective Goals

What I find most helpful is to start by describing goals in general terms before you become specific with regard to your plan for establishing and obtaining your career calling. To be effective, your goals must be:

1. Balanced (Career, Financial, Health and Fitness, Relationships, Spirituality)
2. Beneficial to Others (Contribution goals are the best kind!)
3. Challenging (If they are too easy, what is the point?)
4. Flexible (Goals must be fluid and you must remain versatile)
5. Measurable (How many pounds, by which date, what job title, etc.)
6. Mirror Your Values (And make sure they are in sync with your identity)
7. Purposeful (They must have a reason that you can articulate)
8. Realistic (Regarding time frame to achieve and credentials required)
9. Supported (By family, friends, and mentors)
10. Make Them Your Own (Not mine or someone else's but yours alone!)

The Yale University Study

To illustrate the importance of goal setting, a study was conducted of Yale University's class of 1953, which asked the following questions:

1. Have you set goals?
2. Are your goals in writing?
3. Do you have a plan to achieve your goals?

In response, only 3% of the class had written goals accompanied by a definite plan of action. 20 years later, in 1973, the same class was re-surveyed and the results were predictable. The 3% of the class who set goals and wrote them down were earning, on average, *10 times as much money* as the 97% of Yale graduates who did not. Although monetary reward isn't the only true measure of success, it certainly validates that setting and writing down objectives has a profound effect on income.

Five Proven Success Strategies

The process of goal setting is certainly not a new concept and most likely you are currently in the practice of formulating objectives in at least one area of your life. Maybe you have set a fitness goal to lose weight after the holidays. Perhaps you aspire to save a certain amount of money each month. Setting specific career related goals is challenging because most individuals are short-term thinkers, and long-term career planning is often overlooked. This is a huge mistake! Not setting goals at all is well . . . *self-sabotage!*

Here are some of my favorite strategies:

1. *Study high achievers in your chosen field*
Setting goals is powerful stuff and will elevate you to the top of your field. For example, I am often asked to speak at conferences attended by industry professionals, who seek a competitive edge. To illustrate my point, I will inevitably ask the participants to raise their hands if they can identify the most efficient and effective people in their chosen field. How many of you know whom the people are who have set the standard for success in your field, industry, or occupation? Almost every hand in the room is typically raised, because most people are aware of those individuals achieving excellence in their field (a.k.a. the top dogs!).

My next step is to request again by a show of hands, how many of them have ever made the effort to meet these top performers. Often, not a single hand is raised! Why are people so hesitant to learn from others who may become a mentor to us and who have obviously figured out how to achieve excellence?

It seems so obvious that we could benefit from their wisdom, experience, information or techniques. Most assuredly, you can bet that these top performers are in the regular habit of setting goals.

The message: *Make it one of your priorities and set a goal right now to identify and meet the top two or three performers in your chosen field!*

My suspicion is that you will find that these high achievers are in the practice of not only setting goals, but also have a definite plan for where they want to be 1–5–10 years ahead. From this day forward, I want you to employ the concept of beginning any endeavor with the end in mind; that is, decide what you ultimately want and then fill in the steps needed to get there.

Do not enter into a career or start in a new industry without a plan for exactly where you aspire to end up. Not to oversimplify, but you would not just get in your car and start driving aimlessly, hoping you find a great view or restaurant. No, you hopefully begin your journey with a destination in mind and a set of directions.

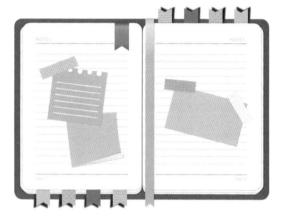

2. Purchase a mini recorder or notebook Goals often originate from our vision or ideas. Purchase a recorder and create an Idea Book—this is simply a device or notebook where you record or write down your day-to-day observations and insights.

It is a powerful tool to expand your awareness. Did you ever have a big idea in the middle of the night? You sit straight up in bed and your mind is racing. Usually, you only have a few seconds to capture that idea before you lose it, or your body says, "Go back to sleep, it is 3 o'clock in the morning!" In fact, you may drift back to sleep, wake up hours later and have completely forgotten what your great idea was. Never lose a great thought again! An old saying that I like is:

"When you think it, ink it!"

3. Establish family goals (at an early age)

Personally, what my family and I do, is create goals around the following categories:

Career
Financial
Hobbies/Entertainment/Vacations
Health and Fitness/Relaxation
Relationships
Spiritual/Contribution/Reflection

What we have determined as a family (and what my wife and I instill in our children) is that when you let other people determine your success, you are sabotaging your future. Personalizing your goals is one of the most important aspects of the goal setting process. Although we have family goals, we encourage each of our children to formulate objectives in key individual areas, even at their young ages (keep room clean, clear the table, school attendance goal, save their pennies, etc.).

Goal setting requires discipline and consistency, which is why most people set goals but do not follow through. If you do not adopt the practice of consistently setting and modifying your goals, you will live to regret it. **It is said that there are two major pains in life. One is the pain of discipline; the other is the pain of regret.** We want our kids to live without regret and teaching them the discipline to formulate goals is an important lesson in this process.

Even though my kids are very young, we already have a *mandatory* family conference every Wednesday night from 7 pm to 8 pm. We create a positive, fun environment, make popcorn and sit in our assigned seats. We keep the meeting notes in a binder and as a family we discuss and address "important issues," like room cleaning, television shows we are allowed to watch, snacks, allowance, trash removal duties, setting the dinner table, and vacation plans.

The important thing is that my children and family know that there is structure, accountability, and a plan for our future. We are setting an example of the importance of goal setting and monitoring progress for *each* member of the Kuselias family. I suggest you do the same with yours. Make it fun, educational, and allow ALL members to share their opinions and objectives. The results will astound you!

In each of our children's rooms, we have created a wall of fame (we also have one in every *Career* TEAM classroom around the nation) where their highlights are visually depicted. Each and every day, these accomplishments (including graded papers, drawings, and photographs with their friends, awards, certificates, etc.) are embedded into their minds. I am convinced this has a positive effect on their attitude, mood, and behavior. The building of self-esteem is another important benefit of this process. The last thing my kids see and observe before going to sleep each night, are the positive aspects of their young lives, visually reinforced. *Research shows that what you see, hear and read 30 minutes before you turn in for the night influences both your sleeping pattern and energy for the next day.*

The lesson? *Be careful what you fill your mind with right before going to bed.* High achievers fill their mind with positive reinforcement, affirmations of their goals, and critical reflection of a great day spent contributing to others. Avoid watching mindless TV, depressing news of war, rape, murder, gangs, scandals, or unproductive reading material. If you decide to have these things in your life, don't do them right before bed. I end each day by brushing my teeth and reflecting on how I assisted others and made the world a better place. I ask myself a single question, which is:

"How could I have been more effective today?"

I do not dwell on my mistakes or question my decisions, because doing so will only negatively affect my rest and abilities the next day to inspire my wife, kids, family, associates, customers, and new people I meet.

4. *Purchase a photo album to create a visual reinforcement of your key goals*

Next, I want to introduce you to the importance of creating visual reinforcement for all of your goals and objectives. Here is a fun strategy to set and visualize your goals:

Buy a large photo album and create chapters for each area you wish to set goals. Within these chapters, I want you to start collecting pictures, which visually emphasize where or how you want to end up. Again, start with the end in mind but reinforce and create a visual reminder of the outcome you seek.

Examples include:

A photo of the body you want
A picture of the house or car you desire
A mock certificate of your targeted educational degree
A mock business card of the title you want to hold
A phantom copy of a charitable donation you aspire to make one day

84

My personal success journal has pictures of:

- The current list of best-selling books designed to help others. One of them, by Jack Canfield, motivated me to spend the long days and nights it took to author this book!
- Photos of my favorite seminar leaders, like John Maxwell and Steven Covey shown in front of large audiences
- Photos of helpful television hosts like Suze Orman, who have their own television or radio program created to assist the general public improve their quality of life
- A picture of my personal fitness trainer to remind me to seek fitness every day
- An article based on interviews with Warren Buffet, a man I respect and admire for his financial savvy on investment strategies

These are just a few of my personal inclusions; what are yours? I think you will find this exercise enlightening and invigorating!

5. Create a goal setting journal

Every successful person I know, have counseled or study, practices the art of setting and monitoring their goals and objectives. The best seem to make a practice of writing down their most important aspirations in a user-friendly format that they can reflect on and feel positive about their progress in life. To demonstrate that I practice what I preach, here is a sample from my current personal goal setting journal. I have recorded my goals in this format for the past 20 years and now have it computerized in a file entitled Annual Goals.

It is inspiring to go back in time and observe what I once thought was a stretch or goal that would be a challenge. Today, some of my goals seem so elementary or simple, it is almost a joke. But guess what? That shows the amazing progress I have made over 20 years by using the same techniques and strategies you are learning. Imagine the fun I will have in 20 years when I look back on what I think is a challenging goal today!

ach year on December 31, I sit at my computer and record my goals for the pcoming year. I begin with a paragraph affirmation and follow up with 5 ategories, which contain my major life goals.

hese include:

1. **Career**
2. **Financial**
3. **Health and fitness**
4. **Relationships**
5. **Spirituality**

ach month, I review my goals and modify them as needed. I may increase or dd new goals based on opportunities that arise throughout the course of the ar. Regardless, I have a blueprint to follow, which provides the course for that ven year. Now it's your turn! When creating your goals, please remember to be specific as possible and include dates, names, numbers, percentages, cations, and amounts.

efore we begin making our goals, let's complete an exercise hat will help us to discover what motivates us!

MOTIVATION

What motivates you? Take this quick assessment to find out! Be sure to check all that apply. Feel free to choose more than one motivator for each of your accomplishments. When you have completed the exercise, be sure to tally up your totals at the bottom of each column.

What motivated you in the past?

List your accomplishments	Money	Recognition	Pleasure	Challenge	Obligation	Pressure	Winning	Acceptance	Friendship	Helping Others	Security	Freedom	Feeling of Accomplishment
Total number of checkmarks													

MY SHORT-TERM GOALS

Now that you have a good idea about what motivates you, it's time to start setting some goals. First, we will set some short-term goals (up to one year). List three things you would like to accomplish within the **next year**. Your goals may fall into any facet of your life: physical, financial, work-related, etc. Examples to get you thinking include: get a job, exercise on a regular basis, buy a car, open a bank account, etc.

Goal 1:

_____

I chose this because _____

_____

Goal 2:

_____

I chose this because _____

_____

Goal 3:

_____

I chose this because _____

_____

MY LONG-TERM GOALS

You are well on your way to making a positive change in your life by creating some goals that you can strive toward achieving! Now, let's turn our focus to a little further into the future. You will now create some long-term goals (3-5 years). Think about your motivators when setting these longer term goals.

My **long-term career goal** (3-5 years) is to be a (an):

_____

A. To obtain this position, I foresee myself having to:

_____

_____

B. The date I have set to obtain this career goal is:

_____

_____

My **ultimate career goal** is to be a (an):

_____

A. In this position, I will perform the following tasks:

_____

_____

B. The date I have set to obtain this career goal is:

_____

_____

DEFINING SUCCESS

As we close this section on Goal Setting, keep the following concepts in mind:

1. THRIVE ON PRESSURE: Beware of the wounded tiger - especially if that tiger is motivated.

2. ESTABLISH GOOD HABITS/ELIMINATE BAD HABITS: Personal calls, office gossip, bringing personal problems to the office, distracting co-workers, cutting corners, fudging the numbers, disorganized, moodiness, excuses, time wasters.

3. LISTEN MORE, TALK LESS: You have two ears and one mouth, so listen twice as much as you talk.

4. BUILD SELF-ESTEEM: In order to succeed, you have to feel good about yourself. The way to do that is to understand that you deserve success. Establish a great work ethic and the discipline to maintain it.

5. ALWAYS BE POSITIVE: The more trying times, the more positive you have to be! *"What I do best is share my enthusiasm"* – Bill Gates, Microsoft Founder

6. LEARN FROM ADVERSITY: When failure occurs, step back, examine your role in the failure, accept the blame and adapt and learn from the experience.

7. LEARN FROM ROLE MODELS: Emulate traits that you admire and learn from other's mistakes.

8. BE VERY PERSISTENT: Persistence, more than anything else helps to achieve success. Success is a long-term commitment. Develop a "PhD" attitude: Poor, Hungry, and Driven.

9. SET DEMANDING GOALS: We all make excuses for our weaknesses, but if you don't conquer them, one by one, they will consume both your time and energy. This will cause you to miss opportunities. Goals will help you to formulate plans to eliminate weaknesses.

10. SURVIVE SUCCESS: Today's success is often tomorrow's failure. Maintain discipline and write down your own secrets to success. Study them. When you do, you will realize that it wasn't luck or good fortune, but rather a chosen life-style.

QUESTION: Does your presence raise the performance of everyone around you?

Section 4:

LEARNING TO LEARN & STRESS RELIEF MANAGEMENT

LEARNING OBJECTIVES

1. Understand what learning is and how to apply how you perceive and understand information.

2. Identify and analyze your own learning style.

3. Understand how emotional intelligence can assist in a long and successful career.

4. Evaluate and understand how anxiety and stress can be managed to enhance your performance.

The capacity to learn is a *gift*;
the ability to learn is a *skill*;
the willingness to learn is a

choice.

Brian Herbert

What is Learning?

In order to get the most out your career, work with others effectively and maximize your education, you need to know how learning takes place and how to use what you learn to your advantage.

Learning is often referred to as:

a somewhat perpetual change in wisdom or actions that is a direct result of your life experiences.

Knowledge is necessary for you to, read, write, speak perform mathematical functions, drive a car, complete assignments, and so on. Regardless of your career path, any career requires you to learn.

What we learn can make us happier, healthier, and more successful. A benefit of learning is that it can help

you to become more **flexible** and **adaptable**, especially when combined with your previous experiences. This means that you can learn to behave in more beneficial ways, rather than harming others and yourself. This also means that each of us **perceives** and **processes** information differently.

We all have different **learning styles** and **multiple intelligences**. We are also **motivated** in a variety of ways that help us to achieve our goals. In other words, if you take a bit of time to understand **HOW** you learn, you can develop a strong foundation for success. This can help you to obtain anything you wish to achieve!

How do you perceive and understand information?

What is your current perception of work or school? Knowing how your brain initially understands the world, what and how you learn, and how you interact with others, begins with how you perceive and understand information.

PERCEPTION

Do you draw conclusions about what a person is saying long before they finish telling you? Of course you do! We all do. But some of the most successful people in the world *ask questions* before drawing conclusions! This helps to deepen their understanding of what is being said. In fact, we all have many perceptions that come from our life experiences that can interfere with our perception of what is really going on around us. Essentially, your own **perceptions** or **"reality"** can hinder or bias the judgments you make.

When you're learning new information in class or in the workplace, especially when you don't possess any relatable experiences, you can easily draw erroneous conclusions. For example, making a very complex situation too simple or applying an inappropriate solution to a certain situation, can have disastrous outcomes.

How does your own reality get in the way of your learning?

This is not an easy question to answer. Often **your perception** *is* **your reality.**

You make decisions based on your perceptions every day. From deciding which clothes you will wear, what types of things you will to buy in a store, whether you or not you trust someone, and so on, are all premises based on your perceptions. To illustrate how your perception can easily change your outlook or misguide you, take a look at the visual examples that follow. As you do, you will also notice that there are some rules known as **perceptional cues** that guide your understanding of how you view the world.

By having a basic understanding of these cues, you will become more aware of your own reality, and consequently gain a deeper level of understanding of how you perceive the world.

But that is just the beginning! You can also learn how others see the world and make decisions, which will be helpful in understanding difficult tasks or important situations that require effective solutions.

Shape constancy allows us to understand objects from different angles. Even though the angle and shape has technically changed, we still comprehend the original form.

Brightness constancy is when the brightness of an object (such as a sheet of paper) remains constant under different light sources, such as in full daylight or at nighttime.

Size constancy is the idea that an object's size remains the same even though the size appears to differ with changes in distance.

There is also a **linear perspective**, which is the idea that lines coincide as they fade into the distance.

Interposition is when objects overlap one another and causes the viewer to believe that one object is further away. [1]

Take a look at the picture of the Manhattan Bridge in New York City. Notice how the bridge appears to be the same size as the buildings?

In reality, the bridge is at least three times larger than the buildings. What is this an example of?

If you guessed **size constancy**, give yourself a pat on the back!

Our perception of the size of objects changes based on our distance from the object.

There is also a **linear perspective**, which is the idea that lines coincide as they fade into the distance.

Interposition is when objects overlap one another and causes the viewer to believe that one object is further away. [1]

This picture of modern day Dubai, India shows us a perfect example of **linear perspective**. In this picture, we see train tracks. As the tracks disappear into the distance, they seem to be converging.

Even though they appear to cross, logic tells us this cannot be true. If the tracks were to actually cross, what would happen? Chaos!

Are you starting to see how our perception of things can be deceiving?

My Perception

As you might have noticed, what you think you are seeing may not be an accurate representation of reality. This means that you may need to be open to different interpretations. These different interpretations can increase your understanding of information or of a certain task that you need to complete. In You can become more flexible in your decisions-making process by allowing room for other interpretations.

Identify a time in which you misjudged a situation or perception cue and made a/some decision(s) accordingly.

_____

_____

Now that you understand how perceptual cues work, what would you have done differently in that same situation?

_____

_____

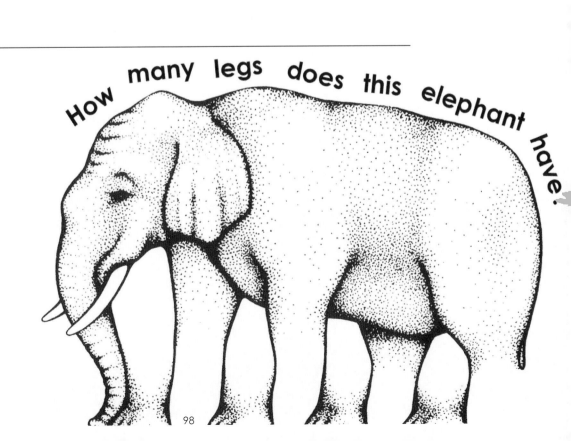

How many legs does this elephant have.

Processing

How You Learn
Top-down Processing

To illustrate top-down processing, read this paragraph:

Aoccdrnig to rscheearch at Cmabrigde Uinervtisy, it deosn't mttaer in waht oredr the ltteers in a wrod appear, the olny iprmoetnt tihng is taht the frist and lsat ltteer be in the rghit pclae. The rset can be a toatl mses and you can sitll raed it wouthit porbelm. Tihs is bcuseae the huamn mnid deos not raed ervey lteter by istlef, rather the wrod as a wlohe.

Bottom-up Processing

This Lego house exemplifies a perfect instance of **bottom-up** design. The parts are first created and then assembled without taking into consideration how the parts will work in the assembly.

How can you remember the difference between **top-down** and **bottom-up** processing? **Top-down** processing is when you take a large object or idea and break it down from general to specific. **Bottom-up** processing is the opposite; you start with the specific details and work towards the large idea. [1]

Different Learning Styles

To further help you understand how learning takes place; you should understand the four learning styles. Everyone learns by one or even a combination of the four types of learning styles listed below.

LEARNING STYLE	STUDY TIP
Using pictures, images and spatial understanding is often referred to as **visual or spatial learning style**.	Use a dry erase board to draw pictures, doodle or graphs of the information you need to understand
Using sounds and music is commonly known as **aural or auditory learning style**.	Listen to up beat music while you study. Be careful to not choose music that you'll mouth the words too. This will take away from your focus.
Using words in writing and speech is usually referred to as **verbal or linguistic learning style**.	Read aloud or talk to yourself about the chapters. Note: If you try this in public, note how many strange looks you get from people.
Using your body, hands and senses is commonly known as **physical or kinesthetic learning style**.	Be active and take several short breaks (5-10 min). Baking cookies while you study with a timer works well. You will have to check on the cookies several times which offers the needed short breaks to reenergize your studying. Bring the cookies to class and you'll be loved by all!

Multiple Intelligences

Understanding which learning style best helps you to retain and understand information is one of the first steps in understanding how your brain works. Garner's Theory of Multiple Intelligences suggests that you can increase your chances for success by understanding each type of intelligence. We each have our own unique blend of intelligences that help us to understand the world we live in, while fine-tuning our approach to quickly learn information and effectively use it.

The theory also suggests that we all have the potential to acquire each type of intelligence and by doing so, can increase our chances for success when confronting various challenges in our personal and professional lives.

The following is a list of nine different types of intelligences. Take a look at the list and identify which types of intelligences you possess. Write a **+** next to the strongest intelligences…

1) **Linguistic Intelligence**: the ability to articulate ideas well through the use of words and language.

   Study Tip: Record yourself reading aloud and play the recording back as you study.

2) **Logical-Mathematical Intelligence**: the ability to calculate and complete mathematical problems to understand abstract concepts.

   Study Tip: Organize the chapter and your notes into a logical flow that makes sense to you.

3) **Spatial Intelligence**: the ability to think in three dimensions by using visual imagery.

   Study Tip: Drawing or doodling works great here. Create a picture that represents the information that needs to be understood.

4) **Musical Intelligence**: the ability to distinguish tone, pitch, rhythm, and timbre.

Study Tip: Listen to music as you study. Create musical jingles of key concepts.

5) **Bodily-Kinesthetic Intelligence**: the ability to manipulate objects and use various physical skills.

Study Tip: Study while doing a physical activity that you enjoy.

6) **Interpersonal Intelligence**: the ability to comprehend and collaborate well with others.

Study Tip: Do you love coffee or tea? Meet with a classmate at your favorite café for a beverage and class discussion.

7) **Intrapersonal Intelligence**: the ability to comprehend one's own ideas, thoughts, and feelings.

Study Tip: Try keeping a brief journal of your reactions (thoughts and feelings) to the information you are studying.

8) **Naturalistic Intelligence**: the ability to comprehend the natural world.

Study Tip: Study in physical locations that are representative of the course material.

9) **Existential Intelligence**: (also commonly known as spiritual or moral intelligence) pose and ponder questions about life, death, and reality. [2]

Study Tip: Pose questions of content that explore what lies beyond life and death, such as why are people born, how they get here, and why they die.

Emotional Intelligence

(Book Smart vs. Street Smart)

High Emotional Intelligence = Higher employability and increased longevity in your career!

Emotional Intelligence is a set of skills that makes up one's ability to accurately assess, evaluate express, and regulate emotions.

Emotional intelligence involves the ability to:

- **Accurately understand others' emotions**
- **Respond to others' emotions appropriately**
- **Self motivate**
- **Understand one's own emotions**
- **Regulate and manage one's own emotional reaction**

Self-Evaluation: Emotional Intelligence

Take a look at this brief self-report rating scale that can help you to understand how emotional intelligence is measured. Write **Yes** or **NO** by each statement. The and – signs designate whether it is considered to be a positive or negative indication of emotional intelligence.

+ 1. People don't have to express how they feel, I can imagine it.

– 2. When conflict arises, it is difficult for me to handle.

+ 3. My goals are always on the forefront of my mind; I do not get sidetracked by impulse.

– 4. When I'm in a bad mood, it takes over my life.

+ 5. I am acutely aware of my feelings as I have them.

+ 6. I understand other's feelings so much that I am sympathetic to their problems

– 7. It is difficult for me to be well prepared when I am nervous about a situation, such as an exam.

+ 8. I am positive and optimistic when faced with misfortunes.

– 9. I explode or keep things bottled up, when I am angry.

+ 10. I am able to articulate unspoken feelings in a group setting or in a relationship.[2]

What motivates you to learn?

Intrinsic versus extrinsic motivation

Do you learn because you are curious about a subject or want to know more about it? If so, you are **intrinsically** motivated. Conversely, do you learn because you are motivated to get a good grade or receive praise from others? If so, you are **extrinsically** motivated. Once you learn how to motivate yourself, you will find that tackling even the toughest of challenges will become a bit easier to manage.

My Story

Think about and discuss your personal history—your story—in relation to **intrinsic** and **extrinsic** motivators.

Think about some of your personal goals and then answer the following questions:

1. What motivators (intrinsic or extrinsic) influenced you to make those goals in the first place?

_____

_____

2. If you have modified certain goal, what motivators influenced you to modify each goal?

_____

_____

3. How do you anticipate your goals changing in the future? Explain why.

_____

_____

"BY FAILING TO PREPARE, YOU ARE PREPARING TO FAIL."

-- Benjamin Franklin

Stress Relief Management

Anxiety is something that every one of us experiences in any stressful situation. All of us feel some anxiety when we take exams, have big projects to complete, have to meet a stringent deadline, when interviewing, and so on. One of the most stressful and anxiety-provoking experiences is taking a test. Feelings of angst can occur before a test, while reviewing for a test, during a test, or even after a test. The experience can produce a nervous feeling in your stomach, sweating, nausea, blanking out, or even becoming physically ill. While all of these are symptoms of anxiety, most people don't experience anything more than a nervous feeling. In fact, a slight amount of anxiety can result in improved test performance!

PREPARATION IS THE

KEY

TO YOUR SUCCESS!

Athletes, actors, singers, public speakers, and other performers count on having some anxiety to be able to perform to the best of heir ability. And so should you! Anxiety can become problematic when it begins to have a negative effect your exam performance. Some of these effects can interfere with every aspect of your life, BUT most can be managed with preparation!

Tips for Managing Test Anxiety & Stress

When anxiety and stress begin to hinder how you perform on exams, there are three main areas you can examine to help to decrease the negative feelings.

1. Mental preparation is a main concern when confronting test anxiety and stress. Before the exam, plan on implementing a variety of strategies:

- **Be thoroughly prepared.** Make sure you have thoroughly studied all topics. If you have confidence that you know the subject matter, you will feel less stressed and anxious.

- **Review the material.** Set aside 15-30 minutes each day to review the material you have learned. Trying to cover two months of material right before an exam is not an effective way to study. By reviewing bit by bit, you will reduce last minute anxiety and stress.

- **Arrive to the exam location early.** If you are early, you will be less stressed and go into the exam with a clear head. Arrive a minimum of 15 minutes early.

During the exam you should be "test-wise" and plan for taking a test.

- When you receive an exam, stop for a minute, take several deep breaths, relax, and then begin reviewing the directions and the test items. Some anxiety is normal- we are all human!

- **READ THE DIRECTIONS** for each section. Students typically lose points on exams because they do not follow the directions, not because they don't know the material.

- On a timed test, spend time on questions that have a higher point value. Try to answer as many questions as possible, thoroughly read each question; do not skim.

- If a question is giving you trouble, come back to it. Don't waste time by spending an over abundant amount of time on one question.

- Learn from the test! Often times, some questions on an exam reveal answers to other questions. Be mindful when reading the questions and look for clues to help you.

- Take your time! Read each question slowly; don't rush through the exam. This is how mistakes are made.

- Most importantly, try to remain calm. If you feel your stress level rising, take a deep breath, close your eyes, and remind yourself that you can do this!

2. Physical preparation is another critical area to keep in mind when preparing for exams.

- **Take good care of yourself.** Make sure to eat healthy foods and get sufficient rest, especially before an exam. When you are tired, you will be less alert and unable to perform at your best.

- **Location, location, location!** On exam day, find a place in the room where you feel comfortable. Avoid sitting near the door or in other high distraction areas.

- **Come Prepared.** Bring all necessary supplies for the exam such as a calculator, pens, pencils, scratch paper, etc.

3. Relaxation is the last way that you can be prepared for an exam.

Along with both mental and physical preparation, trying to relax both before and during the exam can improve your overall performance. When your body becomes physically tense, relaxation removes tension and consequently reduces anxiety – the deeper the relaxation, the greater the reduction in anxiety. There are several things you can do to achieve a state of relaxation prior to an exam:

- **Go for a walk.** Allow adequate time prior to the exam to go for walk. Clear your mind as you walk and enjoy the sense of relaxation.

- **Avoid discussing the test.** Don't discuss the test with anyone, especially fellow classmates as that only serves to fuel anxiety.

- **Breath.** Take a series of 10 deep breaths, holding each breath for 10 seconds. Slowly release your breath.

- **Tense your muscles to relax them.** While sitting, (not laying down unless you want others to look at your strangely) tense all the muscles in your body beginning with your toes and ending at your head. Hold the tension for about 20 seconds. Release and let your muscles relax completely. Repeat, as needed, until you feeling feel less anxious and a deeper sense of relaxation.

Stretch. Stretching your muscles invigorates the body and is a great pick me up, especially if you're groggy. [3]

Anxiety & Stress Triggers

Take a moment to think about the last time you felt anxious or stressed... List the thoughts, concerns, images, and feelings you experienced below.

_____

_____

Now take a moment to ask yourself how preparation could have alleviated most of what you listed. You may be surprised to learn just how important preparation really is.

It's all about preparation!

---

[1] Gardner, Howard. Frames of Mind: The Theory of Multiple Intelligences. Basic Books, 1997

[2] Parker, James D.A. Assessing Emotional Intelligence. Springer, 2009.

[3] Flippo, Rona F and Caverly, David C. Handbook of College Reading and Study Strategy Research, 2e. Routledge, 2000.

Section 5:

TIME

MANAGEMENT

LEARNING OBJECTIVES

1. Learn how to assess your time management skills.

2. Create a timetable that works for you.

3. Assess your priorities and understand how to get them completed.

4. Analyze the different types of procrastination and learn how to manage them effectively.

"Insanity is doing the same thing over and over again and expecting a different result."

- Albert Einstein

If what you're doing professionally, academically, or personally isn't working, then assess your time management skills and **CHANGE YOUR STRATEGIES!**

Successful people know how they learn, what works for them, and when to make changes.

Assessing Your Time Management Skills

By becoming aware of how you spend your time, you can tailor almost any project to fit your needs, preferences, and abilities, while also making time for **FUN!** This means that time management is literally focused on YOU! So if you want to complete projects on time, learn more effectively, and decrease your stress level, let's focus on becoming self-aware. Let's start with the basics!

Making More Hours in the Day

Where does the time go?

7 days x 24 hours in a week	168 Hours
Approximately 56 hours for sleep	-56
35 hours a week for academics and studying	-35
Average 3 hours a day for nutrition and hygiene	-21
About 8 hours every day for work, socializing, chores, exercise, family, and etc.	-56
Total hours remaining	0

My Schedule

Create your own weekly timetable. Be as accurate as possible.

Activity	168 Hours per week
Sleeping	_____ hours
Bathing	_____ hours
Eating	_____ hours
Work	_____ hours
School	_____ hours
Studying	_____ hours
Family	_____ hours
Socializing	_____ hours
Chores	_____ hours
Travel	_____ hours

114

My Ideal Schedule

Take a moment to create your IDEAL timetable below.

Activity	168 Hours per week
Sleeping	_____ hours
Bathing	_____ hours
Eating	_____ hours
Work	_____ hours
School	_____ hours
Studying	_____ hours
Family	_____ hours
Socializing	_____ hours
Chores	_____ hours
Travel	_____ hours

Take a look at both tables.

What are the significant differences?

_____

_____

_____

My Actual Schedule vs. My Ideal Schedule

Take a moment to list the significant differences between your actual and ideal timetables below. Try to think of potential solutions to problem areas.

Actual	Ideal	Potential Solutions

If you feel like you don't have enough time, then you may need to reevaluate how you spend your time. This means you may need to work more effectively, learn to prioritize, stop procrastinating, and learn to say no!

What are the <u>TRUE</u> benefits of time management?

1. Helps to get you started (no time wasted on deciding what to do).
2. Keeps you from forgetting to work on projects or study for subjects you dislike.
3. Provides you with more time to think about and enjoy what you need to accomplish.
4. Promotes effective preparation time and eliminates cramming.
5. Frees your mind (putting it on paper, means you don't have to remember it).
6. Helps you to prioritize.
7. Allows you to avoid time traps and control quick breaks.
8. Keeps you from overlooking opportunities to have **FUN.**
9. Helps you to learn smarter, NOT HARDER!

Using Time Wisely

Take a moment to jot down all of the tasks, projects, and activities that you would accomplish if you were able to manage your time more effectively.

_____

_____

_____

My Tasks - Learning to Prioritize

It is quite helpful to layout your goals and create a plan to accomplish them. You may agonize over some tasks, but after further consideration, they may not take as much time as you originally thought or may even be unnecessary all together!

Using the template below:

- Create a list of the tasks on your "to do" list.
- Create a list of your goals (e.g. get an A in this course, work 20 hours this week, finish my program/degree, etc.).

How does your to do list compare to your goals?

Determine which tasks you need to: 'Do now', 'Do soon', 'Do later' or 'Don't do at all'. For the tasks that you are still unsure about, think about what the consequence would be if you don't complete it. This may help you decide if the task is urgent after all.

Tasks	Desired Goal(s)	Do Now	Do Soon	Do Later	Don't Do
Study every night	Pass this class		X		

Eliminate Distractions

It is difficult to get any real work done when television, family, friends, texts, or status updates on Facebook or Snap Chat distract you? Designate certain blocks of time during which you remove ALL distractions including music, the iPad, television, texting, and social media. Commit to using that time to focus all your attention on projects that require uninterrupted focus.

My Distractions

What distracts you the most when you're attempting to complete a task? List possible solutions to each major distraction.

Distraction	Potential Solution(s)

Do you procrastinate?

One of the best ways to take control of your time is to understand procrastination. Everyone is guilty of occasional procrastination, but if you find yourself consistently putting off projects, it can be a significant issue at school and on the job. Self-awareness is key! When you understand your patterns, it will help to determine if you are habitually putting off projects and why.

Am I a Procrastinator?

Write "**true**" or "**false**" next to the following questions, and see how your score adds up below.

1.   When I am assigned a task, I rarely begin it immediately.
2.   When I wait until the last minute, I perform faster and produce better work.
3.   My classmates or teachers have questioned me about procrastinating on a project.
4.   I wait to start projects because sometimes the deliverables change and I don't want to waste my time.
5.   I'm hesitant to get things started early because a better idea may come to me later.
6.   When I start an assignment, I do not finish working until it is done.
7.   I am often rushed to turn in work reports or school projects by the deadline.
8.   When I delay starting a project, it gives me more time to reflect and strategize.

Number of True: _____   **Number of False:** _____

Mostly true: If you answered true to six or more of the statements above, you are demonstrating tendencies of a procrastinator and need to pay extra attention to the strategies for overcoming procrastination in this section. **Equally true and false:** If you answered true to three - five statements, you are procrastinating some of the time. Once you know your patterns, you can recognize when you are procrastinating sooner, and keep it from getting in the way of your success. **Mostly false:** If you answered true to one – two statements, you are not showing signs of a habitual procrastinator and you probably avoid the stress of last minute work!

My Rationalizations for Procrastination

People that procrastinate commonly use reasons like the examples below to keep the cycle of procrastination going. The real trick is to have a response prepared to help you overcome each statement to stop the cycle. Create a response for each of the following.

1. I produce my best work when I am under pressure, therefore; I wait until the last minute, then, I'll get it done.

   _____

2. I don't even know where to start with this project, so I'll come back to it later.

   _____

3. I'm not doing this because frankly, I don't want to.

   _____

4. Nothing life shattering is going to happen if I wait to start this project tomorrow.

   _____

5. I should be in the right frame of mind to get this assignment done. Right now, I am just not up for it.

   _____

6. Last time, I waited until the night before it was due, and it turned out just fine.

   _____

7. I can't do this right now! My friend is having a party tonight.

   _____

8. After too many hours on this project, I've completely lost interest.

   _____

   _____

Characteristics of a Procrastinator

If you want to understand why you procrastinate, you'll have to delve a bit deeper. First, let's start with the characteristics of a procrastinator. It's important for you to identify if you portray any of the characteristics listed on the next page:

Low Self-Confidence	A procrastinator with low self-confidence may feel incapable of performing at the level he or she aspires to.
I'm Too Busy	A procrastinator that consistently looks at their busy schedule as justification for falling behind on projects. "I can't do this because I have too many obligations." You might spend a lot of time creating excuses, wasting precious time that could be used completing projects.
Stubbornness or Pride	A procrastinator that delays projects in protest. "I will do this on my terms. Not for anyone else."
Manipulation or Control	A procrastinator that delays decisions as a sign of control. "They can't start if I'm not there." Intentional delay is maddening to others .
Coping with Pressures	Overcoming procrastination is a challenge, especially since delaying decisions has become a common method for handling daily pressures. It's easier to have an excuse to delay or put things things off.
A Frustrated Victim	When you can't get a project done, you feel like a victim: you don't understand how others can get things done that are difficult for you to finish. Unfortunately, the reason(s) for this behavior is a mystery to you.

Are You a Chronic Procrastinator?

Take a moment to think about whether or not any of the aforementioned characteristics describe you. List any that do below:

_____

_____

Four Simple Reasons for Procrastination

1. **Difficult** – we naturally gravitate toward doings things we enjoy and avoid tasks or projects that are difficult for us.

2. **Time-consuming** – when you believe a task will take a large block of time, you may avoid it until you think you have enough time. But you may never get started!

3. **Lack of knowledge or skills** – no one wants to spin their wheels on a project that they don't understand. Gather the information you need and learn the necessary skills to complete the project before you start.

4. **Fear** – what will people think if I fail?

Is there a quick solution? Yes! It's truly a mental game. Create positive self-talk! Create affirmations for yourself whenever you feel stuck: I've got this! It's not going to take as long as I think. I will figure this out or I can get help from my teachers and classmates. If you are afraid of what your classmates, friends, or family think, just remember; they too, are working through their own challenges and probably aren't worried about how you do on this project.

Four Complex Reasons for Procrastination

Perfectionism – Maintaining unrealistically high standards that require nothing short of perfection. Everything must go perfectly as planned. Perfectionism may be brought on by outside criticism or self-imposed. The perfectionist is quick to find errors and is rarely satisfied.

- The perfectionist experiences continuous disappointment because they are rarely content with their work on the first attempt. The perfectionist nitpicks everything to no avail.
- A perfectionist may hesitate to start a project because they are anticipating their own criticism and know how frustrated they become agonizing over every detail.
- The Perfectionist's self-talk can be very demanding. "I should get straight A's; I must exceed my boss' expectations, etc.) "If I can't ace this project, I'm not even going to try."
- The motivation of a perfectionist may be rooted in problems with low self-esteem and self-confidence.

Is there a solution? YES:

- During the project, take breaks to reflect and admire the work that you've done.
- Be mindful of your self-talk. When you notice yourself criticizing the project, turn the conversation around! "This work is well done. I've given my best effort on this project."
- Accept that it is impossible to eliminate all mistakes.
- Remember that every student that has ever taken this course has also had to turn in their work at some point.

Anger/Hostility – When you are upset with your boss, an instructor, or a classmate, it is common to "get even" by withholding your efforts. However, there are very real consequences for you in this situation. You could lose your job, earn a low grade in the class, or lose the respect of your classmates.

Is there a solution? YES:

Look at the big picture. How will allowing your frustration in this situation impact your future? You are not going to let one challenging conversation with your manager, or how you feel about one instructor stand in the way of your personal accomplishment, are you?

Low Frustration Tolerance – You are easily overwhelmed by projects and assignments. You believe your boss or instructor's expectations are terribly unfair. Others experience your frustration as whining and complaining. You express self-talk such as "it isn't fair," "this is too hard," and "no one else has to do this." You delay on projects until you "feel better" about doing the work, but you often feel just as anxious the next day.

Is there a solution? YES:

The more you want something and feel like it is out of reach, the more frustrated you will become.

- Find a mentor, tutor, or instructor that can help you master the skills you need to complete the work on your own later.
- Be patient! If you learn to wait for your desired outcome before quitting the task at hand, you will be amazed at how often you achieve your goal.

Self-Downing – Have you ever looked at a project and thought, "There is no way I can do this, I am not smart enough, I do not have the skills required to complete this task." When you continually minimize your own skills and abilities and express doubt about your ability to succeed, this is known as Self-Downing. A person that has already made up their mind about their inability to do something tends to disbelieve even when they have accomplished the task! They may pass off the achievement as "dumb luck." It can also be difficult to accept compliments from a boss or classmate that praise your work. Deflecting praise is an example of false modesty.

After long periods of self-downing, you may start to develop limiting beliefs about your level of achievement and success. You may also start procrastinating because you have developed a fear of success and will subconsciously seek ways to underperform.

Is there a solution? YES:

- When an instructor or manager compliments your work, practice accepting the compliment by simply saying "thank you."
- Fear of success can be deeply rooted in several factors. Try to determine where your fear of success comes from. Did significant people in your life, like a parent or sibling often criticize your accomplishments? Were you taught to minimize your successes? What is it about achieving your goals that is scary? Do you fear judgment from peers if you outperform your classmates? Are you concerned that important relationships could be compromised if you are successful?
- Remember to compliment and praise yourself for work accomplished.[1&2]

The Inner Workings of Procrastination (ABCs)

We have determined that procrastination often stems from emotional responses to pressure and beliefs about success. The ABC method offers a systematic approach for working through emotional hurdles associated with procrastination.

A = Activating Event. The activating event is the task or project you are delaying, such as work, a group project, or studying for a test.

B = Belief System. Your belief system consists of your internal dialog and feelings about a task. If you have had a negative experience with a similar task, you will likely put it off.

C = Consequence. This is evaluating the outcome of different behaviors. There are two approaches: rational and irrational. A rational response is, "I dread monthly staff meetings, but I am going to attend with a positive attitude anyway." An irrational approach is "I hate monthly staff meetings; I'm just going to skip this one and hope my boss doesn't notice."

The goal of the ABC approach is to help you realize that tasks are neutral and that it is your belief system about tasks that drives your behavior. Once you understand your belief system about the task, you can gain elevation and evaluate the consequences of how you choose to handle the situation.

Solutions
- Use this process to realize you are delaying assignments or projects unnecessarily.
- Uncover the "hidden" reasons or beliefs you have about the task. Make a list and remember the list the next time you find yourself stuck on a project.
- Create a rebuttal for each your beliefs to help overcome them. [3]

My Plan

Think of a situation at school, work, or in your personal life that you are actively procrastinating. Write it below. Next, list all the reasons you are delaying the task. Brainstorm your reasons for delay for at least five minutes. These reasons are the controlling influences. Write down as many reasons as possible.

Next, create "Arguments Against the Delay." Once you have overcome your objections to the task successfully, you will be able to start the project.

I'm delaying _____
because...

Reasons **For** Delay:

1. _____

2. _____

3. _____

4. _____

Arguments **Against** Delay:

1. _____

2. _____

3. _____

4. _____

Final tips:

- Point to past successes of a similar task when you are starting a project that is difficult for you.

- Break up a large project into smaller parts. By taking things one step at a time, you will make incremental progress toward you goal.

- Five-minute plan: Only require yourself to commit a minimum of five minutes to the task. You will likely get into the project and finish much more than you expect.

- Make your intentions known with trusted friends, faculty, and coworkers. Once you've publicly stated your intentions, the peer pressure will likely motivate you to finish the task.

- Find a role model. Study with a friend that concentrates easily and won't distract you.

- Change your surroundings – Find out where you study best. Some people do best in the library on campus, while others prefer working at a coffee shop or at home.

- Create a daily plan – Write down a reasonable daily schedule and assign certain tasks at different times in the day.

- Expect some backsliding – Understanding the reasons you procrastinate and creating strategies to overcome them is an ongoing process. Be patient with yourself. When you have a setback, acknowledge it and move on.

---

[1] Burka, Jane B., and Yuen, Lenora M. Procrastination. Reading: Addison-Wesley, 2008.

[2] Adapted from Cal Poly ASC http://sas.calpoly.edu/asc/ssl/procrastination.html

[3] Ellis, Albert, and Knaus, William J. Overcoming Procrastination. New York: Signet Books, 1977.

Section 6:

STUDY

SKILLS

LEARNING OBJECTIVES

1. Critique different study skills and apply those that will work best for you to improve your study habits.

2. Learn how to recall information quickly and effectively.

3. Use the A.S.P.I.R.E study system to master new material.

> "IT IS GOOD TO HAVE AN END TO YOUR JOURNEY; BUT IT IS THE JOURNEY THAT MATTERS, IN THE END."
>
> -- Ursula K. Le Gui

What tasks do you do well?

You have many skills that you use in everyday life such as writing, listening, drawing, talking, and so on. But often, when asked what good study skills you have, the most common answer is, "I don't know!" What most people don't understand is how to take those everyday skills and turn them into effective study habits.

The reality is that academic studying is often considered boring and many don't have the slightest idea where to begin.

Do you believe this?

What's worse is that some of the everyday "content" you learn is constantly changing.

What you learn today may be null and void tomorrow.

So what's the real deal about study habits?

Learning how to learn! If you learn how to learn, it will be beneficial to you throughout your **entire lifetime.** As you have already discovered, there's much more to learning than meets the eye. In order to better understand what study skills will work for you, let's take a brief look at what you already do.

Self-Evaluation:
My Study Habits

Answer **yes** or **no** to the following questions. Be sure to answer every question as accurately as possible.

My Note-Taking Skills

1. If the teacher provides PowerPoints or outlines, I bring a copy with me to class, and take notes on it.
2. I am able to easily recognize main concepts during a lecture.
3. I can typically identify key words when I am taking notes in a lecture or discussion.
4. I listen attentively and take notes on other student's presentations.
5. I often record lectures if the professor allows it.
6. I collaborate with other students to make sure I understood the most important points of the lecture.

My Reading Skills

1. I am able to summarize main concepts in my own words.
2. I review the objectives and summary questions when reading from a textbook.
3. I divide long sections of reading into smaller "chunks."
4. I think about what I am reading and often ask myself questions about the content.
5. I look at chapter titles and headings and ensure that I understand the main points as I read.
6. I make outlines about the material as I am reading.

My Study Strategies

1. I study in noise and distraction free zones.
2. I take breaks as I am studying to give myself time to process the material.
3. I study during the times that I am most alert and awake.
4. I set mini study goals for myself as I study such as, "In the next hour, I will memorize a determined number of terms."
5. I study for a minimum of two hours for every one hour that I attend class.
6. I begin studying the subjects that give me the most difficulty first.

My Time Management Skills

1. I keep track of my upcoming assignments, tests, quizzes, and projects on a calendar.
2. I use my school's resources to help me handle busy times during the course term.
3. I typically complete my work well before the due date.
4. I create lists of things I need to accomplish for any given day or week.
5. I rarely procrastinate.
6. I feel I am well balanced in terms of school, rest, work and social/ family obligations.

My Motivation

1. I have no problem focusing during study time.
2. I have no problem beginning a project.
3. I do *not* have problems telling friends and family that I can't attend social events when I need to work on school projects.
4. I have no problem staying on task while in the middle of a project.
5. I often ask questions while participating in projects or completing difficult assignments.
6. I have both short and long-term goals regarding my future.

My Test Anxiety Management Skills

1. I am rarely anxious and/or stressed when preparing for an exam.
2. I practice positive self-talk during an exam.
3. I use various relaxation techniques when I feel stressed during an exam.
4. I rarely forget material I have studied for an exam.
5. I do not consider myself an anxious person, in general.
6. I tend to get calmer as I am completing an exam.

My Test Taking Strategies

1. I tend to study well in advance of tests so that I am not cramming the night before.
2. I give myself practice tests as I am preparing for an exam.
3. I feel confident in my ability to strategize when taking a multiple-choice exam.
4. I always finish projects and assignments on time.
5. I am acutely aware of what I know and what I need to study when preparing for an exam.
6. I analyze exams that have been returned to me and ask the teacher questions if I don't understand why I got something wrong. [1]

If you answered "No" to two or more items in each section, you will need additional study-skill resources to build and hone your skills. If you do, this is okay. Many of us need to refine our skills. It's always better to have a good idea as to where you need to improve your skills, rather than not knowing at all. List what section(s) you might need some fine-tuning. Identify potential resources that are available to help.

_____

_____

_____

Practical Tips for Different Types of Exams

Multiple-Choice

Multiple-choice exams can be tricky! Start by reading the question and answering it in your head before looking at the answer options. After reviewing the answers, eliminate any that are clearly wrong. If you are left with two that "could" be right, go with your gut-instinct.

Another great tip is to skip questions that have you completely stumped. Don't waste time on these types of questions. Come back to them at the end, time permitting.

Before taking a multiple-choice exam, you should understand the grading practices. For example, some exams penalize you for leaving questions blank while others do not count blank answers against you. Find out how your exam will be graded, if you are not penalized for blank answers; leave the questions blank that you have absolutely no idea what the answer could be. If you can eliminate at least one answer, then go ahead and take a guess. Remember, you don't want to leave too many blank.

A few other sensible recommendations:
- ✓ If two answers are quite similar, minus one or two words, one of the answers is likely the correct response.
- ✓ With number, if there is a wide range (0, 15, 45, 300), choose a number closer to the middle.

True-False

If there is anything at all about a true-false statement that is vaguely false, the correct response is false. Also, if the statement doesn't say it, it is false. If it is not there, it can't be true. Be on the look out for qualifiers such as sometimes, never, rarely, always or almost always!

Short Answer

When an answer requires a brief response, keep it brief. In this case less is more, don't dig yourself into a hole by providing too much information that could be erroneous.

If asked to provide definitions of words, consider studying using flashcards and mnemonic devices to help you remember definitions.

Open Book

This type of exam can be tricky if you are not well prepared. First, invest in some color coded tabs or post it notes and clearly mark each section or chapter so you can quickly find information you need. Next, make sure to go through the book and **HIGHLIGHT** key topics that can easily catch your eye as you are flipping through the book on exam day. Finally, write notes in the margin of the book. You will not have time to consult both the book and your notes, so combine the two sources of information and be speedy on exam day.

Essay Exams

An essay exam is one of the most effective ways for a teacher to decipher how well a student knows the subject matter.

When preparing to take an essay exam, make sure to have a working knowledge of the required material. You will likely need to remember specific details about the subject matter to be able to support your claims. So make sure to study well in advance. Do not attempt to "cram" the night before.

Most essay questions will ask you to analyze, compare, contrast, critique, defend, evaluate, examine, explain, illustrate, or interpret a specific topic.

First, read the prompt and underline what you are asked to write about. You will form your thesis statement based on the writing prompt.

Next, create a quick outline or visual map of how you will prove your thesis. Remember, each paragraph must contain supporting evidence to prove your thesis.

Keep in mind the following:

- The introduction and thesis let the reader know what you are going to discuss.

- The body proves your point (thesis) with supporting evidence.

- The conclusion summarizes how you proved your point (thesis).

Quick Tip: Everything must connect back to your thesis.

Now it's time to write your essay, be mindful to follow your outline or visual map. The most important aspect of writing an essay is to keep your ultimate purpose at the forefront of your mind: proving your thesis. Make sure you do not go off on tangents; remain focused on the task at hand.

Finally, and **most important**! Leave at least five minutes at the end to re-read your essay. It is of utmost importance that you read what you have written. You will undoubtedly find spelling and/or punctuation errors that will need to be corrected.

How should you spend your time? Let's say you have 45 minutes to write an essay:

- 10 minutes: Read the prompt and create an outline or visual map.

- 10 minutes: Write the introduction and thesis statement.

- 15 minutes: Write the body; supporting facts that prove the thesis.

- 5 minutes: Write the conclusion.

- 5 minutes: Proofread the essay and make any necessary corrections.

Memory

To better understand what study skills will work most effectively for you, you need to understand how your memory stores information.

Memory is the process by which information is retained for later use. The basic process by which information is processed follows the following format:

Information is **acquired + encoded** leads to **storage** in the brain leads to the possibility of later **retrieval** (though as you know at test time, is not a guarantee), and the possibility of eventually forgetting the information.

Did you know that your memory is similar to a computer, smartphone, or iPad? Today, it's not uncommon to hear that our human mind can be compared to a computer and our memory, to an information-processing system. If you can take a moment to appreciate this analogy, you can better understand how you store information, how long you need the information (e.g., one hour, a day, five years), and how you can retrieve the information.

Your computer **acquires (or receives)** input from a keyboard or a mouse; it converts the symbols into a special numeric code; it **stores (or saves)** the information on a hard drive, thumb drive, or cloud storage; it then **retrieves** the data from the drive to be displayed on a screen. If the computer crashes or the system is outdated, if there's not enough space on the hard drive, if the file gets deleted, or if you enter the wrong retrieval command, the information becomes inaccessible, or 'forgotten.'

The process by which your memory stores information, is also known as the **information-processing model** and works in a similar manner. Within this memory approach, there are three types of memory: sensory, short-term, and long-term memory.

Memory IS how you learn for a lifetime! And the KEY is Attention.

Types of Memory

Sensory memory (1-3 seconds)

This type of memory is stored for a brief moment ranging from a fraction of a second to three seconds. This is associated with information that registers on the senses.

Short-term memory (about 7 items for 20 seconds)

Short-term memory refers to things we notice; we generally hold a maximum of seven items for approximately 20 seconds. Typically, our short-term memory fades quickly, however; we can commit these items to longer-term memory through repeated exposure. When we refer to "attention span," short-term memory is what comes into play.

Long-term memory (almost permanent)

Long-term memory is considered a more permanent type storage system that holds a large quantity of information over a period of time. Science writer Isaac Asimov thought that long-term memory takes in a quadrillion separate pieces of information over the course of a lifetime. Mathematician John Griffith estimated that, over the average lifetime of a person, (s)he stores about five hundred times more information than the **Encyclopedia Britannica**.[2]

Why do you need sensory memory?

You may be wondering why we even have sensory memory if it only lasts for a maximum of three seconds. Well, it is actually quite useful. As you go through life, it is almost impossible to recognize all of the information that comes our way. Our sensory memory allows us to quickly process information, react to sights and smells, and make quick judgments without having to wait for our conscious thoughts to be processed. Imagine if you had no sensory memory, at the every blink of the eye, you would lose track of what you were seeing. It would be as if you were viewing the world through various snapshots instead of a continuous film.

Take a moment to memorize the following list of numbers. This is part of a self-assessment that you will use shortly.

1 8 1 2 1 9 4 1 1 7 7 6 1 4 9 2 2 0 0 1

Short-term Memory

Think about what your environment is like as you walk from class to class on campus or to work. You're seeing people, trees, buildings, and so on. You're hearing multitudes of conversations, the sounds of cars, the sounds of leaves as they fall. You smell the car exhaust, the perfume or cologne of the person next to you, the flowers that are blooming, and a pungent trashcan that you walk by. More stimuli is probably reaching your sensors than you can think of or write about, but almost never reach your consciousness, and are immediately 'forgotten.' **The key is attention.** Sensations that do not capture your attention quickly tend to disappear, whereas those that we notice, are transferred to short-term memory – a somewhat more lasting but limited storage facility. As you already know, people are selective in their perceptions and can instantly direct their attention to stimuli that is interesting, adaptive, or important.

Self-Evaluation: My Short-Term Memory

Write down the numbers in order that you memorized, without looking!

How did you do? Did you remember all of the numbers? Now, try again but this time chunk the numbers into years like this...

1812   1941   1776   1492   2001

Chunking

Chunking allows you to enhance your **short-term memory** by using your aptitude more effectively. In theory, you are limited to around seven chunks, but you are capable of increasing the size of each chunk. People who do not "practice" can only remember around two to five chunks. However; with practice, you can increase your ability to remember seven or more chunks. With training, you are capable of increasing the size of the chunks that you are able to remember. This will allow you to remember larger quantities of material. Remember, your brain is a muscle that needs to be exercised in order to be in tip-top shape. Exercise it frequently and you will remember more bits of information.

Now, try the numbers again... Without looking!

_____

Were you better able to recall the numbers this time?

Long-term Memory

Once information passes from sensory to short-term memory, it can be passed along to long-term memory.

Self-Evaluation: My Long-Term Memory

What do you remember about your third birthday?

_____

What's the name of your second-grade teacher?

_____

What's the smell of the playground of your elementary school?

_____

Can you describe a dream that you had last night?

_____

Recite the first words of your country's national anthem.

_____

To answer these questions, you would have to retrieve information from the mental warehouse of **long-term memory.** Like a hard drive of a computer or cloud storage, long-term memory is a fairly permanent storage system that has the ability to retain large amounts of information over long periods of time.

But to transfer anything into long-term memory, it is more efficient to use **elaborative rehearsal**. This is a method that allows us to think about learned material in a more relevant way. We can do this by associating the new material with pre-existing knowledge that is already in our long-term memory. Essentially, the more deeply you process something, the more likely you are to recall it later.

Perhaps the most effective form of elaborative rehearsal is the linking of new information to yourself. Am I suggesting you become "selfish?" In a way, yes! By viewing new information as relevant to yourself, you will take that information into consideration and organize it around common themes. **The result is an improvement in recall**. So you need to try and personalize any course material or projects as much as possible, even if it is just coming up with examples of when these things have happened to you. This increases your likelihood of remembering it for an exam or even for your career!

Moving information from short-term to long-term memory is no easy task! Fortunately, some types of knowledge are passed along automatically and without necessarily trying. When you see someone two or three times, you may have trouble remembering their name, but you can easily recall their face. Likewise, we encode information about time, location, and events without conscious effort.

There are different ideas regarding how long-term memories are stored. One idea is that memories are stored in an elaborate web of ideas or **semantic networks**. Another viewpoint is that we store long-term memories linked together by semantic relationships. Regardless of how long-term memories are stored, we can all agree that knowledge is organized in our memories in some way, perhaps the way books are organized in a library.

How We Remember Names and Faces

There are a number of ways in which we remember names and faces. Here are some suggestions:

1. Try associating the person's name with a body part, such as *Nancy* and *nose*.
2. When somebody tells you their name, repeat it various times in your head.
3. Repeat the person's name back to them and imagine how it is spelled.

4. Try linking the person's name to somebody famous. For example, someone named Jennifer could be associated with Jennifer Lopez.

5. If you forget the person's name, ask them to repeat it and this time use one of the tips in numbers 1-4.

Much research supports the idea that memories are stored in **semantic networks.** For example, when a group of students was given 50 terms that fell into four different categories (colors, vegetables, countries, and types of material) – even when the words were shown in a mixed order – they tended to remember them in clusters.[3]

My Recall Skills

If You Don't Encode, You Can't Retrieve it!

Show the importance of encoding by answering the following questions:

1. What color is the suit of diamonds in a deck of cards?

   _____

2. How many rows of stripes are on the U.S. flag?

   _____

3. Whose image is on a nickel? Is he wearing a tie?

   _____

4. What five words besides *In God We Trust* appear on most U.S. currency?

   _____

5. Do you turn a key clockwise or counter clockwise when opening a door?

   _____

You most likely have seen these items thousands of times, but might not recall all of the details because you didn't think about the information.

So how can we improve our memory? Many of us tend to be visual learners. Many books on improving memory recommend that verbal information be connected to visual images. One popular use of imagery is the **method of loci**, in which the items you wish to remember are mentally placed in familiar locations. For example, let's say you want to remember a shopping list of bananas, milk, bread, cheese, and mayonnaise.

Now, take a stroll in your house from the front door to that back door. Along that route, imagine that you pass the dining room table, the couch, the coffee table, the end table and the entertainment center. Now, place each item on one of those familiar pieces of furniture. For example, place the bananas on the dining room table, the milk on the couch, the bread on the coffee table, the cheese on the end table, and the mayonnaise on the entertainment center. When you take a mental stroll through the house, the items on the list should come to mind. The idea is to link new items to other items already stored in your memory.

Sometimes, one learning experience can disrupt memory for another, this is known as **interference**. This happens to students, as material learned in one course can make it harder to remember that learned in another. To minimize the effects of interference, follow these suggestions: first, study right before going to bed and briefly review material before an exam. Second, study for one course at a time. For example, if you study for Spanish, then move to chemistry, then go on to math and back to Spanish, each course will disrupt your memory of the others – especially if the material is similar.

Another idea to be aware of is **context reinstatement.** We can easily remember information when we are in the same setting in which it was first learned – and in the same mindset. The idea behind context reinstatement is that the setting and the mood it evokes serve as cues that help with the retrieval of the new information. This is why actors tend to rehearse on the stage where they will later perform. The next time you have an important exam to take, try studying in the classroom where you'll take it. You never know if it will work until you try!

Quick Tips on Improving Your Memory

- **Practice time:**
    - Practice makes perfect! Spend time studying in short sessions; you're likely to remember more. Do not cram the night before an exam; you are likely to remember less. Your brain needs time to process the information, so give it the time it needs!

- **Depth of processing:**
    - If you cram information into your brain, this may work to keep the information in your short-term memory, but it will not last over time. Have you ever noticed that after you take an exam, you "forget everything"? This is because you have not dedicated the appropriate amount of time to think actively and deeply about material – about what it means and how it is linked to what you already know. Skimming or speed-reading will not promote long-term retention. Spend 'quality' time studying.

- **Verbal mnemonics:**
  - Use rhyming or acronyms to quickly remember various terms.
  - Verbal mnemonics, or 'memory tricks' are sometimes the easiest way to remember a list of items that needs to be recalled. Chances are you have already used popular methods such as rhymes (I before E, except after C) and things like the difference between 'desert' and 'dessert'- dessert has two s's, you often want two servings of dessert.

- **Overlearn Information:**
  - Keep reviewing flashcards or information even after you think you know it.

- **Methods of Loci:**
  - Make sure you mentally associate and place items to be remembered in familiar locations.

- **Study right before sleeping:**
  - Studying right before going to bed helps to remember material better.

- **Context Reinstatement:**
  - Study in the same environment and mood in which you will be taking the exam.

- **Interference:**
  - Study one subject at a time.

The Real Skinny!

What else might you need to know to improve your study skills?

How much do I need to study?

It's suggested that undergraduates study a minimum of three hours for each one hour of class time. The mathematics is simple. If you have a 3-credit hour class, you will spend a minimum of nine hours each week studying for that course. It's likely you will spend additional time preparing for the mid-term and final exams, not to mention research essays.

Is studying hard work?

It doesn't have to be! You're only limited by your creativity. College courses are designed to focus on important key information through repetition: reading, re-reading, writing, re-writing, discussing, re-discussing, thinking, and re-thinking the course material. As you've already discovered, you need to push the same information past your brain in as many ways as possible to remember it: see it, hear it, read it, write it, repeat it all again in as many different ways as possible. The trick is to help yourself learn as painlessly as possible.

How do you

A.S.P.I.R.E.?

A *study system to succeed!*

A: Approach/Attitude/Arrange

Arrange your schedule to eliminate distractions; **approach** your studies with a positive **attitude**. Choose where you like to study:

Quiet place   Study hall   Public venue   Computer/desk

S: Select/survey/scan

- **Select** an appropriate amount of material to study.
- **Survey** the titles, images, headings, comprehension questions to get a sneek-peak as to what's to come.
- **Scan** the content for important words: underline what you don't understand. Highlight or circles keywords.

Mixing with a color wheel
Mixing colors with paints using a color wheel as a guide allows you to visualize color mixtures within a traditional color wheel. This method uses the distance and midpoint between two paints on the color wheel to estimate the saturation and hue of their mixture.

P: Piece together the parts:

- Put aside your materials.
- **Piece** together all of the content that you have reviewed. You can do this alone or with classmates. Then articulate what you don;t understand.

I: Investigate/inquire/inspect:

- **Investigate** other places that can provide you with information such as different books, Internet websites, subject matter experts etc.
- **Inquire** from professionals that are available to support you such as you teacher, tutors, the librarian, etc.
- **Inspect** material that was problematic for you.

Now that you have processed the key words, you need to identify what you don't understand. If the text or your notes doesn't answer these questions, you need to investigate and inquire with other sources.

Where will you go? (e.g., professor/librarian, book/website)

R: Reexamine/reflect/relay

Reexamine the material | **Reflect** on the topic | **Relay** comprehension

- **Reexamine:**

What questions do I still have?
  Did I miss something?

- **Reflect:**

How can I connect this to the work I need to complete? Is there a different way to use it?

- **Relay:**

Can I explain this to someone else?
  Will I make it more meaningful for them?

E: Evaluate/examine/explore:

- **Evaluate** your the feedback you get on tests and assignments.
- **Examine** how you are progressing toward meeting your goals.
- **Explore** possibilities with teachers, mentors, tutors, parents or professionals in your field.[4]

A: Finding the right study space

In order to effectively study, what area works best for you?

- A coffee shop can provide a stimulating environment, background noise, relaxed atmosphere, Wi-Fi, and coffee! It can be convenient for small groups, studying with a partner, or alone. You can also be unknown and unbothered, and easily turn off your cell phone to avoid distractions!
- Your school's study lounge can also be convenient for studying alone or in small groups. However, if the noise, movement, or friends is too distracting, then relocate to where your studying will be more effective.
- Your bedroom/personal space can be a convenient location. Its comfort can be a mixed blessing if you take too many naps!

- Kitchens are conducive to studying, with good lighting and open space for all your materials. You also have nourishment at hand, but snack on fruit and vegetables and avoid heavy foods.
- If you focus better in your basement, great!
- Music can make for good background noise, but make sure it stays in the background; don't lose track of what you are studying.
- Your living room is a great place to study with comfortable seating and enough space, but avoid the distractions or projects around the house. If you love watching the television, it may not be the best option for a study space.
- The library offers professional services, a quiet environment, Wi-Fi, and even windows with a view! An empty classroom provides an even quieter, more secluded space.

S. SQ3R reading method[5]

Survey! Question! Read! Recite! Review!

SQ3R will help you to build a framework to better understand your reading assignment.

Before you read, survey the chapter:

- Review titles, headings, and words in bold
- Read text under images, charts, graphs, or maps
- Review comprehension questions or teacher-made helpers
- Read introductory and concluding paragraphs
- Review the chapter summary

Question while you are surveying:

- Change titles and headings into questions; can you answer them?
- Review questions throughout the chapter; can you answer them?
- Think about remarks your instructor made about the topic.
- Think about what you already know about the topic; how can you apply it?

Note: Consider writing out these questions. This variation is called **SQW3R.**

When you begin to read:

- Try to answer the questions you first asked your self in the "Survey" phase
- Be sure to answer all the questions in the text
- Review text under images, charts, graphs, or maps
- Take special note of all the underlined, italicized, bold printed words or phrases
- Review any graphic aids provided
- Slow down when reading challenging topics
- Stop and review content that is unclear
- Read chunks at a time and "Recite" after each part

Recite after you've read a section:

- After reading each section, ask yourself comprehension questions out loud
- **Take notes** on what you are reading, carefully writing the information in your **own words**
- Underline, highlight, circle the most important points
- Reciting: The more senses you use, the more likely you are to remember what you read. Triple strength learning: **seeing, saying, hearing**
- Quadruple strength learning: **seeing, saying, hearing, *writing*!**

Review: an ongoing process

- **Day One Schedule**
  - After reading and reciting the chapter, jot down the most important questions in the margins.
  - If you took notes while reciting, jot down those questions in your notebook or electronic notes.

- **Day Two Schedule**
  - Review the important points you have noted.
  - Ask yourself the questions you jotted down.
  - Orally recite or write the answers from memory.
  - Develop mnemonic devices for material that needs to be memorized.
  - Make flash cards for the questions that you can't answer from memory/

- **Days Three, Four and Five Schedule**
  - Review the questions that gave you difficulties.
  - Have a friend or family member quiz you.

- **Weekend Schedule**
  - Make a list of all the topics you need to know from the chapter.
  - From that list make a study sheet, visual map, or a study aid that works best for you.
  - Recite the information orally and in your own words as you create your study guide.
  - Review your guide every day until all information is committed to memory.

P: Reading difficult material

Reading difficult material can be a matter of concentration or of simply organizing the challenge into steps:

- To begin, choose a moderate amount of material.
- Get a grasp on how the material is organized: scan the section for titles, headings, sub-headings, and topic sentences to get the general idea; pay attention to graphs, charts, and diagrams.

- If there is a summary at the end of a chapter, read it.
- Check the beginning and the end for leading questions and exercises.
- Read first what you do understand.
- Mark what you do not understand to review later.

As you read, practice *the look-away method*:

- Periodically look away from the text and ask yourself a stimulus question related to the text.
- Phrase the question positively!
- Respond or restate using your own words.

Make connections and associations

Don't use this exercise to memorize--but rather to understand

- **Look up words**

  When there are important words that you don't understand, but that are essential to the subject at hand, look them up in a dictionary.

- **Read to the end**

  Do not get discouraged and stop reading. The more you read, the clearer the ideas become. When you finish reading, review to see what you have learned, and re-read the concepts that are not clear.

- **Organize your notes by connecting ideas**

  Place information in an outline or concept map and pay close attention to the relationships between ideas.

- **Do not confine yourself to words!**

Use representations, graphics, pictures, colors, even movement to visualize and connect ideas. Use whatever techniques work to help you understand.

At this point, if you do not understand your reading, do not panic!

Set it aside, and read it again the next day. If necessary, repeat. This allows your brain to process the material, even while you sleep. This is referred to as *distributed* reading.

Re-read the section you have chosen with the framework (outline or concept map) you have constructed in your mind and separate out what you understand from what you do not.

I: Researching on the Internet

How do I search the Internet?

1. **Narrow your topic and its description;** identify and pull out key words, phrases, and categories.

2. **Use a search engine: Does it contain a directory of topics?**
   - Find the best combination of key words to locate information that you need and enter them into the search engine.

3. **Get assistance from your local research librarian**

4. **Refer to known, recommended, expert, or reviewed web sites**

5. **Refer to professional portals** that may have directories or collections by topic.

6. **Review the number of options returned**
   - If there are too many web sites, add more keywords.
   - If there are too few options, narrow/delete some keywords, or substitute other key words.

7. **Review the first pages returned**
   - If these are not helpful, review your key words for a better description.

8. **Use *advanced search* options in search engines:** Search options include:
   - Key word combinations, including Boolean strings
   - Locations where key words are found
        i. For example: in the title, 1st paragraphs, coded metadata
   - Languages to search in
   - Sites containing media files
        i. Images, videos, MP3/music, ActiveX, JAVA, etc.
   - Dates web sites were created or updated

9. **Research using several search engines**
   - Each search engine has a different database of web sites it searches
   - Some "Meta-Search" engines actually search other search engines; if one search engine returns few web sites, another may return more

10. **Evaluate the content of the web sites you've found**

11. **Track your search**
    - List resources you checked, including the date you checked them
    - Identify the resource, especially its location and the date you found it

12. **When printing, set your options to print:**
    - Title of the page | the Web address | the date printed

R: Thinking critically

Critical thinking reviews a topic or problem with open-mindedness. This exercise outlines the first stage of applying a critical thinking approach to developing and understanding a topic. You will:

- Develop a statement of the topic
- List what you understand, what you've been told, and what opinions you hold about it
- Identify resources available for research
- Define timelines and due dates and how they affect the development of your study

Here is more on the first stage:

Define your destination, what you want to learn

Talk with your teacher or an "expert" about your topic

Topics can be simple phrases:

"The role of gender in video game playing"
"Causes of the war before 1939"
"Mahogany trees in Central America"
"Plumbing regulations in the suburbs"
"Regions of the human brain"

Develop your frame of reference, your starting point, by listing what you already know about the subject

What opinions and prejudices do you already have about this?
- What have you been told about this topic?

What resources are available to you for research?
- When gathering information, keep an open mind.
- Look for chance resources that pop up.
- Play the "reporter" and follow leads.
- If you don't seem to find what you need, ask librarians or your teacher.

How does your timeline and due dates affect your research?
- Keep in mind that you need to follow a schedule.
- Work back from the due date and define stages of development, not just with this first phase, but also when completing the whole project.

Summary of critical thinking:
- Determine the facts of a new situation or subject without prejudice.
- Place these facts and information in a pattern so that you can understand them.
- Accept or reject the source values and conclusions based upon your experience, judgment, and beliefs.

E: Study Guides

Many courses or tutoring centers at your college provide study guides that will be helpful to highlight important areas of the course that you'll need to learn.

My A.S.P.I.R.E Plan

You have just reviewed a whole new approach to studying! It may feel a bit overwhelming to you. Let's break it down into bite-size pieces and see how you can use it to your advantage.

1. When thinking about the A.S.P.I.R.E study plan, something I already do that works well for me is...

_____

_____

2. It works well for me because...

_____

_____

3. In the past, the most difficult part of studying has been...

_____

_____

4. I think this has given me so much trouble because...

_____

_____

5. When thinking about the A.S.P.I.R.E study plan, something new that I plan to try is...

_____

_____

6. I plan to try this because... (State how you think it will be beneficial to you.)

_____

_____

7. When thinking about the A.S.P.I.R.E study plan, something I am afraid to try is... (State something you know would be beneficial to you, but you are apprehensive to try it.)

_____

_____

8. I am afraid to try it because...

_____

_____

9. I am going to make the commitment to myself to try it on my next exam. My next exam is... (State the subject and date of your next exam.)

_____

_____

10. If this particular study strategy does not work for me, the next one I will try is... (State the strategy and why you think this strategy might be beneficial to you.)

_____

_____

_____

LIVE AS IF YOU WERE GOING TO DIE TOMORROW. LEARN AS IF YOU WERE GOING TO LIVE FOREVER.

- Ghandi

[1] Stanley, Constance. Focus on Community College Success (4th edition). Cengage, 2016.

[2] Higbee, Kenneth. Your Memory. Marlowe & Company, 2001.

[3] Small, G. The Memory Bible. Hyperion, 2002.

[4] www.studygs.net

[5] Robinson, Francis Pleasant. Effective Study (6th edition). Harper & Row, 1978

Section 7:

BECOMING AN EFFECTIVE ONLINE STUDENT

LEARNING OBJECTIVES

1. Compare and contrast traditional vs. online learning and success factors associated with online learning.

2. Describe your learning style and identify strategies to maximize your effectiveness as an online student.

3. Identify hardware and Internet speed requirements necessary to access your online courses.

4. Understand how to effectively manage time as an online student.

5. Communicate appropriately and participate effectively with your online community.

Introduction to Online Learning

Welcome to the world of online learning! You are joining the more than 5.8 million students in the United States that take classes online every semester. Online classes today are engaging and use all types of technology to connect you to your teachers and fellow students, as well as to the course material and services you need to succeed in college.

Online learning may not be for everybody. It requires the ability to set a schedule and be disciplined about following deadlines. Younger students sometimes miss the social interaction that occurs in a traditional university, with its dormitories and campus activities. However, there are many benefits afforded to students that take online classes. It enables students to work and still attend school. It allows students to schedule study time around family and work obligations. For students that live in remote areas, it ensures obtaining a degree from an accredited school located anywhere in the United States (or the world!), which saves time and money on commuting. [1]

PREPARING TO LEARN ONLINE

Taking your first online course can be daunting. You have spent the majority of your academic career in a classroom, with a set schedule, and with direct access to your teacher. If you had a question, you just raised your hand. If you needed clarification, you could ask a friend. Typically, you received your book or obtained it at the bookstore on the first day of class. Believe it or not, you can still do all of those things as an online student; you just need to do them differently. If you have a question in an online course, you can email your instructor or message them privately from your course portal. Some teachers even have virtual office hours or are available by phone. If you want to ask a question to a friend or another student, you can post a public or private message in the course portal. Books and other course material can be embedded right into your class for easy access.

So, as you can tell, everything that you can do in a traditional class, can be accomplished in an online class – just differently!

Traditional Learning vs. Online Learning

We have already mentioned some of the differences that you will encounter in an online class. The chart below identifies some additional differences that you will experience.

Characteristic	Traditional Learning	Online Learning
Class schedule	Students sign up for a scheduled course and attend the course at that time.	Students participate in the class discussions and upload assignments according to an established timeline.
Class materials	Students purchase textbooks and workbooks. The teacher may supplement the class with handouts.	Students access e-books and other learning resources that are embedded in the online class or accessed through Publisher's websites.
Class structure	The teacher typically lectures while the students take notes.	Students watch, listen to, or read the course content.
Asking questions	Students raise their hands to ask questions.	Students post or email questions to faculty.
Obtaining feedback	Faculty meet with students in-person or write feedback on assignments.	Faculty schedule a call or a skype meeting to talk with students, or post feedback in the gradebook.
Interacting with peers	Students call, text, or meet up with peers before, during, or after class.	Students call, text, or email peers. Group communication can take place in the class portal.
Faculty's role	The teacher is the primary source of information.	The teacher facilitates the class learning and guides the students to the information.
Student motivation	The student is motivated by the instructor, peers, and environment.	Student is motivated by learning new things and by directing his or her own discovery of knowledge.

While there are many benefits to taking online courses, such as a learner-centered environment, flexibility, and convenience, there are also some challenges. Learning how to access people, services, and your course material are the biggest challenges that new online learners face. Lack of immediate feedback and insecurity about computer skills or having unreliable internet service can also cause concern. By addressing these concerns, and evaluating your learning style, we can provide resources and suggestions to help mitigate your concerns and help you get the most out of your online course.

Learning Styles

Why is knowing your learning style important? Your learning style dictates how you prefer to process information and how you can best learn new things. There are several prominent learning style instruments developed by leading theorists i this field. Three of the most well-known and well-respected instruments include the Myers-Briggs Type Indicator, Kolb's Learning Style Model, and the Fleming VARK Inventory. We will use the VARK inventory to assess your learning style.

The VARK inventory is based on the research of Neil Fleming. VARK looks at modal preferences – only one part of a person's learning style - but an importan one, because it is about preferences for working with information. **The four modalities are Visual, Aural, Read/Write, and Kinesthetic.**

Keep in mind that just because material is not taught in your preferred style does not mean that you **CAN'T** learn it; it just means that it will take more effort on you part.

Take a few minutes to answer the following questions. The questionnaire aims to discover your preferences for the way you work with information. You will have c preferred learning style and one part of that learning style is your preference for the intake and the output of ideas and information. There are no right or wrong answers, and there is no learning style preferred over another. This survey will assist you in developing strategies to help you maximize your success and enjoyment in online classes.

LEARNING STYLE ASSESSMENT

Circle the answer which best describes your preference for each question. Do not be alarmed that the answers do not go in alphabetical order. This is part of the quiz design; it will make sense to you shortly.
Remember, it is okay to circle more than if a single answer does not match your perception.

1. You are about to give directions to a person who is standing with you. She is staying in a hotel in town and wants to visit your house later. She has a rental car. Would you:
a) draw a map on paper
b) tell her the directions
c) write down the directions (without a map)
d) pick her up from the hotel in a car

2. You are not sure whether a word should be spelled `dependent' or `dependent'. Do you:
c) look it up in the dictionary
a) see the word in your mind and choose by the way it looks
b) sound it out in your mind
d) write both versions down on paper and choose one

3. You have just received a copy of your itinerary for a world trip. This is of interest to a friend. Would you:
b) phone her immediately and tell her about it
c) send her a copy of the printed itinerary
a) show her on a map of the world
d) share what you plan to do at each place you visit

4. You are going to cook something as a special treat for your family. Do you:
d) cook something familiar without the need for instructions
a) thumb through the cookbook looking for ideas from the pictures
c) refer to a specific cookbook where there is a good recipe

5. A group of tourists have been assigned to you to find out about wildlife parks. Would you:
d) drive them to a wildlife reserve or park
a) show them slides and photographs
c) give them pamphlets or a book on wildlife reserves or parks
b) give them a talk on wildlife reserves or parks

6. You are purchasing a new stereo. Other than price, what would most influence your decision?
b) the salesperson telling you what you want to know
c) reading the details about it
d) playing with the controls and listening to it
a) it looks really smart and fashionable

7. Recall a time in your life when you learned how to do something like playing a new board game. Try to avoid choosing a very physical skill, e.g. riding a bike. How did you learn best? By:
a) visual clues -- pictures, diagrams, charts
c) written instructions
b) listening to somebody explaining it
d) doing it or trying it

8. You have an eye problem. Would you prefer that the doctor:
a) tell you what is wrong
b) show you a diagram of what is wrong
d) use a model to show what is wrong

9. You are about to learn to use a new program on a computer. Would you:
d) sit down at the keyboard and begin to experiment with the program's features
c) read the manual that comes with the program
b) telephone a friend and ask questions about it

10. You are staying in a hotel and have a rental car. You would like to visit friends whose address/location you do not know. Would you like them to:
a) draw you a map on paper
b) tell you the directions
c) write down the directions (without a map)
d) pick you up from the hotel in their car

11. Apart from price, what would most influence your decision to buy a particular textbook:
d) you have used a copy before
b) a friend talking about it
c) quickly reading parts of it
a) the way it looks is appealing

12. A new movie has arrived in town. What would most influence your decision to go (or not)?
b) you heard a radio review about it
c) you read a review about it
a) you saw a preview of it

13. Do you prefer a lecturer or teacher who likes to use:
c) a textbook, handouts, readings
a) flow diagrams, charts, slides
d) field trips, labs, practical sessions
b) discussion, guest speakers

Scoring:
Give yourself one point for each A, B, C, or D response. Tally up the number of times you chose each letter option in the second row. Next, total up the number of tally marks for each response. Which column has the highest score? This indicates your preferred learning preference(s).

Answer	A	B	C	D
Tally up the number of times you chose each response:				
Learning Styles	Visual	Aural / Auditory	Read / Write	Kinesthetic

Now that you have an idea as to how you prefer to learn, read the suggestions that follow. You are armed with knowledge! Use this to your advantage; you are in the driver's seat when it comes to how you process information! [2]

Visual (V):

If you have a visual (V) preference you prefer information to be presented in charts, graphs, labeled diagrams, and separated into colored textboxes. You prefer important information to be highlighted or pointed out with arrows or circles. In online learning, lessons tend to rely heavily on the use of PowerPoint, which primarily presents words on a slide. This is not optimal for visual learners. As a matter of fact, you are probably glossing over these words and focusing in on the diagrams already. That's ok! Now, let's take a moment to learn about ways to maximize your study time by turning written cues into visual cues.

Let's say the lesson this week is about US presidents and their important contributions. Chances are the PowerPoint presentation will include a list of the presidents in one column and their contribution in another.

Obviously, you can't change the way the information is presented in your course, but you can change the way you use that information to study. As a visual learner, your brain responds to symbols and colors. When studying for the exam, and as you take notes, turn the words into pictures. Associate the words with an image that you will remember.

Aural / Auditory (A):

This perceptual mode describes a preference for information that can be listened to and/or spoken. Students with this modality report that they learn best from lectures, tutorials, recorded material, group discussion, and lively discussion. It includes speaking out loud as well as talking to yourself. Often people with this preference want to sort things out *while* speaking, rather than sorting things out and *then* speaking.

If you are an auditory learner, you will perform best when you attend synchronous classes or listen to recorded lectures that might be offered as a part of an online program.   Also, just because you are taking your class online, doesn't mean that you cannot reach out to your peers by phone or through skype.   Many textbooks have a free "companion site" for students. The companion site usually includes audio files with key vocabulary pronounced. Many also have the chapters in audio files that you can download to an IPod or MP3 player. You can listen to the chapters while commuting or when you have some down time. Auditory learners can also benefit from the resources that are available for visually impaired students. Although you are not visually impaired, the Americans with Disabilities act (ADA) has encouraged publishers to find ways of converting printed material to auditory material and these files are available to everybody. You just need to ask where to locate them!

Read / Write (R):

This preference is for information displayed as words. Not surprisingly, many academics have a strong preference for this modality. This preference emphasizes text-based input and output - reading and writing in all its forms. People who prefer this modality often prefer PowerPoint, the Internet, lists, dictionaries, quotations and words, words, words...

Online courses are perfect for students with a preference for the read/write modality. Many eBooks enable learners to highlight, cut, and paste notes. These activities bring the class to life and make the material much easier to learn.

Kinesthetic (K):

By definition, this modality refers to the "perceptual preference related to the use of experience and practice (simulated or real)." Although such an experience may invoke other modalities, the key is that people who prefer this mode are connected to reality, "either through concrete personal experiences, examples, practice or simulation" [Fleming & Mills, 1992, pp. 140-141]. It includes demonstrations, simulations, videos and movies of "real" things, as well as case studies, practice and applications.

Your online course has plenty of opportunities for kinesthetic enrichment. There will be case studies to review, puzzles to test your knowledge, and opportunities to write about how you are connecting the class information to your real world experiences.

SETTING UP YOUR LEARNING SPACE

Now that you understand your learning style and how you learn best, let's take a look at ways to structure your physical environment and schedule to maximize your success.

Online learning requires organization and structure. Many new online learners make the mistake of assuming that the flexibility and convenience of online classes also means that less preparation is required. This is not accurate. You must prepare yourself and your environment for this learning modality.

Computer Requirements

Online learning requires that a student has access to a computer and the internet. You can choose a laptop or desktop. Generally, if your computer is less than five years old, you should have no problem using it to access your class. The same goes for Web browsers. You always want to make sure that you have the latest version of Explorer, Safari, Firefox, Google Chrome, Opera, or other up-to-date browsers that you use. Be sure to locate the computer requirements document on your school's website or learning management system and update your computer accordingly. Remember, your instructor is not an IT director; it is your responsibility to make sure your computer is ready for an online learning experience.

In addition to your hardware, you will want to obtain some useful software. You should ask your school for a list of software required for your courses, recommended browsers, and see if your school offers any educational discounts before you purchase your computer and software. Since the majority of your professors will require that you submit papers in Microsoft Word, it is good to have access to the Microsoft Office Suite. Other software that may be required includes Adobe Reader, Adobe Flash, Java, instant messengers, and anti-virus software.

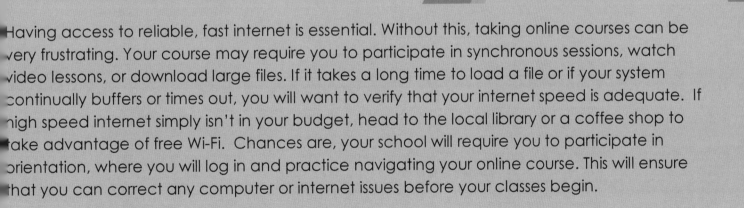

Having access to reliable, fast internet is essential. Without this, taking online courses can be very frustrating. Your course may require you to participate in synchronous sessions, watch video lessons, or download large files. If it takes a long time to load a file or if your system continually buffers or times out, you will want to verify that your internet speed is adequate. If high speed internet simply isn't in your budget, head to the local library or a coffee shop to take advantage of free Wi-Fi. Chances are, your school will require you to participate in orientation, where you will log in and practice navigating your online course. This will ensure that you can correct any computer or internet issues before your classes begin.

While it may not be a requirement to have a headset, flash drive, or a webcam to get through your coursework, sometimes a small investment in these items can make a big difference in how easy or enjoyable it is to complete coursework and participate in online discussions. Your school should be able to recommend some helpful accessories, but if they don't, post an inquiry in the chat area and see what your peers are using.

Study Space

Carve out a small space in your home or at your office to keep your school material. It is essential to have organization, even if it's just a few folders — a physical one for important papers, and an electronic one on your computer where you keep your assignments. Put your books, notebook, pens, and highlighters all together in one place. If you are planning to use multiple computers like one at home and one at work, buy a backpack to neatly transport your school material from place to place.

Navigating Your Online School

Online schools contain the same locations as a residential campus – minus the cafeteria and dormitories! Just as if you were walking around a new campus, you will need to explore your virtual campus so you know where to find things.   Almost every online course is built in a course management system or learning management system (LMS). WebCT, Blackboard, Angel, Desire2Learn, Sakai, Canvas, and eCollege are some of the LMS' that you may have heard about. There are also proprietary systems that colleges develop. Some schools refer to the LMS as the "online portal" or "virtual classroom." Regardless of what it is called, you need to know how to access your courses. Your school will provide you with credentials (user name and temporary password) and a link to take you to the LMS.

As soon as you receive your credentials, log in. Click on different links to see what is available and get familiarized with your school. Most schools hide important student information behind a firewall to protect you, so you may need a separate password to access things like your grades or financial information. Your school administrator will let you know if that is the case.

Once you've logged on, locate the bookstore or list of required materials, and order your books for your course(s) if they are not embedded in your class already. Sometimes it takes 10 days to get the book to you, so you want to do this right away. It is also helpful to visit the online library. Many schools offer writing and research assistance and there are books and full text articles that will help you with your papers and projects.

Remember your first day in high school when you wandered the hall looking for your class? Finding your online class on the school portal can also feel daunting. Don't wait until the day before the course begins to access the virtual classroom. Practice getting online from your computer, your tablet, or your smart phone, if allowed. Store your password and log in information securely on your smart phone so you are never without it. If you can't figure out how to access your classroom, there is a help desk available to assist you and frequently asked questions that can guide you.

Once you access your classroom the fun begins! Check out every link and all the icons. Try rolling the mouse over an unfamiliar icon (known as hovering), often times, it will tell you what it is. Remember, you cannot break anything, so feel free to explore. Investigate the discussion board, the assignments page, the e-mail system, and anything else you can access just as if you were checking out the physical space of a classroom. It is to your advantage to learn how to navigate the course and contact your instructor before you begin class. Nothing adds to frustration more than having to learn how to do something or where to find something when you face a deadline.

Once you investigate the various components of the online classroom, find the syllabus and read it. This will give you an idea of what you are going to study, the types of assignments you will be responsible for, the grading scale, and a plethora of other useful information. Knowing what to expect will enable you to develop a schedule to keep you focused and not feel overwhelmed.

Most online courses begin by having the students write an introduction about themselves or even make an introduction video (more on this later). Find a few students in the class who have similar interests as you and send them a private e-mail using their school e-mail address. Let them know you like their posting and why. Keep it short and simple. This could be the beginning of a new friendship! Having a friend in an online class is important — you can compare notes, share thoughts, and keep one another motivated.

TIME MANAGEMENT

The 6-Ps will remind you about the importance of organization –
Prior, Proper Planning Prevents Poor Performance.

Just because you are taking classes online, does not mean that you don't need to change your schedule to accommodate study time. Online classes are not the same thing as an independent study course. You are required to complete assignments and participate by the established timelines. There is flexibility in online courses but you must still set aside time to complete your work by the deadlines. You are a college student. Success in college, regardless of the learning modality, requires discipline, hard work, and preparation.

Setting priorities is essential to succeeding online. Since there is not a set time that you must attend class, some online learners fall into a bad habit of putting off their assignments until the last minute. Create a schedule and stick to it. Perhaps it is first thing in the morning, so other tasks can't creep in later in the day and steal your attention. Maybe it is after you put the kids to bed. If you find that distractions are negatively impacting your ability to study, grab your laptop and go to a public library or a coffee house. It is also helpful for you to put your study time on the family calendar. Even well-meaning family and friends may not understand why you can't just "do your homework later." Education is a gift that you give yourself – so don't short change yourself. Give yourself the time you need to succeed. [3]

MOTIVATING YOURSELF TO SUCCEED

Motivation can be intrinsic or extrinsic. Intrinsic motivation comes from within. It is the feeling of satisfaction from a job well done. It is the personal reward that results from participating in something worthwhile. Extrinsic motivation occurs when a person engages in an activity for the sake of a reward. That reward could be financial or some other type of recognition.

For some students, getting high grades is motivational. Other students relish positive feedback from faculty and peers. Some students are motivated by the joy of learning something new or applying that knowledge to their job.
When you begin your program, it is natural to be a little anxious, but also excited and motivated to succeed in college. As you progress through the courses, and being a college student becomes your natural routine, your motivation may begin to falter.

Sometimes this results in putting off assignments, procrastinating, spending less time studying, and getting lower grades. If you feel yourself starting to get distracted, consider the following strategies to get you back on track.

- **Reward yourself.** Sometimes getting a good grade is reward enough. However, if you are struggling to keep motivated, there is no time like the present to reward small successes. Make yourself a study plan for the week. If you stick to it, reward yourself. A reward doesn't always have to be expensive. Perhaps it is giving yourself permission to take a night off without doing school work or to enjoy a movie

- **Do the hard stuff first.** Lack of motivation can happen when you are anxious or stressed about a big assignment or major exam. Discipline yourself to do the hard assignments first. Tackling the most unpleasant tasks will give you a sense of accomplishment and assurance that you have the skills to succeed in college.

- **Get support.** Taking the time to update friends, family, and teachers on how you're doing and where you're having issues, can open the door to good advice and increased motivation to keep trying. Taking classes online can feel lonely, even though your peers and faculty are just a call or click away. Reach out to your online community, as well as your family and friends at home.

- **Remember the big picture.** It's easy to forget why you're taking online course in the first place. All of the work you're doing, whether big or small, is being done for a reason: to help you reach your goal of obtaining a degree and taking life in the direction you want to go. It can be helpful to remind yourself of this when you're struggling with motivation and potential burnout.

COMMUNICATING ONLINE

Interacting in Class

Online courses can be just as rewarding as classes taught on campus. Think back to high school. The students that did not want to be noticed by the teacher sat in the back of the classroom. Not actively participating in the weekly discussions or message boards is like sitting in the back of the classroom.

Much of the learning that takes place in an online course is done by reading and responding to the posts of your instructor and fellow students. If the syllabus says you are required to respond to comments posted by two students every week, consider doing more. Post meaningful feedback instead of just stating that you like or agree with the comment. One strategy for expanding the conversation or obtaining more information about a topic that interests you is to use the Socratic Technique.

The Socratic Technique is a way to explore subjects in depth. Rather than asking a student a question that can be answered with a yes or no response, phrase your question in an open-ended manner. Open ended questions cannot be answered with just a yes or a no. Here are a couple of examples:

- **Closed-ended question** – I read your introductory post about the reason you returned to school. Are you happy with your decision?

- **Socratic Technique** - I read your introductory post about the reason you returned to school. Tell me more about that.

- **Closed-ended question** – I read your post about the three branches of government. Do you believe that the founding fathers set up the US structure of government properly?

The Socratic Technique

"I read your post about the three branches of government. Why do you believe that the founding fathers set up the US structure of government with three branches?"

Using the Socratic technique when you participate in your classes will enrich your experience by obtaining perspectives and life-experiences held by your instructor and peers.

Now it's your turn! Turn each of these close-ended questions into an open-ended question using the Socratic Technique. [2]

Original Question	Open-ended Question
Did you take this course so you can get a better job?	
Do you agree that climate change is causing the ice to melt and the oceans to rise?	
Is there anything else you would like to talk about related to the importance of aseptic techniques in nursing?	
Are you understanding the comments I am providing?	
Do you want to study tonight?	

Communicating with your instructor

As we have discussed, you can communicate with your instructor both publicly and privately. You can email your instructor or reach out by phone during his or her office hours. There are also unique ways that your instructor will communicate with you. Make sure to find out his/her preferred method of communication and follow it. When communicating with your instructor in written format, be mindful of appropriate language, grammar, and punctuation.

Feedback is important in an online course. Your instructor will attach feedback to your assignments or post it in the gradebook. The gradebook may be located in the class LMS or any accompanying websites that your instructor may be using.

The gradebook includes a record of all your graded assignments and all the points you have earned. By clicking on an assignment grade, you can see the feedback that the teacher provides. Sometimes the feedback provides positive affirmation for a job well-done! Other times the feedback may address specific parts of your assignment or provide suggestions for improvement. Be sure to read the feedback thoroughly and contact your instructor if you have questions about any of the comments.

If is a good practice to check your gradebook regularly. Sometimes errors can be made or an assignment lost. If you know you submitted an assignment and it is not listed in the gradebook, reach out to your instructor for clarification.

Become part of the community

Just like a traditional academic campus is made up of multiple buildings, the virtual campus also has "virtual" buildings. Chances are there are links that take you to a virtual library, chat room, and social media page for the course. Take advantage of those. Research shows that students that are actively engaged in their classes have a much higher rate of graduating.

As previously mentioned, don't do the minimum. Your syllabus will identify what you are required to do, but you can always go above and beyond. If you are required to comment on two student posts, comment on three. Once you respond to your instructor's post, check back later in the week to see the feedback that was posted to your comment. Feel free to ask further questions or make additional comments. Your online course will come to life once your weekly posts turn into meaningful dialogs.

College is about more than just accumulating knowledge. Many lifelong friendships are formed in college. Go beyond the computer screen. Reach out to your peers by phone or by text. See if there are students that live in your community. If so, set up in-person study sessions or time to just relax. If not, use skype or another video messaging tool to make a more personal connection.

Netiquette

Netiquette is a term that refers to appropriate ways to communicate over the internet. When you communicate electronically, all you see is a computer screen. You don't have the opportunity to use facial expressions, gestures, and tone of voice to help communicate your meaning.   Therefore, it is easy to misinterpret what somebody means.

When communicating from an electronic medium, whether it is online, through email, texting, or in your LMS, remember this – Would I say what I am about to write to the person's face? If you would not, then think again before typing it. The posts that you are responding to are from people. It is not appropriate to call their ideas stupid or to embarrass somebody in writing. If you disagree with a point of view, ask them to clarify it or back up the opinion with facts. It is also not appropriate to post your response in all capital letters. ALL CAPS, when used online, signifies that you are yelling or angry. There is no need to have this type of anger in an online course.

What you write says a lot about you. Would you show up to work disheveled and leave your office space a mess? Hopefully not! In an online class, your words reflect who you are. When responding to the course threads, use proper English and grammar. Use spellcheck. Do not use emoji's, abbreviations like LOL, LMAO, or IDK, or excessive punctuation marks for emphasis. However, when you are communicating in the chat rooms or other areas set aside for social conversations, you can be much more casual in your communication.   Remember, to always keep the topic of conversation appropriate, everything you type is "forever." Once you hit "submit," you cannot delete it. So choose what you say wisely!

FORMAL VS. INFORMAL COMMUNICATION

Can you identify the correct way to communicate? Next to each sentence or group of sentences, state whether it is an example of formal or informal communication.

Statement	Type of Communication
Thank you for responding to my post.	
Ur welcome. LOL. Enjoy the class.	
R U planning on doin the synch session today?	
IDK. Doubt it.	
Attending the synchronous session would be very beneficial.	
I LOVED your example about presidential debate!!!!!!!!!	
Thank you. I enjoy watching political debates and putting myself in their shoes.	
I hope we are in another class together. Perhaps we could hook up since we live so close together. What do you think?	

LEARNING ONLINE

Reading and Writing in the Online Classroom

The reading and writing skills that are effective in a traditional classroom also apply to virtual the classroom. Your syllabus will indicate what reading is required. It will also include information about the writing expectations of the course. Depending on the course, you may be required to use APA style for your papers and for noting your research sources.

Getting used to reading an e-textbook or course material on a screen takes practice. Play with adjusting your screen height or the brightness on your computer to see what works best for you. Whenever possible, interact with the material. Highlight important sections or cut and paste sections of text to create your own study notes. Skim the reading assignment instead of reading every word, paying special attention to the first sentence of every paragraph, as well as the introduction and conclusion. Once you have skimmed the entire assignment, go back and thoroughly read the sections that contain pertinent information. This technique will help you get through a greater amount of material in a shorter amount of time and cut down on eye strain and reading fatigue.

Just as there are places for formal and informal communication in your online course, there are also appropriate places for formal and informal writing. Any assignment that is being graded, should be written using formal writing. This includes your weekly posts to any questions posed by your instructor, your responses to student posts, and any assignments that you upload for grading. I this context formal writing means that your material does not contain abbreviations such as LOL, IDK, U, etc. Your writing should not contain emoji's, excessive punctuation, and capital letters to communicate anger or emphasis. Consider formal writing as if you were writing to your boss.

Review your syllabus so you that know the expectations for your writing. Some colleges require students to use APA format and include bibliographic citations. The syllabus may state that papers need to be double-spaced or be written in a 12pt font. Don't lose easy points on an assignment because you didn't follow the directions.

Your syllabus may also discuss academic dishonesty and plagiarism. Plagiarism is when you use the words or ideas of another person without giving them credit. Many online schools require students to submit their work through a plagiarism checker. This software reviews your words and compares them to all other known works. Your paper receives a score that indicates the percentage of the paper that is plagiarized. Plagiarizing material off the internet is a serious code of conduct violation and may get you expelled from school. If you are concerned about plagiarism or want to know more about preventing it, you can access some of the information about plagiarism located in the LMS.

Informal writing can be used when writing in chat rooms and for blogging. Keep in mind, just because you are communicating between friends, doesn't give you permission to use vulgar language, to send inappropriate pictures, or to be offensive in other ways. Informal writing means that you don't need to use complete sentences or worry about grammar and punctuation. It also means you can talk about subjects that are not school related, such as your family, pets or vacation. This type of language is NOT recommended in any academic setting.

MY ONLINE COMMUNICATION

Let's see if you can modify each sentence so that it is appropriate to post in your online course. (There is not one correct answer).

Original	Rewritten
I AM CONFUSED AND NEED HELP!!!!	
Your bio pic is hot!	
I agree with everything that everybody said except for Frank. His posts are always worthless and off topic.	
Did you see the score of the ballgame last night? I didn't have time to get any work done since it went into overtime.	
IDK how to do the problams. R U online?	
I HATE THIS CLASS ☹	
I enjoyd ur video presentation. Way cool!!!!	

nteracting in synchronous and asynchronous courses

'ou will encounter different types of online learning formats. Sometimes your course will be entirely asynchronous. This means that all the coursework can be completed without any set course dates and times. Synchronous learning essions occur when your instructor schedules a time when students must log in and participate. Sometimes this participation is done through real-time chat essions. More and more however, online learning is incorporating more ophisticated synchronous elements like live video presentations by students.

f you need to create a presentation in your online class, PowerPoint (or similar presentation software) is an excellent tool because you can use it both ynchronously and asynchronously. PowerPoint allows you to convey ideas using ooth words and images. You can also add audio to PowerPoint slides and easily upload the file. This way, other students and your instructor can view it asynchronously. You can also incorporate PowerPoint slides into your presentation during a live session. Either format will make it clear to the instructor that you know your stuff! Below are some hints for creating great PowerPoint oresentations.

- **Words matter.** Don't use too many words on the screen. The purpose of PowerPoint is to capture the main idea or theme. Through your audio or video presentation, you will explain and elaborate about the words and images on the screen.

- **A picture is worth 1,000 words.** PowerPoint enables you to use SmartArt and other graphics to convey your messages to your audience. These features are especially helpful when you are comparing items or creating timelines.

- **Clear and concise.** In addition to using clear and concise language, be cautious about having too many competing colors and fonts. You want your page to be interesting, but not distracting. Also, be sure that your font is readable. Typically, you don't want to use font sizes under 18pt on PowerPoint. Script writing and other fonts with fine lines may also not be a good choice.

- **Timing is everything.** PowerPoint has a feature that allows you to time the length that your slide is on the screen. This is helpful when you are recording a presentation that will be watched asynchronously. You can also manually move the slides as you create the audio that accompanies them

Unlike asynchronous sessions that you can attend in your PJs, attending synchronous sessions are like going to class, especially when video is included. Because of this, it is important to be prepared to participate in the discussion and to dress and act appropriately. [4]

When participating in a synchronous session, remember your surroundings. It will be distracting to other students if there are dogs barking in the background, crying babies, or if you are recording yourself while watching TV in the living room. Consider your synchronous session just like a residential class. You would not take your dog or children to school, so modify your environment so you can have a quiet place to participate in the session. Likewise, think about your backdrop. Ideally, you record yourself in front a solid color wall or in front of a sheet. Also be cognoscente of your attire. If you are giving a presentation to the class, you should dress as if you were going to an interview. Business casual would be appropriate. If you are interacting one-on-one with the instructor or attending a session in which you are just a participant and not a presenter, you can be a little less formal. Tank tops, shorts, and other clothes that do not convey a professional image should be avoided. You only have one chance to make a first impression.

As a part of your synchronous courses, you may be asked to develop a Video Resume, create a Video Post, or write on a whiteboard. Your school will post information to teach you how to create these. The same rules apply to creating these as they do for appearing live in a synchronous session. Dress professionally, record in a professional environment that is free from distractions, and act appropriately. You should also test your equipment to ensure that the sound quality and lighting in your videos is adequate.

Getting help online

As an online student, you have access to a whole host of support personnel. It is critical that you are proactive in asking for assistance. Don't wait until you fall behind. The staff will be able to provide you with more options if you proactively communicate with them.

The contact information for these staff people, as well as others, will be located in the LMS. Copy the contact information and put it in your cell phone or school binder so that you have access to that information even when you are not online.

In addition to your instructor, your school employs the following people who are here to assist you.

- **Admissions** – Assists with questions about your enrollment in college.

- **Registrars** – Assist with questions related to registration in courses or about your grades or attendance. Registrars often provide student transcripts and are the person to contact in case you need to change your schedule.

- **Financial Aid Personnel** – These employees provide information about your financial aid or payment arrangements. You can also contact them if you have questions about tuition obligations.

- **Student Services** – Student Service personnel are sometimes called academic advisors. They assist students in finding solutions to issues that are impacting your ability to succeed in school. Perhaps you are having issues with a course and need to set up tutoring or maybe you have hit a wall and need ideas to get back on track.

- **Librarian** – Most schools will have a librarian to assist students with research. The librarian can recommend scholarly articles for your research papers.

- **Technical support** – For online students, having access to technical support personnel is critical. These employees can troubleshoot computer difficulties with the LMS and help you navigate the online system.

MY ONLINE READINESS

Are you ready to be an online student? Let's put your knowledge to the test! Take the following 10-question quiz. See the answers at the end to grade yourself and see how you did.

1. T or F   A person's learning style will determine if he or she can succeed in an online course.
2. T or F   The Learning Management System is the technology that houses that online courses.
3. T of F   Online courses are typically easier and require less preparation than traditional, on-campus courses.
4. T or F   Online students have access to the same services and personnel that an on-campus student has; they just access the services differently.
5. T or F   Synchronous learning sessions require to participate at a specific time.

6. Which of the following is NOT needed in order to take an online course?
    a. A brand new computer
    b. Reliable internet
    c. Software
    d. Plug ins

7. Which of the following is not a learning style described in the VARK learning style inventory?
    a. Visual
    b. Abstract
    c. Read/Write
    d. Kinesthetic.

8. Which of the following sentences is written using the Socratic technique
    a. Do you want to study tonight?
    b. Are you understanding the course material?
    c. Is there anything I can do to assist you?
    d. Tell me more about why you feel that way.

9. Which of the following should you consider when recording a video for class?
    a. Your attire
    b. Noise level
    c. Lighting
    d. All of the above

10. Which of the following activities is appropriate in an online forum?
    a. Typing in all capital letters
    b. Using vulgarity
    c. Challenging another student respectfully
    d. Discussing personal information

ANSWERS: 1.F 2.T 3.F 4.T 5.T 6.a 7.b 8.d 9.d 10.c

8-10 correct- You are ready to be a successful online student!

6-7 correct- You should review this section again.

0-5 correct- Perhaps you are better suited for face-to-face classes.

---

[1] Boettcher, Judith V. and Conrad, Rita-Marie. The Online Teaching Survival Guide (2nd edition). John Wiley & Sons, 2016.
[2] http://vark-learn.com
[3] http://www.planetofsuccess.com
[4] http://www.usnews.com/education

RESPONSIBLE BORROWING & BUDGETING

LEARNING OBJECTIVES

1. Describe loans, grants, scholarships, and GAP financing.

2. Create a budget that includes discretionary income, minimizing debt, and financial options with accrued interest.

3. Understand the importance of your credit score and learn to prevent identity theft.

4. Evaluate different loan options while avoiding default.

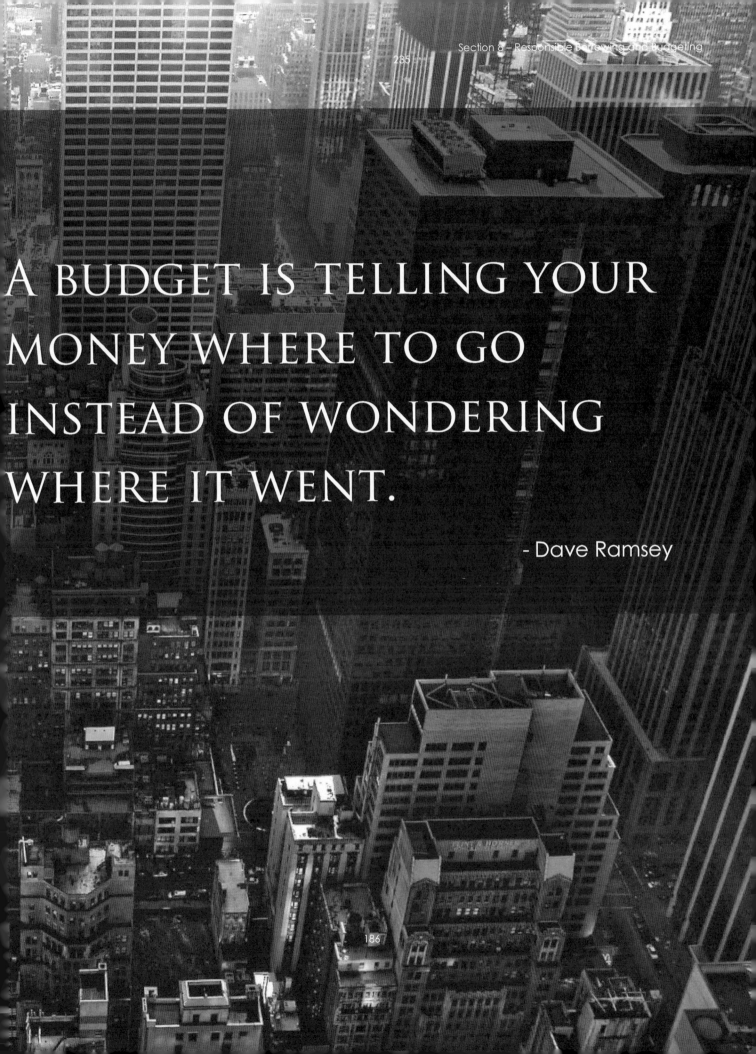

A BUDGET IS TELLING YOUR MONEY WHERE TO GO INSTEAD OF WONDERING WHERE IT WENT.

- Dave Ramsey

Managing your money is an important part of being a responsible adult. Quite often people say, "I have no money to manage because I'm a broke college student!" When you start paying attention to your sources of income and where your money goes, you might just be surprised to find out that there is more financial complexity to manage than you think. To succeed as a college graduate, it is just as important to have a sound financial plan, as it is to have a sound academic plan.

Choosing to go back to school is an exciting time. Once you select the perfect program, your emphasis needs to shift toward paying for your education. Hopefully, you have been saving for college and can afford the college of your choice. If you're like most students however, you need to find alternate options for covering your college education. There are several methods that are available for financing education, including:

- **Self-financing**

- **Government loans**

- **Government grants**

- **State funding**

- **Private loans**

- **Scholarships**

Self-Financing

Self-financing includes money that you have saved or have available to pay for your education. This can include education savings accounts that have been set up by your parents or grandparents, or money that you or your family has set aside for you to use for college. Self-financing is an excellent option that will enable you to graduate without debt.

Government Loans

A loan is money that you borrow that needs to be paid back. The US government has a program called "Title IV" that manages the distribution of student loan funds. Unlike private loans, which use credit score and income requirements as factors for approval of the loan, the government loans are available to almost everybody at low interest rates. Interest begins accruing on the money you borrow after you graduate, if you meet low-income criteria. It may begin while you are in school, if you don't meet low-income criteria. To find out if you qualify for government sponsored student loans, you will need to complete the Free Application for Federal Student Aid (FAFSA).

Government Grants

The US Department of Education awards over $150 billion dollars every year in grants and work-study money to low-income students who qualify. A grant is money that does not need to be repaid and will not increase your debt. Work-study is a program that allows you to work at your college and receive a paycheck that you can use to help pay for school or other expenses. Not all colleges participate in work-study, so you should check with your college. To find out if you qualify for grant funds, you will need to complete the Free Application for Federal Student Aid (FAFSA). The government also has grants available for active military personnel, veterans, and their spouses.

State Funds

State college funds are usually grants that do not need to be repaid. Even if you do not qualify for federal financial aid, you might still be eligible for a grant from your state. You should contact the state grant agency where you live, to determine if your state has a program to assist you in defraying your college expenses.

Private Loans

Private loans are loans offered by agencies like banks and credit unions. These loans typically have higher interest rates than federal student loans. In order to qualify, there are certain income and credit score requirements. If you have not yet established credit, or have poor credit, you may want to try and obtain a co-borrower or co-signer to help you qualify or reduce your interest rate. Shopping around locally or online for a loan with the best interest rates is the sign of a smart borrower!

Scholarships

Scholarships are funds that do not need to be repaid and are awarded on the basis of academic achievement or other merits, such as sports acumen, or community service. Colleges and other organizations award scholarships. Almost all students can find a scholarship with a little hard work. Sites like fastweb.com and scholarships.com have lists of scholarships for students like you. Perhaps you have a parent that works for a major corporation like General Electric or Microsoft that have scholarships for students of employees, or maybe they belong to a fraternal organization like the Knights of Columbus or Rotary Club. These organizations have money available and you can find it online.

Once you have exhausted your grant options, applied for scholarships, and submitted your FAFSA to determine the federal aid that you can receive, you may still need money to cover your education-funding gap. "Gap funding" is the amount of money needed to cover your educational expenses above what you have received. Your goal should be to minimize your gap, since gap financing typically comes with higher interest rates. Consider talking to your parents about obtaining a Parent+ loan, which is a government-financed program that allows parents to assist their children with their academic expenses. Some students are even setting up an account at a crowd-sourcing site, like GoFundMe.com/education, where friends, family, or strangers can contribute to their education.[1]

My Student Loan Payment

- The Internet is full of sites that enable you to estimate your monthly student loan payment. Select a site by searching "Student Loan Repayment Calculator" or use the calculator at aie.org/pay-for-college.
- Enter the estimated amount of student loans you will have.
- Don't include grants or scholarships, since those are funds that don't need to be repaid.
- Next, assume a 6% interest rate and a loan term of 120 months.
- Once you know what the estimated monthly payment will be, answer the questions that follow.

1. What is your estimated monthly payment?

_____

2. List two strategies to **increase your income** so that you can afford the monthly payment.

_____

_____

3. List two strategies to **decrease your other expenses** so that you can afford the monthly payment.

_____

_____

4. Besides increasing your income or decreasing your other expenses, what are some other strategies you can do to lower the monthly payment on your student loan? List at least three.

_____

_____

Budgeting IQ

It's time to get smart about managing your money! Regardless of your age or income level, creating a budget is an important first step in creating positive financial habits. Just as you study for an exam, you also need to study your income and expenditures in order to establish a workable financial plan.

A simple budget includes tracking your monthly income and monthly obligations. Income includes sources such as your take home pay from your job, tips, alimony, child support payments you receive, or unemployment benefits. Any money that you receive on a regular basis should be included as income in your budget. Monthly obligations or expenditures are the payments you are required to make each month. When determining your monthly payments, use the minimum amount due. For example, if you owe $5,000 on a credit card and the monthly minimum payment is $100, use $100 for budgeting purposes even though you will be encouraged to pay more than the minimum if you have money left over.

The money that is left over after you subtract your expenses from your income is called "discretionary income." Some people call discretionary income "fun money" since it is the money available for entertainment or to buy gifts. Smart students don't use all their discretionary income for fun however; they establish a "rainy day fund" for emergencies, or to pay down debt, save for retirement, or cover educational expenses.

If your monthly expenses exceed your monthly income, don't panic! You are going to school so that one day you can graduate and obtain a better paying career. In the meantime, get creative. Sell your unwanted items on eBay or host a garage sale with other students. Take a part-time job that works around your school schedule. Get a roommate or set up a babysitting coop to save on childcare expenses. Tightening your belt may be a bit uncomfortable in the beginning, but graduating with less debt will save you countless financial woes in the future.[2]

Smart Borrowing

Smart borrowers shop for the best deals, just like smart shoppers scour the Sunday ads and clip coupons. The cost of borrowing is expensive because of the interest that accrues and fees associated with obtaining a loan or using a credit card, so you never want to borrow or spend more than you absolutely need. Just because you qualify to borrow more, does not mean it is in your best financial interest to take more. Think of it another way – just because you *want* that third helping of chocolate cake, doesn't mean you *need* it.

Americans often rely on credit cards to make ends meet. Credit cards have high interest rates and fees and should be used sparingly and as a last resort. Typically, the higher your credit score, the lower your interest rate will be. We will talk about credit scores later in this chapter, but for now, let's explore interest rates.

Annual Percentage Rate (APR) is the annual interest rate you pay on all

purchases when you use a credit card. APR is applied every month to the full amount you charged. APRs can be variable or fixed. Variable APRs adjust based on the interest rates that are being charged by the Federal Reserve, which is essentially the bank for the US government. Fixed APRs do not change unless you miss a payment or violate other payment terms, at which time the APR can be raised.

To find out how much interest you're paying on your balance each day, you can convert your APR to a daily percentage rate. To do this, divide your APR by 365 (the number of days in a year). At the end of each day, you can multiply your current balance by the daily rate to come up with the daily interest charge. Let's look at an example:

Let's say you have an outstanding balance of $2,000, with an 18.5% APR. If you made just the minimum monthly payment, it would take over 11 years to pay off the debt. In addition, you would pay an additional $1,934 for interest charges. That added interest almost doubles the total cost of your original purchase. This is why credit card balances don't seem to shrink and why you should always make more than the minimum payment. It is also a good idea to select a credit card that has a **grace period**. A grace period is the time between the date of a purchase and the date when interest begins. If your card has a standard grace period, you can avoid finance charges by paying your monthly balance in full. If there is no grace period, the credit card company imposes a finance charge from the date you use your card to make the purchase.

Smart borrowers select cards with a low interest rate, minimal fees, and a generous grace period. It pays to read the fine print before applying for any credit card or loan.

Credit Score

Having a good credit score is as important as acing your final exam! A high credit score means that you will be able to borrow money at lower interest rates, with fewer fees; and enable you to qualify for the loans you might need for a car, home, or education. The credit score was developed by an organization named the Fair Isaac and Company (FICO). Therefore, sometimes your credit score is also called your FICO score. Credit scores range from 300-850. Companies often use the following scale to determine your credit worthiness.

Score	Grade
720 and Above	Excellent
680-719	Good
620-679	Average
580-619	Poor
500-579	Very Poor
Less than 500	Not Credit Worthy

Several factors go into determining your credit worthiness. Some of the most important factors are as follows:

- History of paying your bills on time
- How much debt vs. income you have
- How much credit you have vs. how much you have used (high balances on loans and credit cards)
- How much credit you have applied for recently

It is important to know and manage your credit score. You can obtain your free credit at freecreditscore.com or by contacting one of the three companies that rate your credit and provide your score to lenders.

- EQUIFAX – (800) 685-1111 equifax.com

- EXPERIAN – (888) EXPERIAN (397-3742) experian.com

- TRANS UNION – (800) 916-8800 transunion.com

Consumers have rights when it comes to their credit. If you have been denied a loan, you are entitled to a free credit report from one of the three credit bureaus and they must provide you with the reasons for the denial. If you find errors on your credit report, you can work with the agencies to get the discrepancies removed from your report to improve your score.[3]

Knowledge is power!
Be sure to know your credit score prior to applying for any loan.

My Credit Card

- If you have a credit card, call the customer service number on the back of the card and ask the representative the questions that follow.
- You can also visit the card's website to obtain the information.
- If you don't own a credit card, look one up online. It can be a major credit card like a MasterCard or Visa, or a retail card, like Costco or Shell Oil.

YOUR CARD

Type of Card (MC, Visa, Discover, etc.)	
What is the APR?	
Is the APR fixed or variable?	
How much is the annual fee?	
How much is the late fee?	
Describe the grace period.	
Other card Benefits (cash back, airline mileage points, insurance on purchases)	

FICTIONAL CARD

Type of Card (MC, Visa, Discover, etc.)	Discover Card
What is the APR?	19.0%
Is the APR fixed or variable?	Variable
How much is the annual fee?	$50
How much is the late fee?	Yes. $35
Describe the grace period.	There is no grace period.
Other card Benefits (cash back, airline mileage points, insurance on purchases)	You earn one airline mile for every dollar you spend.

Compare the features of your credit card and the fictional credit card. Which credit card is preferable? Why?

_____

_____

_____

Identity Theft

Identity theft is on the rise. Identify theft is a crime in which an imposter obtains key pieces of your personal information, such as your social security number, driver's license number, or date of birth, and uses that information to obtain access to your financial accounts or apply for accounts in your name. These thieves run up debt and can ruin your credit.

Although a criminal might access your personal information by hacking into the database of a bank or credit card company, experts agree that the most common way your information is stolen is through dumpster diving! Thieves sort through your trash and obtain information from your discarded bills and personal paperwork.

To prevent identity theft, it is important to shred all documents that contain ANY personal information. Destroy unsolicited credit applications and never give out your personal information over the phone or through email. It is also important to regularly check your credit report and FICO score in order to determine if accounts have been opened in your name. If you find that this has occurred, you will need to report such activities to the authorities immediately.[4]

Strategies of minimizing debt

Debt is an amount of money that you owe to a person, bank, or company. Debt is a way of life for almost every adult. Having a small amount of debt is important so that you can establish a credit score. Unfortunately, if you are not disciplined and do not stick to your budget, it is easy to let your debt get out of control. The smartest way to control your debt, is by not overextending yourself in the first place. Reevaluate your priorities and truly assess your *wants* versus your *needs*. Needs include debts that you must pay to live. They include items like:

- Rent
- Utilities
- Transportation
- Food
- Insurance
- Loan payments

You can get creative to reduce the impact of your needs on your monthly budget. Choose a roommate to share rent and utility expenses. Having a car requires gasoline, maintenance, and insurance. Consider selling your car, taking public transportation, and using the proceeds to pay down your debt. Consider carpooling to cut your fuel costs in half.

Food costs are a necessary expense that you can control. As the old saying goes, some people have "a champagne taste on a beer budget." Why pay more for name brands groceries, when store brands can save you up to 60%? Instead of eating out, pack a lunch. You can also sign up to receive free coupons through email. Small changes in your eating habits can help you save big.

Reducing the interest rate on loans you already have is another strategy that can put some money back in your pocket. Call your credit card companies and ask for a reduction. If you have made timely payments, you will have leverage to get your rates reduced. You can be your biggest advocate by speaking up for yourself. You will never know until you ask!

Many times, your wants can feel like needs. Purchasing holiday gifts for your family, throwing a birthday party, or purchasing a new outfit may feel like needs. A key to financial stability is never to use credit cards to pay for your *wants*. Non-essential items should be paid for with discretionary funds or savings. If you don't have discretionary income to pay for the items you want, get creative! Give handmade gifts, scale back the party, or purchase an accessory to wear instead of buying a whole new outfit. Keep in mind that nothing feels as good as being debt free!

Consequences of Financial Irresponsibility

Being a responsible borrower is just as important as being a responsible student or a responsible parent. It indicates to creditors that you pay your bills on time and you care about your good credit. Sometimes bad things happen to good people, such as a major emergency or a job layoff. If you can no longer afford to make your loan payments, there are right ways and wrong ways to handle the situation.

- Increase your income – Take a part-time job or sell some of your non-essential items on eBay.
- Ask for help – Everybody needs a helping hand now and then. Ask friends or family to borrow some money. This is preferable over obtaining a high interest-bearing loan. Many cities have emergency funds for families in crisis to pay for housing or utilities. Obtaining assistance for those items may enable you to continue to pay your other debt obligations until your situation stabilizes.
- Communicate with creditors – Don't ignore the calls from creditors, as this will cause them to racket up the pressure to collect the debt. Instead, reach out to them. Explain your situation. Creditors will usually work with you to reduce your monthly payments temporarily.

Special considerations for student loans

Unlike other debts that can be discharged through bankruptcy, federal student loans cannot. The consequences for defaulting on a student loan are severe. The Department of Education can garnish your tax refund without any type of court order. If you filed your taxes with a spouse, their portion of the refund will also be garnished, and put toward your defaulted student loan.

Wage garnishment is another tool used to collect defaulted student loans. Up to 15% of your wages could be garnished to cover your student loan obligations.

Defaulting on a student loan ruins your credit, making it impossible to qualify for low-interest car loans or home loans. You also lose your eligibility for additional federal student aid in the future. If you are unable to make your student loan payment, there are options such as deferment, forbearance, or a repayment plan. Once you default, you lose your right to use those strategies. Let's look at each one.

Deferment

A deferment allows you to temporality postpone making your federal student loan payments or to temporarily reduce the amount you pay. If you are experiencing financial hardship, go back to school, are unemployed, or are on active duty military service, you may qualify to postpone your payments with a deferment. During a deferment, subsidized Stafford Loans do not accrue interest. Unsubsidized Stafford loans, PLUS loans, and consolidation loans, do accrue interest during the deferment that will be added to the principal of your loan and increase the amount you owe. Other types of deferments are available for students that qualify under the following categories:
- Armed Forces
- Domestic Volunteer
- Economic Hardship
- Full Time Teacher in a Teacher Shortage Area
- Graduate Fellowship
- Internship
- Military
- Parental Leave
- Peace Corps Volunteer
- Post Enrollment
- Public Health Services
- Rehabilitation Training
- School
- Tax Exempt Volunteer
- Temporary Total Disability
- Unemployment
- Working Mother

Forbearance

Like a deferment, forbearance, allows you to suspend making monthly loan payments. If you work an internship, perform certain types of community service, or find yourself experiencing financial hardship, you may be qualified to postpone payments with forbearance. Loans continue to accrue interest during forbearance. If possible, you should continue to make payments on the monthly interest rate so the total amount you owe will not increase. Special types of forbearances are available for students that qualify under the following categories:

- Active Military
- Corporation for National and Community Service
- Department of Defense
- Hardship
- Internship/Residency
- Reduced Payment
- Student Loan Debt Burden
- Teacher Loan Forgiveness

To find out more information about these deferment and forbearance programs, visit ed.gov or studentloans.gov.

Payment Plans

Like other creditors, the federal government or your student loan servicer would prefer to get some payment in rather than no payment at all! They will work with you to select a repayment plan that meets your needs. Examples of repayment plans include:

- **Standard Repayment Plan:** Spreads out the payments equally over 10 years. Unless you change your payment option, you will be enrolled in a standard plan.
- **Graduated Repayment:** This plan takes assumes that you will make more money over the life of your career, so your payments start low and increase every two years. Keep in mind that you will pay more interest with this plan than with the standard plan.
- **Extended Payment:** If you have over $430,000 in federal student loans, you may qualify for the extended plan that allows you to pay of your loan over 25 years instead of 10 years.
- **Income Sensitive Repayment Plan:** The payments on this loan are adjusted annually, based on your monthly gross income. You may choose this plan for up to five years, after which, your account will revert to either the Standard or Graduated Repayment Plan

Managing your debt is essential. There are options to help you remain in good standing and maintain your good credit if you do a little homework. Communication is the key.

My Personal Budget

Complete the budget template below for next month and then answer the three questions that follow.

Month	
My monthly financial goal is:	
My financial goals for this year are:	
Monthly Income (include sources such as your take home pay, tips, unemployment compensation, child support or alimony, other sources)	
Income Source	**Total**
Income Grand Total	
Monthly Expenses (include items such as your rent/mortgage, utilities, gas/transportation, insurance, child care, food, credit cards, child support or alimony payments, other loans or obligations)	
Expense Source	**Total**
Expenses Grand Total	
Income Grand Total – Expenses Grand Total	

[1] https://studentaid.ed.gov/sa/
[2] https://tomhitchens.com
[3] https://www.credit.com
[4] https://www.identitytheft.gov

Section 9:

WORKING IN TEAMS

LEARNING OBJECTIVES

1. Identify attributes of a successful team.

2. Understand how to resolve conflict.

3. Define roles and responsibilities of team members.

4. Describe four communication styles.

5. Determine your leadership style and utilize social and emotional intelligence to be a successful leader.

You have probably heard the saying, "There is no 'I' in team." While this is a true statement, the "I" the quote is referring to is you – and you are an important part of many teams. Teams are all around us. Your family could be considered a team. Perhaps you sing in the choir at church or play softball. Maybe you have formed a study group in class. All of these are teams with participants, roles, responsibilities, and a purpose. The more you know about how teams work and how to interact appropriately in your role on the team, the more successful you will be.

Dictionary.com defines teamwork as the "cooperative or coordinated effort on the part of a group of persons acting together as a team or in the interests of a common cause." Teamwork should lighten the burden on each individual and result in superior outcomes because it incorporates expertise from many people. Why then do some people dread the idea of being on a team? Chances are, people who dislike being part of a team have had a bad experience.

Often they have been on ineffective teams that wasted time and didn't achieve the goal, or maybe they were forced to participate on a team that was comprised of members that either dominated every meeting or were lazy and didn't contribute. Let's take a look at some of the attributes that lead to a successful team, so we can avoid bad team experiences.

ATTRIBUTES OF A SUCCESSFUL TEAM

When you think about creating a successful team, remember the acronym

S-I-M-P-L-E!

It will remind you of the six key attributes necessary to develop a high functioning team. [1]

Shared goal. A successful team is committed to the achievement of the goal. Individual members are engaged and motivated. They share in the successes and take responsibility for missteps for the good of the entire team.

Interdependence. Successful teams need all of its members. Team members draw on their strengths and support the contributions of others. The vast experiences and expertise of each team member results in an environment where the final product is vastly superior to the outcome that would have been reached by an individual.

Make-up. The composition of the team is essential to its success. Teams need diversity to fill various roles and each team member needs to be given expectations based on their role. The composition and size of a team needs to be appropriate for the mission. Successful teams have an engaged leader, subject matter experts, and a supporting cast of other people who have skills that complement one another.

People Skills. Successful teams are comprised of individuals that have exceptional people skills. These individuals have the ability to discuss issues openly and honestly. If they disagree, they share their point of view respectfully, without negativity. Being able to give and receive constructive criticism is a sign of high social and emotional intelligence. Teams that are made up of members that have strong social and emotional intelligence tend to be more successful. This is because they have an ability to put the needs of the team above their individual needs. They check their ego at the door!

Leadership. Successful teams have effective leadership that values best practices, new ideas, and proven processes. All team members, including the leader, are accountable to the team and its mission. Successful teams utilize shared decision-making and problem solving.

Excellent Communication. Clear, concise, honest communication is the hallmark of a successful team. Individual opinions are valued and constructive feedback is encouraged. Excellent communication also includes the methods used to memorialize the ideas and activities of the team. Keeping thorough notes, which are referred to as "meeting minutes," is necessary to keep the team on track and to ensure accountability.

MISSION AND GOALS OF THE TEAM

Every business has a mission. It is its reason for existing. The mission focuses the organization around a singular objective. Just as a business needs a mission, so does a team. Every year, athletic teams have the mission to finish first in their sport and they establish goals and activities throughout the season to help them achieve the mission. As a college student, your mission is to graduate. Decisions you make should always take into consideration their impact on your goal. Skipping classes, dropping a course, or not studying for an exam will have a detrimental impact on your mission to graduate. Forming a study-group and setting aside time to focus on your homework ensures that you achieve your mission.

In order to achieve their mission, teams must first establish goals. Goals should be *SMART* (Specific, Measurable, Achievable, Realistic and Time-bound).

Specific: Goals should be specific enough so that they are easily understood by new team members. They should also be related specifically to achieving the mission. If your mission is to launch a new line of furniture, one of your goals might be to create a 3-D prototype of the furniture using a graphics program within the next 90 days. This goal is specific because it explains what you will do, how you will do it, and when it will be completed.

Measurable: Accountability is essential in high functioning teams. Having measurable goals ensures accountability. "Completing research before the next team meeting" or "selling 10 cars this month" are examples of measurable goals. Measurable goals should be made published within the team and aieving the goal should be celebrated.

205

Achievable: Having achievable goals is not only important for the success of the project, it is also essential for the morale of the team. Nobody wants to be on a team that cannot be successful because the goals are not achievable. "Stretch goals" are objectives that may be just out of reach. However, with teamwork and resolve, the goal might be achievable. It is healthy for a team to have some stretch goals, but not all goals should be stretch goals.

Realistic: Similar to being achievable, goals should be realistic. If management is not supportive of an idea or there is not money in the budget to fund it, there is no reason to include that as a goal. It is not realistic. Having unrealistic goals frustrates team members who just feel they are spinning their wheels. Unrealistic expectations also lead to frustration.

Time-bound: Smart goals are written in a way that includes a deadline. Examples of time-bound goals include revising the department manual by the end of the month or selling $1,000 worth of furniture next week. Placing a deadline on a goal or a due date on a project focuses attention on that item as the deadline draws closer. Resources can be allocated to ensure that the goal is met.

Establishing a singular mission and creating smart goals help teams operate effectively and efficiently. Even an "ad-hoc" team, which is a temporary team typically established to achieve a specific task in a short amount of time, deserves to have a stated mission and goals. It is also a good idea to solicit input from the team regarding the mission and goals. Inclusive goal-setting builds camaraderie and buy-in to the project.

SMART GOALS

Think back to the elements that result in the creation of SMART goals (Specific, Measurable, Achievable, Realistic, and Time-bound) and rewrite the goals below, making them smarter. [2]

ORIGINAL GOAL STATEMENT	REVISED GOAL STATEMENT
Our team will finish the product roll-out on schedule.	
We intend to save the company $20,000 next month.	
Our new initiative will increase customer satisfaction.	
Our team will hit its numbers.	

ROLES + RESPONSIBILITIES OF TEAM MEMBERS

Successful teams have clearly defined roles and responsibilities. Think of a choir or football team. In a choir, the conductor is the leader. The other participants stand where directed. The altos stand with the altos and the sopranos stand with the sopranos, etc. On a football team, the coach is the leader. He determines the plays and the strategies. On the field, the quarterback executes the plays. Each player understands where they are supposed to be and what they are supposed to do.

Researcher Dr. Meredith Belbin, identified nine distinct team roles. Successful teams select individuals with skills and characteristics that complement each role. Just as a slow runner should not be assigned to be running back on a football team, neither should a person be selected as the team leader if he or she does not have the temperament for the job. Good people sometimes fail because they are put in the wrong role.

Role	High Performing Team Characteristics	Strength (People, Action/Task, or Thinking
Shaper	• Performed by people who are natural leaders • Work well under pressure and like a challenge • Keep a positive attitude and can motivate others • Tend to have a "Type A" personality • Extroverts and have the ability to communicate with and motivate team members	Action/ Task
Implementer	• Performed by people that can get things done • Practical, efficient, and well-organized • Turn the team's ideas and thoughts into action plans • Tend to be conservative, rigid, and slow to accept change	Action/ Task
Completer/ Finisher	• Performed by people with an eye for detail • Tend to be the people that find errors and are considered perfectionists • Tend to be self-conscious and concerned with problems or delays • May also resist delegating assignments to others	Action/ Task

Coordinator	• Performed by people that are confident and possess exceptional listening skills • Guide the activities of the team to complete the task at hand/good at delegating duties • May be manipulative when it comes to prioritizing activities based on what they feel is most important	People
Team Worker	• Performed by people who are good at conflict resolution and who appreciate team harmony • Support everybody and are thus popular within the team • Tend to avoid taking sides during decision making because they don't want to alienate people • Put team harmony ahead of their decision-making abilities	People
Resource Investigator	• Performed by people who are inquisitive and have good networking skills • Obtain external contacts for the team and can successfully negotiate resources on behalf of the team • Tend to be extroverts who easily relate to others • Quick thinkers/learners with the ability to obtain information from other people	People
Monitor-Evaluator	• Performed by people who are serious, cautious in nature, and can think critically about situations • Carefully analyze information before drawing any conclusions • Tend to be slow in decision making and are more concerned with the outcome than they are about motivating others • Don't mind stepping on toes	Thinking
Specialist	• Performed by people who have expert knowledge in a particular area • Their priority is in maintaining professional standards and they demonstrate great pride in their area of expertise • Tend to show little or no interest in the expertise of others or of other aspects of the team beyond their contribution	Thinking
Plants	• Performed by people who are original and innovative • Find creative ways to help the team solve problems or overcome challenges • Tend to be introverts and prefer to work alone • May not possess good communication skills • React well to praise and are greatly affected by criticism	Thinking

While high performing teams need to have all of the roles filled, often times, one person will serve in more than one role. This is especially true in small organizations. Once you know what role or roles you are serving, you need to know your responsibilities and expectations. If you are not given a list of expectations for your role – ask! Better yet, draft a list of expectations and responsibilities that you believe are essential to your contribution on the team and present them to the team leader.

Assembling a High Performing Team

If you have had a bad experience serving on a team, chances are it is because the team was not assembled to maximize effectiveness and efficiency. Sometimes being selected for a team seems like a personality contest. As you have learned however, surrounding yourself with people that act like you and have the same skillset as you, will not result in a high functioning team. Team leaders may feel that selecting all Specialists will ensure a positive outcome. In reality, Implementers, Coordinators, and Monitors are also required to ensure that the mission and goals of the team are accomplished.

When assembling a team, it is important to know something about the skills, competencies, and personalities of the people that may be serving on the team. How else would you know what role each person would be best suited to perform? Some companies use personality profiles to assess the attributes of each employee. One personality type is not better than another, but one personality type might be better suited for a particular role on a team than another.

For example, you would not want to put a scientist or an introvert in the role of Resource Investigator but you would want to assign them to the role of Specialist or Monitor-Investigator. If you do not have access to results of a personality inventory for the people you are considering for your team, just interview them. Ask a series of questions about their working style, likes, and dislikes. Personality-inventory questions like those below will provide you with insights into your potential team members:

- **Do you prefer to work independently or in a group?**
- **Do you consider yourself an introvert or an extravert?**
- **What skills will you bring to this team?**
- **How much time do you have to devote to this team?**
- **Describe other projects you have worked on in the past.**
- **When learning something new, do you prefer to read directions, watch a demonstration, or try it yourself?**
- **What are your top two attributes?**
- **In what two areas could you use improvement?**
- **What motivates you?**
- **If I asked your current manager to describe you, what would he or she say?**
- **Why do you want to serve on this team?**

Once you assess general information about potential team members, explain the project and expectations. Describe the various roles and ask them which ones they feel best suited to perform. Explain the mission and goals of the team and make sure that each person supports the mission. High performing teams put achieving the mission and goals of the team ahead of their own goals. They do not have a hidden agenda. Regardless of what role they serve, if a person does not believe in the mission, he or she should not be selected for the team.

Just as there is no ideal personality type to be successful on a team, there is no magic formula to determine the appropriate size of a team. One philosophy is summed up by the adage, "Many hands make light work." This philosophy ascribes to the notion that the greater number of members within a team, the more resources that are available to achieve the goal.

An alternative philosophy is conveyed in the saying, "Too many cooks in the kitchen spoil the broth." This philosophy realizes that as the team size increases, so does the number of conflicts, thereby resulting in decreased levels of cohesion and productivity. To determine the correct size of a team, the leader must evaluate the mission, goal, tasks, roles and available resources to determine how few members can work effectively and harmoniously together while still having enough people to accomplish the requirements on schedule.

TEAM ROLES

Imagine that you are the team leader with the responsibility of assembling a team. Review the profile of each potential team member and select one or more roles that would complement each person. Justify your selection.

Team Member Profile	Role	Justification for the Role
Mary is a perfectionist. She loves participating on teams and often takes on too many tasks because she wants to ensure that they are done on time and on budget!		
Tim is a peace-maker. He often mediates disagreements between his co-workers. He has the ability to make everybody feel better about the result, even if it was not in their favor.		
Paul is a born delegator. He listens attentively and then guides the activities of others to get the job done.		
Jan is a doer. She makes things happen. Some people say that Jan is too inflexible but nobody can question her results.		
Kenny is outgoing. He is a born leader whose positive attitude is infectious. He is competitive and loves a good challenge. He won't let you down.		
Dr. Tom is a technology expert. He literally wrote the book about cybercrime. He is interested in providing assistance but has reservations about having to participating in operational and organizational team meetings.		
Ashley is a people-pleaser. It is known that she will work endless hours to make you proud. She is known for being good at thinking outside of the box.		
Mike is not known for being warm and fuzzy. His favorite saying is "just the facts, ma'am." People tend to overlook his curt attitude because nobody is better at analyzing evidence and making good decisions.		
Ellen is a real social butterfly. She is energized being around people. She belongs to many groups and has contacts that can add value to any project.[3]		

Communicating with and Motivating a Team

Even if you are not the team leader, chances are you will still need to manage certain components related to your portion of the project. Remember, communication is key. On some teams, the primary form of communication takes place in meetings and is memorialized in meeting minutes. Other teams communicate regularly through email or on conference calls. Sometimes on small teams, communication is very informal and takes place in cubicles, lunchrooms, and in passing. Although this type of impromptu communication can yield important discoveries, keep in mind that off the cuff communications may not always involve all participants, so making notes about those discussions to share later with the rest of the team is important.

Teams are made up of individuals with different communication styles. Have you ever felt like no matter how much you tried, you just couldn't get through to some people? There could be many reasons why you struggled to be understood, but one possibility is that your communication style is different from the person you are trying to communicate with. The book "Men are from Mars Women are from Venus" outlines some of the communication differences between males and females. Pop culture is always deciphering the best way to reach millennials, Generation X, and Baby boomers. By knowing how best to communicate with your team mates, and by knowing how to adjust your communications to match the preferred style of the recipient, you will have a better experience on the team and become a more valuable team member.

Research into communication styles began in the 1940s and revealed that there are four styles of communication. The styles include the **Controller**, **Promoter**, **Supporter**, and **Analyzer**. Each person tends to communicate in the style that they prefer since it comes naturally to them. However, if you want to be the most effective, you should practice altering your style so you can reach as many people as possible.

Team members that communicate using a **Controller** style tend to focus on the conclusion and results and only provide details if asked. Their communication style is direct and to the point. They do not include pleasantries in their communications and are not verbose. They are the "just the facts" type of communicators.

Team members that communicate using a **Promoter** style tend to express ideas and conclusions using stories and metaphors. They use examples. Their communications are laced with niceties. They want to know about the subject of the communication, as well as about the person sending it.

Supporters make up the largest portion of the population. They are good listeners who avoid conflict. Their communications often include pros and cons so they do not offend people. They do not challenge people or ideas in writing. Supporters are uncomfortable when you ask them to make a snap decision.

Analyzers respond best to facts, figures, charts, and graphs. They communicate less in words and more with numbers or graphics. Like controllers, they get straight to the point in their communications.

Recognizing different communication styles and adjusting your style to effectively reach your team mates is one way to improve your performance on the team. Another is determining what motivates each person – what makes them tick?

Motivation is a personal thing. Some people are motivated by money, a job title, power, or fame. Knowing what motivates and inspires each team member is essential to a high functioning team. Receiving recognition at an awards luncheon may excite some team members, but may actually unmotivate an introvert that avoids from public praise. Some people may aspire to a corner office, while others just want a higher paycheck. Figuring out what motivates each team member and individualizing the ways you express recognition and appreciation, demonstrates awareness and commitment to their needs.

Motivation can be intrinsic or extrinsic. Intrinsic motivation comes from within. It is the feeling of satisfaction from a job well done. It is the personal reward that results from participating in something worthwhile. Extrinsic motivation occurs when a person engages in an activity for the sake of a reward. That reward could be financial or some other type of recognition.

While it is unlikely that anybody would turn down financial compensation for serving on a team, sometimes offering money as an incentive is not an option. In those circumstances, what can you do to motivate your team to achieve the mission and goals?

According to research from Gallup, employees that receive regular recognition and praise are more engaged, produce at higher efficiency levels, and stay longer with the company than those that just receive additional monetary compensation. As we have mentioned, different people respond differently to motivators, so utilize a combination of techniques to keep your team engaged and performing effectively.

- Say thank you! While public recognition is nice, sending a handwritten note will make an impact on team members.
- Acknowledge progress. Waiting until the mission is accomplished to acknowledge participants may demotivate employees that are working hard over an extended period of time. Establish and recognize milestones instead.
- Be flexible. Many people respond favorably to increased freedom. Allow team members to work from home on occasion or to take an afternoon off when a major milestone is accomplished.
- Public recognition. Nothing says "thank you" more than being named employee of the month! Having an employee's picture displayed, their name on a plaque, or reserving a parking space for them costs little but means a lot.

- Give your time. Many team members want access to the executives. "Pizza with the President" or similar initiatives gives top performers the visibility they crave.

- Casual Fridays. Employees relish the opportunity to dress casual at work. Establish deliverables for your team and if met, allow them to dress casually once a week or once a month.

  - Feed them. Whether it is treating your team mates to a long lunch or bringing in a meal to share, the hospitality shown will be appreciated. Stocking the office refrigerator with snacks that your team members love, not only shows that you appreciate their work, but also that you care about them enough to know what they like.

  - Upgrade their space. Everybody likes to get something new. Maybe a team member needs a new desk, a better chair, an office clock or a desk lamp. Show your appreciation by helping them get items that will make them more effective or make their time at work more pleasant.

  - Pay for a night out. Purchase your hard working team members a pair of tickets to the movies or a concert.

  - Team titles. Even if you don't have the authority to change their job title, you can have creative titles for team members. Titles like "statistics guru" or "planning master" are lighthearted but also indicate an appreciation for their role and contribution.

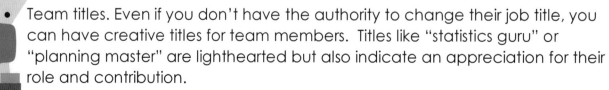

COMMUNICATION STYLES

Review the information about communication styles. Then, in the space below, identify your style. Next, make a list of five people you communicate with on a regular basis and identify their communication style. Finally, describe ways that you could adjust your communication style to more effectively communicate with each person.

My communication style is (Controller, Promoter, Supporter, Analyzer):	
What characteristics do you have that made you choose that style?	

Person with whom you communicate with regularly	His/her Communication Style	How can you adjust your style to communicate more effectively with this person? Be specific.
1.		
2.		
3.		
4.		
5.		

AVOIDING PITFALLS THAT OCCUR IN TEAMS

Even well-managed, well-trained teams with a clear mission can succumb to problems. One common problem that occurs in teams is called Groupthink. Groupthink is defined as the practice of thinking or making decisions as a group in a way that discourages creativity or individual responsibility. We have all heard employees referred to as a "yes-man" or "yes-women." These are derogatory terms that seem to indicate that the person always agrees with the boss, even if the decision he or she is agreeing with is not a good one. This type of agreement in a team setting, without evaluating alternatives or having debate, is called groupthink. Sometimes groupthink occurs, not because employees want to curry favor from the boss, but because they want to avoid conflict.

Groupthink is not healthy for a team. One strategy to avoid groupthink is to place emphasis on the Monitor-Evaluator role when assembling the team. It should be made clear from the beginning that the role of this team member is to challenge decisions and the status quo. Another strategy is to have regular brainstorming sessions where all ideas can be shared without the risk of embarrassment. Allow team members to take turns leading group sessions so the team experiences different styles and perspectives.

Another pitfall that occurs in teams is poor group dynamics. Some team members might shirk their responsibilities. This breeds resentment from other members that pick up slack. Establishing clear roles, responsibilities and accountability measures for each role will help avoid this problem. The opposite issue is equally problematic. Sometimes a team is dominated by one person or small group of people. These individuals monopolize the conversation and appear to have influence over the decisions since they have the loudest voices. The productivity of the rest of the team declines when they feel unheard and unimportant. Setting team norms at the outset, including limiting the "floor time" in meetings, enables the leader to respectfully limit the presence of these problematic individuals.

GROUP DYNAMICS

Review each challenge related to group dynamics. Write a couple of sentences explaining how you would handle each of these individuals.

Issue	My Solution
Bully in Meetings	
The Yes-Man	
The Lazy Team Member	
The Attention Hog	
The Wall Flower / Pushover	
The Over-extender	

READY TO LEAD

verybody is a leader and a follower at various times of their lives. Regardless of whether you are the leader of your family, a Girl Scout troop, a Little League team, or your neighborhood association, knowing your leadership style and practicing good social and emotional ntelligence, will help you to be more successful in that role.

Ken Blanchard, researcher and author of "Leadership and the One Minute Manager" dentified four leadership styles: **Supporting**, **Coaching**, **Empowering**, and **Directing**. It is mportant to note that while people have a preferred style, the appropriateness of each style will change based on the situation. You may feel most comfortable using a coaching style, but in an emergency situation, you may be forced to use a more directing method.

- The **Supporting** approach to leadership utilizes praise, listening, and facilitation. It works best when you are managing highly competent employees who have varying levels of commitment to your team.
- The **Coaching** approach to leadership is direct and supportive. It works best when you are managing people that have moderate levels of competence and commitment to your team.
- The **Empowering** approach to leadership utilizes a high degree of delegation and trust in your team. It works best when you are managing highly competent individuals with high levels of commitment to the team.
- Finally, the **Directing** approach to leadership utilizes a high degree of structure, control, and supervision. It works best when you are managing people with low competence but who are highly committed to your team.

Knowing your style will enable you to lead others in a way that they will respond to. This is similar to what you learned about communicating and motivating others. There are several free leadership-style quizzes online. Google them so you can learn a little bit more about yourself and your strengths and weaknesses as a leader. As a team leader or a team member, you have the ability to impact others by changing the way you interact with them. There is no right or wrong approach but some approaches will certainly yield better results than others.

People that show an ability to adjust how they respond to others tend to have high social and emotional intelligence. Individuals that have high social and emotional intelligence make better leaders because they recognize and are attuned to the needs and desires of the people around them.

This makes them invaluable on a team! Emotional and Social Intelligence refers to competencies linked to self-awareness, self-management, social awareness, and relationship management. These competencies enable people to understand and manage their own emotions and the emotions of others during social interactions. Psychologists agree that a person who is aware of their strengths and weaknesses, and who works at improving their social and emotional intelligence, is better prepared to influence and impact others. Let's take a look at ways to enhance your competencies that will result in high social and emotional intelligence, namely: Self-Awareness, Self-Management, Motivation, Empathy, and Social Skills.

Self-Awareness.

Becoming more self-aware can be tricky since often times individuals do not recognize a lack of self-awareness in themselves. A great way to start is to obtain feedback from other people. Ask them to list your strengths and weaknesses. Compare results from multiple people and look for trends and patterns. Try to see your behaviors from their points of view. It is also helpful to keep a journal of your emotions. Write down details about what happened that day, how you felt about it, and how you handled it. After a month, look back to see if you can spot any trends or types of situations that bother you or make you overreact. Reflect honestly about why you are affected by certain situations.

The key is to look inward as opposed to focusing on external factors. For example, you might find that every time you have a meeting with a colleague, you end up in a bad mood. Rather than justifying your mood on the fact that your colleague is self-centered, pushy, and monopolizes the boss's time, focus on how you react. Is it possible that you are subconsciously annoyed that you don't speak up more for yourself or that you are not confident enough to share your ideas? Honest, internal reflection will help you change the way you respond to interactions with others.

Self-Management. Once you have determined what triggers various emotions within yourself, you can start utilizing techniques to control them. You cannot always control what makes you feel a certain way, but you can always control how you respond to it. Self-management enables you to react appropriately. It means learning to control outbursts, disagreeing respectfully, and avoiding activities that undermine yourself, such as self-pity or panic. Before responding to a negative email, count to 10 or breathe deeply. If a co-worker makes you angry, take a walk outside. Sunshine stimulates endorphins in your brain that affect your mood. If you are frustrated, try exercising. Making a slight change to your physical environment, can dramatically impact how you deal with your emotions. The bottom line is to turn emotions that feel overwhelming into something positive.

Motivation. When used in the context of emotional intelligence, motivation means having an intense, internal desire to complete something. It does not come from an external promise of a reward, like a raise or promotion. Since motivation comes from within, you must assess your values in order to select activities that will motivate you. Write the answers to some basic formational questions: What are my values? What is important to me? Am I currently doing any activities that are contrary to my values? What do I want to accomplish in my life? A person that is motivated to improve their career will go back to school, apply for new jobs, or work towards a promotion. A person that is motivated to save the planet may recycle or alter their lifestyle to leave a smaller carbon footprint. People that understand the root of motivation can use this knowledge to bring out the best in themselves and their team members.

Empathy. Empathy is more than "feeling bad for other people." Individuals that have strong social and emotional intelligence understand that empathy is about walking in a person's shoes and internalizing their feelings in order to relate to that person. You can increase your ability to empathize with others by practicing arguing an opposite point of view. If you believe your boss made a poor decision, try defending her actions in your head. Once you establish credible arguments that support the boss's actions, ask yourself if you would have made a similar decision under similar circumstance. Being able to see another person's point of view and listening without bias are invaluable skills to have when you are on a team.

Social Skills. Social intelligence includes a range of abilities related to interacting effectively with others. It includes being aware of other people's feelings and being able to adjust how you interact with people to obtain the optimal result. It also means having the ability to resolve problems and disagreements without involving inappropriate emotion. People with high social intelligence "fight fair" meaning they don't throw people under the bus or manipulate to gain an advantage. They are also mindful of their nonverbal communication, as well as the nonverbal signals of others. Crossed arms, rolling eyes, or a furrowed brow do not communicate a desire to resolve a conflict. Those types of behaviors escalate tension. Whether you are using social intelligence on the job or in your personal life, you want to end a conflict on a cooperative note. Let your boss, coworker, or significant other know that even though you have different views, you want to work towards the same goal. Reflect empathy and take responsibility for your role in the disagreement or conflict. This is not a sign of weakness, rather it demonstrates self-awareness and integrity and will expedite a successful resolution. By incorporating the techniques related to empathizing and self-management you have learned, you will be more prepared to negotiate conflicts and be a team leader.

Leadership Styles

Review each situation and determine which leadership style (Coaching, Supporting, Empowering, Directing) would yield the best outcome. There may be more than one style that is effective, so be sure to justify your selection.

Situation	Preferred Leadership Style	Justification for the Style
You were just assigned to lead a team to quickly finalize the new employee manual that is due in a week. The people on your team do not have Human Resources or writing experience, but they are motivated to complete this project due to the fact that the current manual is so out of date.		
You are leading a group of customer service representatives. Their previous manager told you that they responded well when he had contests to reward the representatives who provided the most accurate product knowledge and got the highest customer ratings.		
You were chosen to mentor a team of managers-in-training. Each one has strengths and weaknesses. With some individual attention, you are certain that you can make them exceptional managers.		
You have had the opportunity to work with this group of team members before, when you were opening a new store location. They did a great job and you trust their ability to select the next location. They can't wait to get started.		
You have been asked to put together a new team of real estate agents that reside throughout the region. These individuals have never been put on a team, but the agency believes that they will perform better if they learn best practices from you and other successful agents.		
You have been asked to lead a team that is investigating the uses for a new pharmaceutical drug. The structured drug trials are confidential and the team members are not privy to many details because of the nature of the study.		

If your actions inspire others to dream more, learn more, do more and become more, you are a leader.

– John Quincy Adams

¹ Tarricone, P & Luca, J. Successful teamwork: A case study. Edith Cowan University, Perth, Australia. 2002.
² https://www.thebalance.com/
³ https://www.liquidplanner.com

CULTURAL DIVERSITY

&

CONFLICT RESOLUTION

LEARNING OBJECTIVES

1. Describe how cultural differences directly affect communication.

2. Discuss the ways in which gender stereotypes define traditional roles.

3. Analyze how conflict arises by ineffective communication.

4. Improve communication by modifying modes of expression.

PEACE IS NOT ABSENCE OF CONFLICT,
IT IS THE ABILITY TO HANDLE
CONFLICT BY PEACEFUL MEANS.

– Ronald Reagan

Gaining awareness of the many differences in any given culture and learning to effectively manage conflict will significantly improve your chances for success in school and on the job. The key to success in both areas is communication. Communication can take place verbally, through tone of voice, through body language, or can even be expressed by the clothes you wear. Understanding one's culture and the various ethnic nuances will help you to communicate in an effective and respectful manner. This type of communication can eliminate distracting phrases or body language that can be offensive and can cost you or your organization time and money.

If you wish to get your message across in an email, text, on social media, or a written report, it is crucial to express your ideas in a manner that is not offensive. The more diverse a community is, the more challenging it can be to communicate, listen, and understand the different cultural norms. Fortunately, you don't have to be an expert communicator or even a cultural diversity specialist. You do, however; need to be aware of your own communication style! And that, you can do!

Cultural Diversity

Different cultures have different behaviors, values, and often communicate in a variety of ways that may drastically differ from your own culture. **Ethnocentrism** is the belief that your culture is superior to other cultures. This commonly held belief could lead to devastating results in your career or even your relationships, if left unchecked. It is not uncommon to have this belief and not even be aware that you have it, until it is challenged!

Some of the most typical ethnocentric challenges can revolve around different religious views, politics, gender stereotypes, family values, sexual orientation, clothing, and so on. Your company or school's mission statement may explore, assess, review, and even make conclusions about these topics. If you are curious about certain topics that may be perceived as sensitive or controversial, think carefully about how you will pose questions to classmates or co-workers from different cultural backgrounds.

Some of the best places to work are known for their neutrality and judgment free zones on these topics. It's always best to ask questions about any differences that present themselves, rather than assuming what those differences might mean.

In both your professional and personal life, asking questions will increase your focus on your goals and objectives at hand. Being mindful of the way you ask a question is perhaps the most crucial part of this lesson.[1]

Imagine that you are at school and a classmate comes to class wearing a headscarf. You are curious about it, but want to make sure that you ask questions in a respectful manner. Which would be the best way to address the topic?

1. "That is a beautiful headscarf! Would you be open to explaining why woman typically wear headscarves in your culture?"
2. "I like your headscarf, what do those things mean anyway?"
3. "What are you wearing on your head?!"

Which did you choose? If you chose #1, you are well on your way to asking questions in a respectful manner that shows you are truly interested in understanding more about different cultural values. You are opening the door to conversations that will allow you to not only learn about another culture, but will also give you the opportunity to share something about your own culture.

The other options, while may be seemingly appropriate, imply that you are not really interested in knowing about the cultural significance of the headscarf. In fact, they may imply disrespect, contempt, or ethnocentrism.

Assumptions

Think of a time when you were working on the job or in school and a supervisor or faculty member assumed something about you that was not accurate.

What was the topic of the conversation?

_____

_____

What was your reaction(s)?

_____

_____

What emotion(s) did you feel?

_____

_____

Was it appropriate to address the subject with you? Why?

_____

_____

If yes, what question(s) would have been more appropriate and less assuming to ask?

_____

_____

Gender Stereotyping

Did you know that your gender identity develops as a child and with that identity you acquire gender-role stereotypes? **Gender-role Stereotypes** are beliefs about the characteristics and behaviors that are appropriate for boys and girls. All societal groups have expectations of acceptable behavior based on gender. Parents, siblings, extended family members, friends, religious affiliation, magazines, television, social media, and other social influences construct these norms from early childhood. Overtime, we assume these stereotypes as part of our identity.

ction 10 – Cultural Diversity & Conflict Resolution

Gender Stereotyping: Positive and Negative Aspects

Stereotyping can be either negative or positive, but in either case, below you will find three examples of how stereotyping can be harmful:

- Stereotypes inhibit our ability to treat others as individuals because we immediately make assumptions based on gender.
- Stereotypes create limited expectations for behavior based on gender.
- Stereotypes lead to faulty assumptions. Unfortunately, we tend to look for explanations for specific behavior based on gender stereotypes, which come from those faulty assumptions.

Gender stereotypes often inform attitudes and expectations between sexes. These stereotypes greatly vary across cultures. Many cultures favor a male in a dominant poser position (a position of authority). The United States' culture is no different. In the 1950s the United States had some incredibly stringent gender stereotypes.[2]

Gender Roles

Today significant progress is being made in the workplace, in school, and by the mass media to neutralize gender bias. For example, feminist groups are working diligently to propel the "equal pay for equal work" initiative that often refers to pay inequality based on gender. Disney has introduced more female characters as heroines, and children's books are removing gender bias by using the words "male" and "female" as opposed to "boys" and "girls." Despite social progress, many of us grew up with strict gender messages like those that follow.

Review the statements below and discuss how they have affected your views on gender.[1]

Males	Females
Play in the dirt	Play with Barbies
Brave	Nice
Handsome	Beautiful
Play Football	Cheerleaders
Carpenters	Housekeepers
Breadwinners	Homemakers
Doctors	Nurses
CEOs	Administrative Assistants
Pilots	Flight Attendants
Presidents	First Ladies

Body Language and Gestures for Different Cultures

It's difficult to know about the cultural norms in every group. Trying to follow all the rules is even more challenging. However, the more rules you know, the more groups you can effectively interact with. Here are a few examples of cultural differences you may find in the workplace, at school, or in different countries around the globe!

Eye Contact

In the United States and Canada, **intermittent** eye contact conveys that you are interested and listening to what the other person is saying. This type of eye contact is appropriate for males and females in mixed company.

In some European cultures, it is considered completely appropriate to **stare** at individuals for extended periods of time.

In many Middle Eastern cultures, you can expect **intense** eye contact as a sign of trust and connection. However, this is only appropriate between individuals of the same gender. Particularly in Muslim cultures where anything more than **brief** eye contact is inappropriate with members of the opposite sex.

In some Asian, African, and Latin American cultures, **extended** eye contact insinuates that you are "challenging" the other person.

In Japan even **brief** eye contact is considered uncomfortable.

Finally, in some cultures, a woman is expected look down when talking to a man.

Handshakes

While handshakes have been a method of greeting for centuries, cultural rules vary in different parts of the world. Below you will find a several examples of appropriate handshake etiquette.

In some Northern European countries, handshakes are quick, firm, and typically "one-pump."

In some Mediterranean cultures, and Central and South America, handshakes are longer and often include more meaningful touch. For example, the left hand may touch the clasped right wrist or the elbow.

In Australia, women should offer their hand first when greeting a man, and women typically do not shake hands with one another.

In Turkey, a firm handshake is considered rude and aggressive.
In some parts of Africa, a limp handshake is appropriate.

Men and women in Islamic countries never shake the hands unless they are close family members.

In some countries like China and the United Emirates, it is important to offer a handshake to the oldest person in the group first.

Greetings

In the United States, we typically greet someone by saying: "Hello, my name is..." or "Hi, I am...." While offering a firm handshake. People from different cultures will most likely assimilate to the local or dominant culture, however; there are other forms of greeting that you should be aware of.

For example:

In Japan and China, people bow. The bow often indicates someone's age and social status.

In some countries like Italy and Spain, people kiss each other's cheeks on both sides of the face.

Personal Space

Personal space varies a great deal across cultures. Keep in mind that personal space preferences vary widely based on your upbringing and preferences.

If you travel to China, you may notice people infringing on your personal space. Strangers regularly touch when standing on the subway, sitting on buses, or waiting in lines.

Conversely, some cultures require much more space than in America like Germany, for example.

Quick Tip: When you are in a group and are unsure about the personal space rules, start with your comfort zone, and allow others to take the lead on what makes them comfortable.

Touching

Touching is usually NOT appropriate in the American work environment.

Certain sects of Judaism only allow physical touch between husband and wife.

In Japan, Scandinavia, and England, personal touch is less common.

In some Mediterranean and Latin cultures, touching is encouraged and it is often considered rude if you are less affectionate.
Quick Tip: If you're unsure, let the other person guide what is appropriate to them.

Personal Hygiene

In some cultures, men do not shave facial hair and women do not save legs or underarms. Wearing deodorant is not customary in some cultures and others bathe less frequently. That said, odors that are odd to you may be acceptable in another culture. Be mindful or your reactions when you observe a difference in hygiene and be careful not offend anyone.

Gestures

One of the easiest ways to offend someone from another culture is to miscommunicate using gestures! Gestures mean different things in different cultures. To be on the safe side, when you are learning about a new culture, keep your gestures to yourself. In some cultures, the middle finger is used as a pointer. In other cultures, it might not have any effect at all. Conversely, the American "A-OK" sign has negative connotations in other countries. For example, by flashing the "A-OK" in Portugal or Spain, you are actually signifying to someone that they are worthless! The thumbs-up has different meanings in other cultures as well. Try searching on the Internet for, "Gestures in different countries." You will be amazed at all the different meanings for common gestures!

Time

Time differs for many countries. Polychronic cultures (many things at the same time) such as parts of Europe, the Middle East, and Latin America, believe that time cannot be controlled and that it is flexible. In Japan however, showing up on time for meetings, dinner, and work is a sign of respect. If you're working for a Japanese boss and everyone is advancing but you, make sure you're on time (early) for everything![3]

Quick Tip: When learning the norms of another culture, if you are uncomfortable or nervous about doing or saying the "right" thing, let the other person lead the interaction. Additionally, you can always ask! "May I ask how this [_____] differs in this culture?"

When in doubt, always ask!

Different Dialects

Even if someone speaks the same language as you, it is sometimes difficult (and can be amusing) to understand and communicate effectively. **Dialects** are regional or social variations of language, including pronunciation, grammar, and vocabulary. For example, in the south you might hear the following:

Agonna	I'm Going To
Y'all	You All
Warnt	Was Not
Bard	Borrowed

Think about some of the dialect that makes your local area unique!

Writing

When communicating with anyone, especially in writing, write (type) in complete sentences. Many people, whose second language is English, often learn proper English, which might not include colloquialisms, jargon, or cultural metaphors that are used for informal conversation.

Here are a few examples:

She needed a **fix** of chocolate.

Getting admitted to the college of your choice has become a **crapshoot**.

It was just **smoke and mirrors**.

Choose language that is appropriate to your demographic (audience) and review your message at least once to ensure it relays the information you intend. If you use examples, make sure the example is clear and concise. It can often help to have someone else review the information to clarify tone and message.

Remember, all emails, texts, and social media posts are often public. Keep this in mind at all times. Your work devices such as computers, emails, smart devices, and so on are not for personal use.

Appropriate Language

Revise the sentences that follow without using jargon or slang.
Example: He is totally trippin.

He is being unrealistic.

_____

She has all of that <u>coin</u> in her pocket.

_____

It takes time to learn the <u>setup</u> around here.

_____

He didn't have the <u>guts</u> to try it.

_____

I'm not <u>down</u> with that.

_____

There <u>ain't</u> nothing wrong with this.

_____

Managing Conflict

Now that you've learned about cultural diversity, you can better understand why **conflict** arises when there's a breakdown in communication. There are various reasons for this, and several have already been discussed (e.g., cultural differences, assumptions, stereotyping and so forth.) Let's focus on ways to improve your communication.

Improving Communication

Be more accepting
We usually want others to be accepting of our ideas and thoughts, even when they might not be clear to the other person. Try to do the same.

Be attentive
Most of us like to think that what we are talking about is important or at least meaningful. Paying attention to the person speaking "says" that you're listening.

Listen between the lines
If you pay attention to the nonverbal signals as well as the words, you have a better opportunity of understanding the full message.

Share responsibility for connecting

All parties participating in the conversation need to be involved and make sure they are clearly understanding each other.

Using "I" Statements

It is usually better to state your own thoughts, emotions, and needs rather than telling others what they should do or how they should think.

Inappropriate Statements	Appropriate Statements
I can't believe you did that!	Help me understand what happened.
You're wrong!	I see your point, however; have you considered this information?
No!	That's actually…
Uh huh.	Yes, of course.[4]

Example: Joe arrives late for work for the 2nd time this week. Without asking for an explanation, his boss, Rick says, "You are late! One more time, and you are FIRED." Joe is upset by this and stomps off the job. What Rick doesn't realize is that the reason Joe is late is because he was asked by another manager to stop by a client's office on his way to work to make sure the HVAC system was installed correctly. Joe quit over a **miscommunication**.

If Rick had said, "Joe, I noticed you were late again this morning. Can you help me understand why you were unable to arrive on-time?" Joe would have been able to explain that he was making sure the HVAC system was properly installed on a jobsite. Rick would likely have responded with, "I understand, thanks for doing that. Next time you are going to a job site before work, can you text me and let me know? I don't always know when you've been called off site, and it would really help me to better plan."

Analyzing Statements

Now it's time for you to try "owning" your own statements by using the phrases below. Think of a situation in which you were disappointed by a family member, friend, colleague, or classmate. Then complete the following statements:

I think _____

I prefer _____

I have found_____

It appears to me that_____

What I'm feeling is _____

In my opinion _____

What I'm hearing is _____

Am I being clear about _____?

What is normal behavior?

Distinguishing normal from abnormal behavior can be difficult and quite treacherous. Applying empathy (not sympathy) is always the best practice. Being sensitive to your own and other's needs and desires will help you in any situation, however; recognizing what is socially acceptable and what isn't can be difficult at times.

SEEK FIRST TO UNDERSTAND

THEN TO BE UNDERSTOOD.

- Stephen R. Covey

[1] Bucher, Richard. Diversity Consciousness. Opening Our Minds to People, Cultures, and Opportunities (4th ed). Pearson Education, 2014.

[2] http://www.healthguidance.org/entry/15910/1/List-of-Gender-Stereotypes.html

[3] Lewis, Richard. When Cultures Collide: Leading Across Cultures (3rd ed.). Nicholas Brealey Publishing, 2006

[4] Sharland, Alan. The Communication and Conflict Guide to the Principles of Effective Communication and Conflict

EFFECTIVE COMMUNICATION & NETWORKING

LEARNING OBJECTIVES

1. Identify why mentors are essential and how to meet them.

2. Create a system to organize contacts.

3. Develop effective styles of communication.

4. Devise an approach to overcome rejection.

Connecting to mentors and building your network is like a muscle;

The more you work it, the large it gets.

Let me start by telling you that the Bureau of Labor Statistics estimates that the average American knows approximately 500 people. By knowing 500 people, you may have developed a bigger network of contacts and friends and a support system larger than you ever realized. Each of the 500 people you know has contact with 500 people of their own. The net result is (500 × 500 or 250,000) potential contacts. ***That many people would fill Yankee Stadium five times!***

Making contacts is crucial to your career success. I encourage you to network at all times. Taking advantage of obvious and not so obvious people connections a positive step to ensuring career success.

This exercise will serve to construct a visual depiction of your current centers of influence, people who have the potential to assist you. What I would recommend doing first is to develop what I call a *tree diagram*.

MY NETWORK

Write your name on a blank piece of paper, and from that form little branches or clusters of your immediate family; then from that add your secondary family, until you get to your 3rd cousins. Next, list your friends or professionals or work associates, neighbors, your doctor, your dentist, people you've come to know, your former professors or teachers, the people who you've met through friends or a friend of a friend, and people you've met at social events. By creating this tree diagram, you'll find that you know a great many people.

Take a look at the sample diagram below. Create your own visual representation of your personal network. You can use a graph, a tree, or anything else that comes to mind. Get creative and include as many contacts as possible.

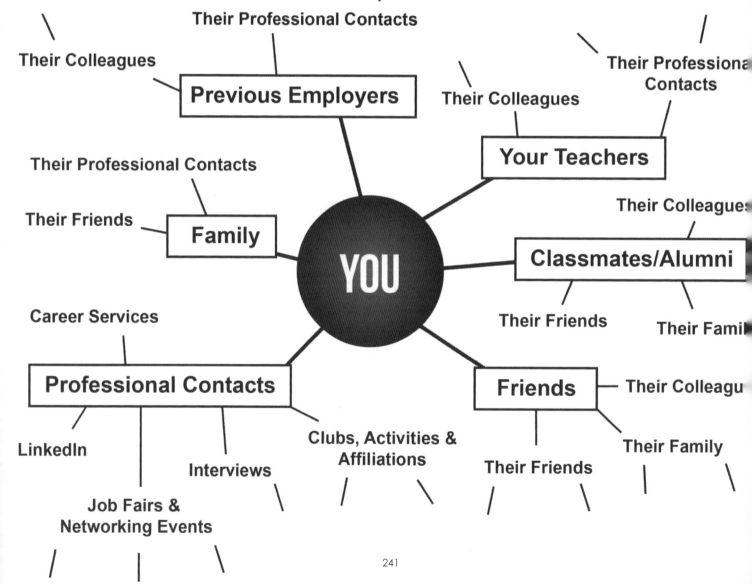

To initiate this process, ask yourself the following questions:

Whom do you know? . . .

From your family?
From your friends?
From your childhood?
From your old job?
From your school or college?
From your civic activities?
From your health club?
From your church?
From your PTA?
From your neighborhood?
Who is your attorney?
Who is your banker?
Who is your doctor?
Who is your dentist?
Who is your insurance agent?
Who is your realtor?
Who sold you your car?
Who do you look up to?
Who has a successful business?
Who do the people you know, *know*?

MY CONTACT LIST

In the chart below, list as many contacts as you can by name, occupation (field) and type of relationship. If possible, also include the method you will use to contact each individual.

Example:

Name	**Occupation**	**Phone/email**	**Type of Relationship**
Joe Smith	Teacher	714-555-0067	Friend of Bill Jones

Set a goal to increase your Contact List by one person per month. Remember to keep an active file!

Name	Occupation	Phone/email	Type of Relationship

Organizing Your Contact List

Each time you contact a person about a position, fill out a computerized index card (or create a similar system) and record the key information. Finding your career calling can be a very competitive process. There is often a fine line between success and failure. But in terms of competition, everybody you meet who is relatively friendly, may have many friends. But recognize that there are a lot of people looking for that same calling.

Understand that you can only expand your contact network by keeping track of the people you meet. Monitor your progress and record names, job titles, and employer name, not on a napkin, but in an organized, professional manner. If you do not actively maintain and build your network of connections, you will most likely never find your true calling.

Some do, but I never found it valuable to join unemployed networking groups. If you are between jobs, it simply does not make sense to attend "pity parties." Instead, associate with job givers—people who can hire—not folks who are without work.

All contacts are important in some way; the key is to figure out which are worth maintaining. If a person cannot directly hire you, they may refer one or two other names to you.

The Power of Asking

"'How come you never told us any of this?' the bosses inquired. 'How come you never asked?' the workers replied."

- Christopher Locke

I am constantly amazed at how many people are afraid or hesitant to ask for something that they know will benefit them or their family. Have you ever heard the saying, "The squeaky wheel gets the oil!" Asking for what you want and deserve is not only your right, it is your obligation! *Why?* Because asking for a person's assistance or for him/her to become one of your key mentors, is merely your attempt to obtain more knowledge. Here's a useful acronym to remind you about asking:

Always

Seeking

Knowledge

So why do people stumble when they have an opportunity to ask?

Essentially, there are three reasons:

1. They have a belief system that says it's not right to ask.
2. They lack confidence.
3. They fear rejection.

Scipture says, "Ask and you shall receive, seek and you shall find, knock and it shall be opened to you."

Effective Communication

The definition of communication is: to send and receive messages. *Every day you send and receive thousands of messages.* There are essentially five types of communication. They include:

1. **Verbal**: Messages sent from one person to another through the spoken word.

2. **Non-Verbal**: No words are spoken. You can send messages through your actions, or you can receive messages by observing another person's actions.

3. **Written**: Reading or writing a message.

4. **Listening**: Receiving messages by hearing and by focusing on the spoken word. By definition, there is no communication unless someone hears or reads what you are saying.

5. **Technological**: Sending and receiving messages through technology.

How I Communicate...

Think about your day yesterday. List ten people with whom you communicated and what type of communication was established. The communication may be verbal, non-verbal, written, listening, or through technology or it may even involve several types of communication at the same time.

PERSON	TYPE OF COMMUNICATION
1. _____	_____
2. _____	_____
3. _____	_____
4. _____	_____
5. _____	_____
6. _____	_____
7. _____	_____
8. _____	_____
9. _____	_____
10._____	_____

This exercise allows you to ponder on how communication is used. How do you tend to communicate?

Types of Communication

Instructions: Write an example of how you have communicated in the past using each type of communication.

For example:

Verbal: *In a calm voice, I asked my child to clean his room. He ignored me; this made me angry. Then I asked him to clean his room; this time I yelled!*

1.**Verbal:** _____

_____

2.**Non-Verbal:** _____

_____

3.**Written:** _____

_____

4.**Listening:** _____

_____

5.**Technological:** _____

_____

Think about the examples you just wrote about. Choose one of the situations that could use improvement. Write about how you could improve upon your communication skills.

I chose _____ type of communication. I could improve my

communication skills by _____

_____

_____

Defeating the Fear of Rejection

We just briefly reviewed different ways in which we communicate, now let's turn our attention to rejection. I must admit that at times I am a bit nervous when it comes to contacting key individuals, not out of fear of rejection but out of concern that I will not convey *my* contribution to them. Remember, true networking is the process of finding creative ways to help *other* people be more successful. What helps me to relax is to remind myself of the following:

My decision to proceed is not one of success or failure, but rather between choosing greatness (which requires risk) or accepting certain mediocrity and the guilt associated with an inability to master my own emotions.

There are three basic strategies for overcoming fear and anxiety associated with contacting a potential mentor:

1. Acknowledge that it is perfectly normal to be anxious about the prospect of calling on a stranger. This is not a skill that comes naturally to most people; it is a learned behavior. Confidence is developed through experience, practice and rehearsal of your contribution and how it can be of mutual benefit to connect.

2. Understand that overcoming this fear through proper preparation and practice is absolutely essential to improving your technique and building a world class Rolodex.

3. Make a 100% commitment to improving your networking skills and making it part of your personal brand. Remember, 21st century superstars are master networkers and connectors!

Responding to Objections

COMMENT:	REPLY:
I am too busy . . .	*What is a better time to chat? Or Are you sure? I was told you were extremely helpful to passionate career seekers like me and your wisdom and knowledge was invaluable . . .*
I am the wrong person . . .	*May I please have the appropriate contact? Can I use your name as a referral?*
Email or send me your resume.	*Will do. Can we also set a time and date for me to present myself in person?*
We only hire experienced candidates . . .	*Understood. But wouldn't you agree that passion can overcome perceived shortcomings? I promise not to waste your precious time.*
We aren't looking for anyone right now . . .	*Understood. As a key person in my chosen industry, can we spend a few minutes sharing information? It would be greatly appreciated.*

I cannot overemphasize the importance of being persistent!

Remember, you have value and are looking to solve problems. The people you are calling simply need to be made aware of what your contributions are and how you can help them! Do not be afraid or feel you are imposing. You have tremendous value and, unfortunately, the only way that a potential employer can learn about you is for you to make the connection.

The problem is that too many job seekers are unprofessional and have given legitimate seekers who have taken the time to learn the proper process a bad name, so many hiring authorities are skeptical and waste a lot of their time with unfocused career seekers. Show them you are focused and professional and they WILL talk with you!

Differentiating Yourself

It isn't enough to be at the right place at the right time, you must be the *right person in the right place at the right time!*

One of my favorite questions in life is, *"What is unique and compelling about you?"* Whether you are pitching a new product to a venture capitalist, trying to convince someone to date you, or attempting to get potential mentors to assist you in pursuit of your career calling, you must identify and be able to articulate your unique and compelling advantage. What *differentiates* you from others?

The most powerful way to differentiate yourself is by mastering the use of language. The better your vocabulary, the faster you will achieve your objectives. Your vocabulary creates a first impression, helps you to overcome obstacles, points out your sincerity and, above all, is the bond that creates lasting relationships. Whether you are speaking directly to a contact or using technology (email, etc.), word choice is powerful.

Contrary to opinion, you can improve your skills in this area. Many people make the excuse they were not born with, "*the gift of gab*" or lack charisma. Nonsense! It is simply a matter of committing to

improving the way you describe yourself, your experiences and your contributions. I have found that charming people are simply those that are themselves and do not try to put on an act.

Each of us is unique and compelling in some way; that uniqueness is your power.

As the Founder of *Career* TEAM, I am proud of our accomplishments in building the nation's workforce, particularly in the area of assisting welfare recipients achieve self-sufficiency and become gainfully employed. Many of these folks come from incredibly challenging upbringings filled with abuse and neglect. We have worked in major cities across the country. Whenever we initiate a new training program, we always begin the first day by asking each attendee to write down four things about themselves- three that are true and one that is false. *We call this exercise, "Three Truths and a Lie."* We ask them to consider things that are unique and compelling, things that other people might find interesting. We are looking for a window into the person.

You would be amazed at the contributions folks have made or obstacles they have overcome but have not been afforded the chance to share with others. Often, their verbal skills are out of practice or they have forgotten their uniqueness. They are each required to stand in front of the group and share their list, which in itself requires a certain confidence.

But because they are talking about subjects they are intimately familiar with, their anxiety and nervousness is somewhat diminished. Classmates are asked to guess which three are true and which one is the lie or is a goal not yet attained. We have met chefs, heroes, foster parents, world travelers, artists, singers, poets, and so on. This exercise sets the tone for one of the primary foundations of our conversion training:

No matter who you are, where you come from, or what hardships you have endured, we all have something unique and compelling to offer.

We just have to identify what it is and communicate it to others! But always remember to think before you speak! Remember: Never let your emotions control your dialogue; have a specific plan every time you meet with a potential new mentor.

Often, people will ramble or let their emotions take over, but not you! Do not be afraid to share aspects of your personal life with new contacts. I learned this valuable lesson when I was once attempting to negotiate a contract to serve a large group of at risk youth with the Director of a large Washington, D.C. based federal government agency. For months, I had attempted to get a meeting and had leveraged my connections and sent multiple letters and email messages creating a justification for the meeting. Finally, a breakthrough came as the timing of our program to assist the nation's youth coincided with this agency's priorities. The appointment was set two days before Christmas, not the ideal time but I knew I most likely wouldn't get a 2nd chance. After waiting in the lobby for 45 minutes, I was called into the office.

During the meeting, the dialogue was progressing but not at the pace or in the direction that I ideally wanted it to go. We were engaging in small talk and beginning to discuss our business, but I felt that something was missing. *There was no bonding occurring;* we were simply two people sizing each other up but without a connection toward a common objective. I began by sharing my passion for youth and how our program would benefit their mission (*always give before you get!*).

As I was talking, I noticed that my contact kept looking at the door of his office and into the reception area. Glancing over, I noticed an elderly looking woman sitting there who did not look like she belonged in a government office. I was tempted to continue but noticed that my contact seemed very distracted by his next visitor. My instincts told me to address the issue or my presentation might not get the attention I wanted. So I stopped my presentation and suggested that my contact greet his new visitor. As it turns out, the visitor was my contact's mother, who had flown in from out of town to see her son, the well to do government director. Being extremely close to my mom and understanding his perspective, I suggested that we shorten our meeting so my contact could spend time with his mom, an obvious priority. His mom came into the room, we shared a few stories of my family values and childhood memories and our respective plans for the holiday. I was like one of the family!

My contact was so impressed with my sensitivity to the event and closeness to my own family, that we became friendly and established a business relationship that exceeded my wildest expectations. He later expressed that my professional attire and bottom line approach gave the impression of a "stick to business" mentality and masked my strong family beliefs and willingness to give "props" to moms. I shared that behind the large government building and button down shirt, I assumed that he was probably stodgy. We were both wrong; the end result was we were awarded a contract to serve youth!

The lesson:

Do not be afraid to let people in to meet the real you; it lets them know you are humble, honest, and more than just a person with their hand out looking for assistance.

Here are a few suggestions to further give you a competitive edge:

1. **Always keep good eye contact.** Looking away makes you appear unconfident or sneaky.

2. **Keep a reasonable distance and acknowledge your understanding with a confirmation** (uh-huh or a nod)

3. **Be relaxed and mirror the actions of your contact.** If they sit, you sit. Also, never cross or fold your arms as this creates the appearance you are guarded. If your contact has their arms crossed or folded, they are most likely uncomfortable or in a defensive posture. Try to loosen up the conversation if this occurs.

4. **Attempt to ease tension by physical contact meaning a handshake or by touching your contact's elbow, which is a bit more personable than a regular handshake.** Ever watch a master politician glad hand a new group? They often (gently) grasp an elbow and acknowledge a new person. Hugs for first meetings are genuinely not recommended!

5. **Always smile when you meet a new contact and an early compliment (if it is sincere) always helps!** I remember a friend once recounting a story of his initial meeting with a powerful, elderly contact. In the influential contact's office for the first time, my friend, a bit nervous, tried to make small talk and offered a feeble attempt at a compliment by commenting how pretty the contact's daughter was from the photo on his credenza. Imagine my friend's embarrassment, when the contact said, *"That isn't my daughter, young man, it is my new wife."*

6. **Focus on the other person's interests first and show genuine curiosity.** Encourage your contact to discuss these interests and share their passions.

Best Strategies for Making Connections

At this point you may be saying, "Well, that sounds great, and the information is very helpful. But I really have stage fright as far as how to actually go about contacting a potential employer or somebody else who can help me. I can do my own research online, in a library or through company published information. I can find a list of contact names. But when it comes to actually making the contact, I'm at a loss. I'm paralyzed with fear. I don't know exactly what to do." Many people have what I call *paralysis by analysis*, which means that they analyze too much and never take the action.

Without a plan, the process of developing a career contact network can be very difficult. But keep in mind that there are a number of different methods for contacting key individuals.

When I made the decision to write this book, one of my immediate objectives was to meet and learn from a successful author in the business motivation category. I targeted Jeff Fox, a successful businessman, speaker and best- selling author of *How to Become A Rainmaker, How to Become CEO, How to Become a Great Boss, How to Become a Marketing Superstar, Don't Send A Resume, How to Make Big Money in Your Own Small Business,* and *The Dollarization Discipline.* When doing research to find out how to contact him, I discovered that he lived in my state.

Rather than call or email Jeff and ask for his assistance in helping me overcome obstacles (that no doubt consumed his precious time and energy early on) or spend days trying to determine a person we both knew, I approached him with an opportunity to promote his published works in our company e-newsletter. I mentioned a couple other industry authors he would know who had also participated. In each issue, we would simply extract an excerpt from one of his books, include his photo and bio and presto, instant free publicity for Jeff to an audience of workforce professionals around the country.

To initiate a dialogue with Jeff, I requested a luncheon (in his town with a choice of two specific dates) to meet and discuss the publicity offer. I closed my request by indicating that he might be helpful in guiding me in my new book offering. As it turns out, Jeff is a great guy and was helpful in terms of suggesting certain strategies: clearly a win–win scenario.

Here are a few hints and suggestions that I used:

1. **Never make a cold call.** Always begin by referencing a common person, event, educational experience, work experience, organization or award that creates a common bond. As my first boss used to say, "Cold calling is for suckers." I never, ever make cold calls; they are a waste of my time and do not work. I have the reputation for being able to make a connection with virtually any person I set my mind to meeting. My secret? While some people say I was born with the "gift of gab" or have the unique benefit of extensive negotiation training, you and I now know the true reason for my success . . . *I always give before I ask for anything in return.*

2. **Another tip is to call people at unusual times.** Busy people are more likely to answer their own phones when their assistants or receptionists are not in the office, meaning before 8 am or after 6 pm. I know I do! Also, there isn't the competition for signatures or interruptions as most other staff has gone home.

3. **Make warm calls!** Begin by referencing a familiar reference (person, club, or institution) to establish a common bond and peak interest.

4. **Indicate immediately how *they* will benefit from meeting *you*; your needs are secondary.**

5. **Be flexible with regard to a meeting time and date.** Make it easy and convenient for the contact to say yes!

6. **Do your homework!** The Internet, via name search, provides instant access to information on your targeted connections.

For example, start by saying something like this:

"I am currently in the process of exploring several career alternatives. But before making any final decisions regarding employment, I'm trying to benefit from the counsel or guidance of an experienced individual such as you. I've had a great deal of experience in the field of . . . Then list your field . . .

Next, you want to say something like, "I'm particularly interested in learning more about specific employment opportunities, the skills and responsibilities required, the advantages and disadvantages of the profession, as well as the future outlook in your field. Could you please take some time from your busy schedule to meet with me for 15 minutes and share your knowledge and perspectives?"

It is important to proactively build your connections in areas where you feel passion or purpose. Today's hobby is tomorrow's occupation.

Here are five networking methods I recommend:

1. **Meet new contacts for 15 minutes over a cup of coffee.**

2. **Use food to break the ice . . .** breakfast, lunch, an after work drink or even dinner.

3. **Share a hobby:** play golf, workout or attend a sporting event. Find out your desired contact's interests in advance and show respect by selecting a venue that they feel comfortable with.

4. **Conferences:** If you are in a particular town and want to meet someone, why not invite them to a workshop or ask them to partake in lunch. Note: The American Society of Association Executives (ASAE) reports the meeting industry is an $83 billion market, with over $56 billion spent annually on seminars and conventions.

5. **Have a dinner party!** Invite a few guests who may benefit from knowing each other and, *presto*, instant connection.

Gaining an Appointment by Letter

Date
Mr. Ray Green
Vice President
XYZ Enterprises, Inc.
16 Glenn Road
Anywhere ST Zip

Your Name
Your Address
Your City, ST Zip

Dear Mr. Green:

I am exploring career opportunities in order to select a particular field or occupation. I thought it might be a good idea to obtain valuable insight from a more experienced individual like yourself. I am particularly interested in learning about the responsibilities, skills, outlook, and opportunities in (*Name of field or industry*).

I know you are extremely busy, but if you could provide me with 15 minutes of your time, you could really assist me in moving closer to my career goals.

I will be calling you or your secretary to determine your schedule, and, with your approval, solidify a mutually convenient time and date. Should you wish to contact me in the meantime, please do not hesitate to call me at (*insert your telephone number*).

Sincerely,
Signature
Your Name

* Note: Do not enclose your resume in a letter of this type because, if you do, you will look like a typical job seeker and that could turn the person off.

My Mentor Letter

Now it's your turn, write a letter to a prospective mentor/employer asking to meet. Be sure to include the following in your letter:

- Begin by doing a little research; choose your field of interest and research who might be a good person to contact.
- Remember, you are seeking out a potential contact that could help you to jumpstart your career!
- Now that you know whom you are writing to, follow the model and be sure to use a proper business letter format and language. Remember, you want to make a good first impression!
- Start your letter by telling the person why you are writing to him or her.
- Next, let the person know why they should make time to help you: state your unique value proposition! Remember, everyone has something unique and compelling about him or her.
- Sell yourself, but don't be too overzealous, this is about getting your foot in the door, not getting a job…. yet!
- Suggest a meeting time and date and let the person know how you will follow up.
- Be sure to include your phone number and e-mail address.

Important! You are at a crucial time in your life, make sure your ring back tone and/or voice mail message is appropriate and professional! Use an e-mail address that is also professional. Remember, you never have a second chance to make a first impression!

Mentor Letter Template

Following the model, use the template below to write a letter to a potential mentor.

_____   _____

_____   _____

_____   _____

_____

_____

_____

_____

_____

_____

_____

_____

_____

_____

_____

_____

_____

_____

Gaining an Appointment by Telephone

Sell the appointment; do not ask for a job! Never talk about your need to find a job on the phone unless you can actually make and conclude the sale without seeing the prospect personally. Inexperienced career seekers, in their eagerness to get appointments with career mentors, often share their personal needs or hardships in the first couple of sentences. If you do this, you will ruin the opportunity with a potential mentor.

Your approach must break the preoccupation of the contact. Assume everyone you call on is busy and thinking about things unrelated to your career aspirations. Most people are completely involved in their own problems, work, family, health, business, or bills.

Try this approach:

"I need about two minutes of your time. Is this a good time to talk?"

Remember:

1. You only have about 30 seconds at the outset of your discussion to get the prospect's complete and undivided attention

2. The first 25 words out of your mouth will set the tone for the rest of the conversation, so be prepared!

3. Be certain that you are speaking to the right person before making any attempt to set up an appointment

Improve Your Telephone Prospecting

Two things you can do to improve the quality of your telephone prospecting are:

1. **Stand up when you speak to the prospect.** Standing will force you to project your voice and lends itself to more confidence. Sitting may lessen your enthusiasm.

2. **Smile into the phone when you speak.** The person on the other side may not see your face, but they will sense your enthusiasm if you "dial with a smile."

How to Obtain an Information Interview

1. **Know the name of the person you are calling.**
2. **Confirm how the person prefers to be addressed.** (Mr., Mrs., Miss, Ms., Dr., Etc.).
3. **State how you got their name** (referral source).
   a. Name (friend)
   b. Article in magazine
   c. From teacher or associate
4. **State the purpose of your call** (wish to meet personally to discuss opportunities.
5. **Deliver your message.**
   a. Refer to any previous letters sent, if appropriate.
6. **Overcome objections.**
   a. "I will be brief."
   b. "I know you are busy; would Tuesday be better?"
   c. "Should I contact your secretary?"
7. **Close the presentation.**
   a. Ask for a personal session (time and date).

Success Tip: *In an information interview, it is rarely appropriate to ask for a job!*

Networking (interviewing) is Communicating . .

> "A farmer went into his attorney's office wanting to file for a divorce from his wife. The attorney asked, '*May I help you?*' to which the farmer replied, '*Yeah, I want to get one of those dayvorces.*' The attorney said, '*Well, do you have any grounds?*' and the farmer said, '*Yeah, I got about 140 acres.*' The attorney said, '*No, you don't understand. Do you have a case?*' and the farmer replied, '*No, I don't have a Case, but I do have a John Deere.*' And the attorney said, '*No, you really don't understand. I mean do you have a grudge?*' And the farmer replied to that, '*I got a grudge. That's where I park my John Deere.*' The attorney, still trying, asked, '*No, sir, I mean do you have a suit?*' The farmer replied, '*Yes, sir, I got a suit. I wear it to church on Sundays.*' The exasperated and frustrated attorney said, '*Well, sir, does your wife beat you up or anything?*' The farmer replied, '*No, sir. We both get up about 4:40.*' Finally, the attorney says, '*OK. Let me put it this way. WHY DO YOU WANT A DIVORCE?*' And the farmer says, '*Well, I can never have a meaningful conversation with her.*'"
>
> —Steven Covey, *The 8th Habit*

Communication is without question the most important skill in life. **There are basically four modes of communication: reading, writing, speaking and listening.** And most people spend of their waking hours doing those 4 things. The one that represents 40% to 50% of our communication time is listening; the other modes we have had the least training in.

Listening continuum:

1. Ignoring
2. Pretend listening (patronizing)
3. Selective listening
4. Attentive listening
5. Empathic listening

There are two ways to penetrate the hidden job market and arrange an information interview: via the telephone or via direct letter. You can use the telephone to help you get the job you want and set up the information interview; many people have some form of phone fright, where they have a fea of picking up the telephone. Their hands get sweaty. They begin mumbling their words.

I teach people to avoid or overcome this problem through practice and by being prepared. The best way to guard against stumbling over the phone is to prepare a script or dialogue. And don't take anything for granted. Include everything from your name and how you're going to introduce the particular call to your background and accomplishments so that you don't appear unprofessional.

Also, preparing a script will keep you from omitting or forgetting important information you want to share with the person so that when you hang up you don't say, *"Darn it. Why didn't I tell him about that accomplishment or my other accomplishment or my other activities?"*

REFLECTION: HOW WE COMMUNICATE

1. **Listen**. Listen quietly to what a person says without interrupting. Use "verbal attends" such as "uh huh," "um," "yes," and "I see" to show the speaker that you are following what he/she is saying.

2. **Maintain adequate distance**. We all have "personal space." When someone invades this space, we become uncomfortable. Conversely, when someone is too far away from us, it may feel as if they are not engaged in the conversation. Most people in North America use the distance of about an arm's length to separate two people engaged in a conversation.

3. **Avoid touching.** The appropriateness of touching another person will vary depending upon the circumstances. Some people are extremely uncomfortable when another person touches them. A handshake is acceptable in most cases, but refrain from other physical contact with people with whom you are not familiar.

4. **Maintain good body posture.** Stand up and pull your shoulders back. Erect posture conveys confidence, while slouching indicates the opposite. If you lean slightly toward the person with whom you are speaking, you will convey interest and intelligence.

5. **Control facial expressions.** Your face communicates a wide variety of attitudes and emotions. If you raise your eyebrows, you may look surprised. If you poke out your lips, you may convey anger, disagreement, or confusion.

6. **Maintain eye contact.** Good eye contact (not staring) shows that you are listening and are interested. North Americans often feel that when someone won't look you in the eye, they can't be trusted.

7. **Control personal odors.** In person-to-person contact, this aspect of communication is often overlooked. Obviously, cleanliness is essential. In addition, you should avoid strong perfumes and colognes or any scents that are strong enough to distract another person from their interaction with you.

8. **Control gestures.** Make a point of thinking about what your gestures convey. For example, clenched fists may indicate aggression or anger, and crossing your arms may indicate that you are defensive or suspicious. These are closed gestures that create nonverbal barriers. Use open gestures such as keeping your hands at your sides. Don't wave your arms or hands too much; as this may distract the person with whom you are speaking.

9. **Maintain your overall appearance.** What you wear to work depends upon the job you do. Remember, that whatever you are required to wear should be clean and neat. This will convey your competence and respect for your position.

10. **Get the Edge!** Follow these simple guidelines and you are on your way to becoming a great communicator

REFLECTION: GOOD LISTENERS

"You can't learn anything with your mouth open!"
- Edgar Bergen

Five common mistakes are:

1. **Concern about having the right answers.** The listener spends so much time trying to formulate an answer that he or she misses what is really being communicated. Sometimes an answer isn't even required; the speaker may just need understanding.

2. **Thinking that you know what is going to be said.** This habit can cause you to "tune out" and dismiss what is being said.

3. **Allowing interruptions.** If you are opening mail or carrying on a "side conversation" with a co-worker while on the telephone with a customer, it tells the customer that you do not think that what he or she has to say merits attention.

4. **Reacting to specifics.** Sometimes a customer will use language or a style of speaking that offends you. It's easy to stop listening and start focusing on your own feelings. Listen to the "big picture."

5. **Daydreaming.** The daydreamer pretends to listen, but really is focusing on something else.

After reading these, ask yourself, "Do I know anyone who does these things?" "How does it make me feel?"

If it makes you feel this way, it will make others feel the same way.

REFLECTION: AM I A GOOD LISTENER?

1. **Stop what you are doing and be ready to listen.** Often a speaker will state the main point when he/she begins speaking. You don't want to miss this vital information.

2. **Indicate that you are listening.** Use body language to show you are engaged in the conversation.

3. **Ask questions if you are unclear about the information.** You might say, "Did you say that you have a flight to catch today at 6 a.m. or 6 p.m.?"

4. **Take notes and write down important details.** Unless you have unlimited recall (and few of us do), writing down important details is essential to avoiding mistakes and misunderstandings. Listen for details. Clue words will help you recognize these details. Examples of clue words are names, dates, times, addresses, places, numbers, and products. It will also help you keep focused on what is important instead of on minor items.

5. **Restate the main points.** After the person has finished speaking, restate the main points to convey that you understand what the person has said. Use your notes to remember the details.

Section 12:

PROFESSIONAL BRANDING: RESUME & COVER LETTER

LEARNING OBJECTIVES

1. Compare the three resume types and create a resume that best suits your situation.

2. Write a professional cover letter.

3. Prepare a professional wardrobe.

Your Essential Marketing Materials: *Resume Time!*

It is now time to itemize your marketing materials. While certain aspects of careering have changed dramatically (for example, Internet job boards, personality type assessments, etc.) certain aspects remain surprisingly similar. Much like a brochure or company website, the resume and cover letter represent your calling card; that is, how you create a first impression in print.

While in the past, the postal service served as the primary means of distribution (remember the dreaded mass mailed resume!), today, career seekers use email and employer based websites to distribute their credentials. I am not a fan of mass-producing your credentials (neither via print nor the Internet) and strongly advise you to adopt a more targeted campaign aimed at specific employers or contacts.

One thing is clear: *The creation of the resume serves the valuable purpose of inventorying your unique and compelling contributions. It is a summary of your brand and acts as your one-page marketing campaign, a tradition still honored and recognized in the 21st century workplace.*

270

One Candidate . . . One Page . . . One Shot!

Resumes don't get candidates hired . . . mainly they serve to screen people out!

Now that you have determined your brand, interests, targeted your job aptitudes, researched opportunities in your area of interest, studied different markets or industries in terms of who is hiring and who is not, narrowed down specific employers, your next step is to inventory your credentials, so that you can talk intelligently about your past accomplishments and potential worth.

The creation of a resume is a task that most people dread, because it itemizes the sum total of your professional career in one document, typically on a single page! ***The end result produces two responses:***

> 1. You get really excited and are proud of your accomplishments when you see your finished resume.
> 2. Seeing your credentials reinforces the fact that you have not done your best work, have spent time in unfulfilling occupations and wasted precious time.

Let me remind you that it is not where you start, but how you finish. Regardless of how you initially feel about your professional summary to date, there is always the opportunity to improve yourself and build credentials that will provide a strong sense of accomplishment.

So what is a resume? A resume is really a digest of your qualifications that inform the employer of **five** things:

> 1. Who you are
> 2. What you know
> 3. What you have done
> 4. What you would like to do
> 5. How you can benefit the employer

Think of yourself as an individual with unique qualifications. Portray yourself as a candidate who has a strong sense of self and stands above the competition.

Resumes should be brief and to the point, no more than one to two pages.

Unless you have a specific long-term history, probably one page will suffice. Remember that you will never get the second chance to make a good impression unless the interviewer takes an interest in your resume. So, stand out! If you take advantage of the hidden job market and develop a career contact network, one effective strategy is to have a friend of the interviewer or influential person write a personal note on your resume praising your abilities. The core of your resume is a list of facts, activities, and experiences that summarize your accomplishments to this point in your life.

The very first step in putting together your resume involves making a complete list of all your achievements. After you have developed a list—and don't exclude anything from your academic, job experience, or personal life—edit those items that do not pertain to the targeted position. If it does not help your cause, *leave it out!*

A Hiring Authority is Looking for Two Things:

1. *Actual facts that indicate your qualifications*: your educational background, your employment history, and your social activities

2. *Patterns reflecting different aspects of your character or skills*: leadership ability, initiative, determination, and actions of that nature

Highlight your most essential qualifications. For example, if the position requires strong leadership, tailor your resume to demonstrate those instances where you have been a leader.

From the information obtained in an information interview, learn what credentials top people in that organization exhibit on a consistent basis. Remember that question from the information interview? Once you know that, you can tailor your resume to the area most important to the employer.

An Overview of the Resume

Definition:

By definition, the *resume* is the primary written vehicle of a productive and successful search. You must develop your ultimate career objective in language that can be effectively communicated. It also requires you to assess your previous training, experience, skills, abilities, and other characteristics that qualify you for the position. In short, the resume must tell the employer what position you seek and what you have to offer.

Style:

There are three types of resumes from which you can choose:

- **the chronological**
- **the functional**
- **the targeted**

Hint:

Let experienced people review your resume to make sure that it contains your best attributes. Focus on the most important accomplishments and be flawless in resume appearance.

What Employers Seek

1. The ability to become part of a team and have a great attitude
2. The ability to be flexible, versatile, and to multi-task
3. The ability to challenge previous ways of thinking and bring new,
fresh ideas to the table

Regardless of your background, show your ability to take risks, set high standards, and behave professionally. *One top human resource director stated that when evaluating resumes, the number one requirement is a progression from jobs of lesser responsibility to jobs of greater responsibility, especially within the same organization.*

How to Begin

Through our previous exercises in critical reflection and goal setting, you should have a specific career target in mind and be able to identify an industry or employers of interest.

At this point, your resume should be a brainstorming effort. Start your momentum by writing down your name, address and phone number. Then jog your memory by identifying your objectives. Immediate goals may be one to three years; long-range goals may be three to five years or longer. List your previous professional experience, including any training you've had beneficial to the position sought. Include the names of companies and the specific responsibilities. List your specific talents and skills. Now it's your turn!

274

Brainstorming Your Resume

State your career objective: _____

_____

What skills are required? _____

_____

What experience is required? _____

_____

Describe your ideal employer (location, size): _____

_____

What type of training is required for your ideal job? _____

_____

State your competitive edge over your competition: _____

_____

What transferable skills have you acquired in your previous jobs? _____

_____

List all your prior jobs held:

_____   _____

_____   _____

List all of your proudest accomplishments:

_____   _____

_____   _____

_____   _____

_____   _____

List any associations or organizations that you belong to or should join:

_____   _____

_____   _____

_____   _____

_____   _____

List any associations or organizations that you belong to or should join:

_____   _____

_____   _____

_____   _____

List your most enjoyable hobbies and non-work related activities:

_____   _____

_____   _____

_____   _____

List at least 5 people that can provide an accurate assessment of you as a person and as an employee. Remember, the best references are a former teacher or professor, a former employer, and a character reference (typically a close friend).

Name & Phone	Title	Relationship
_____	_____	_____
_____	_____	_____
_____	_____	_____
_____	_____	_____
_____	_____	_____

Update Your Resume on a Regular Basis

Remember, your resume is apt to change as your accomplishments, experiences, and knowledge levels change. Update your resume on a regular basis and make sure that it is as current as possible.

Useful Resume Tips

Before being offered employment, you must convince the employer of your talents in three areas: yourself and your personality; your abilities and credentials; your potential, that is, your future worth to the company. Emphasize your strengths, downplay your weaknesses, and demonstrate your flexibility and versatility. Understand the employer's competition and their culture. Listen carefully, question intelligently, be aware and sensitive to the employers' needs, and show persuasiveness. Your resume should introduce you as a creative problem solver, a person who is organized, persistent, and knows how to follow through.

A resume should answer who you are, what you know, what you have done, what you would like to do, and what you can do for the employer.

Utilize numbers in your resume wherever possible. Quantify your achievements. For example, "Duties included coordination of entire sales team of 15 individuals with a budget responsibility of $10.2 million dollars." *Wow!*

Those sentences seem to jump off the page at you. Consider . . . "Won the quarterly award from a total pool of 200 competitors" or "was responsible for opening 13 new client advertisers." Every role has a quantifiable aspect to it. How many boxes did you lift, millions did you manage, software programs did you install, how many words per minute do you type? Remember, the competition is successfully using this strategy . . . you should as well!

Compile a list of image-building words even before you know how you're going to incorporate them. Don't be too flamboyant or flashy. Don't try to oversell or glorify a low-level job. Be honest and use your head. But don't be too timid or modest.

Recommended Phrases for Your Career Objective Section:

- Achieved . . .

- Attained . . .

- Demonstrated . . .

- Introduced . . .

- Launched . . .

- Proven performer in . . .

- Significant experience in . . .

Recommended Power Words to Command Respect:

- Designed . . .

- Eliminated . . .

- Increased . . .

- Improved . . .

- Prevented . . .

- Reduced . . .

As I mentioned, *be concise.* Provide the interviewer only the bare materials or information to make them want to meet the person behind the resume.

Entice them!

Basic Resume Overview

1. The first section is the *identification*. The identification is your name, your permanent or temporary address, phone numbers, email, and LinkedIn profile URL if you have one.

2. The second section is called the *profile or summary*. This may be the first place an employer looks. They want to know who you are in a short paragraph with possibly bullet points. This description of who you are professionally, should include a little about past, present, and future skills. Once you have decided on a particular occupation and employer, incorporate phraseology and buzzwords that correspond with that occupation.

3. You can title this third section *education* or *educational history*. List the name of the high school, trade school or college, graduate school, the location, your degree or degrees, and a major or a minor, if applicable. Indicate areas of specialization or extensive course work, internships, or training courses, especially if it relates directly to the position for which you are applying. Seminars and specialty training that relate to the position sought should also be included.

4. The fourth section of the resume is *employment history*. Indicate the name and location of the organizations that you worked for, the dates of your employment and the position, title and responsibilities. It is much better to spend more time on one or two positions that relate specifically to the job that you're applying for than to put down five or six non-related positions. Too many positions indicate a lack of focus or inability to maintain a job.

5. *Achievements, awards, certifications, volunteering, other.* This section should be structured the same as your employment or education. It should include the name of the achievement, name of the organization affiliated, date it was received or accomplished, and a possible description to explain to the reader what exactly that extra activity was for.

Now it's your turn, create a quick "snapshot of your resume by completing the following exercise.

My Resume: A Snapshot

Name: _____

Home Address: _____

Telephone: _____

Email: _____

LinkedIn URL: _____

SUMMARY or PROFESSIONAL PROFILE: (Describe yourself)

_____

_____

_____

_____

EDUCATION:

School: _____ Town: _____ State: _____

Major: _____ From: _____ To: _____

High School (GED): _____

EXPERIENCE:

Company: _____ Town: _____ State: _____

Title: _____ From: _____ To: _____

RESPONSIBILITIES/ACHIEVEMENTS:

- _____
- _____
- _____

MISCELLANEOUS:

Professional Organizations/Clubs: _____

Special Skills: _____

As mentioned, there are three basic resume formats:

1. **The first is called the *chronological* resume**. The chronological format spells out job history from the most recent job backwards, with the most recent job having the most space and getting the most attention. Advantages of the chronological resume are it's easy to follow, it emphasizes continuity and career growth and highlights names of employers you've worked for. The disadvantages to this type of resume are if you have breaks in your work history, when you are changing your career direction or when an individual changes jobs quickly and frequently.

2. **The second type of resume is the *functional* resume**. The functional resume is designed to emphasize your qualifications and not previous employers. This type of resume is useful for a person who has related experience in the position sought. The advantages to using the functional resume are that it gives considerable flexibility in your emphasis. It emphasizes skill areas that are marketable, in demand, and relevant. It masks employment breaks or prior positions irrelevant to the position currently sought. The disadvantages to the functional resume are that it does not relate accomplishments to the specific employer. Many employers consider a candidate's prior affiliation when judging their accomplishments. Also, the same accomplishments may seem more impressive if gained with an established company rather than a lesser-known company.

3. **The third resume format is the *targeted* format.** The targeted resume format is designed with a specific job title in mind. It is not the type that you send out in an email blast or mass mailing. It's tailored to that particular employer, so the actual name of the company may be referenced in the resume. You can use industry titles or buzzwords specific to that industry in this type of resume.

The disadvantages to the targeted resume is that it's costly, when individually produced. It's very time-consuming if you are targeting more than one employer in a specific field and you need to weave in the names of specific people directly on the resume. It allows for less flexibility. However, the targeted resume can be the most productive in terms of specificity to a particular employer.

In today's competitive job markets, I prefer the targeted resume. It is specific, not generic.

RESUME "DOS" AND "DON'TS"

Dos:

- Do use one to two page maximum unless there are special requirements
- Do verify accuracy of all information
- Do use the "buzz words" from your field
- Do select quality paper and print
- Do select one of the three formats
- Do be specific, not generic
- Do start each sentence with action words such as: *Organized, Assisted, Developed, Operated, Programmed, Designed, Planned, Analyzed, Coordinated*

Don'ts:

- Don't include any irrelevant information
- Don't include inaccurate information
- Don't list references on your resume
- Don't be too wordy (be concise)
- Don't have any typos or spelling errors
- Don't list many personal hobbies

 # Resume Check List

Introduction Appearance

- Name
- Address
- Phone number(s)
- Email address
- Margins correctly spaced

Profile or Summary

- Easy to understand
- Interesting

Prior Experience

- Underlining and capitals
- Employer name Correct choice of style
- Employer location *Double-check*
- Responsibilities Eliminate typos
- Achievements (numeric) Check spelling
- Job description Verify punctuation
- Job title *Format*

Education

- Consistent and accurate
- Name of Institution Logically organized
- Degree(s) Correctly spaced

Miscellaneous

- Associations and memberships Avoid abbreviations if possible
- Awards and honors Cite specific details and accomplishments
- Include updates
- Use short sentences with action verbs

The Cover Letter

The purpose of the cover letter is to introduce you to the employer, to spark an interest in your potential value to the employer and, ultimately, to get an interview. The cover letter should identify the specific position or type of position sought and should also illustrate your familiarity with the skills and training needed for effective performance. The cover letter should motivate the reader to want to meet you in person! The cover letter should be typed in standard business format on 8-by-11 white bond paper and should include your name, address, and date. It should not contain any spelling errors or typing errors and should be neat and grammatically correct. In all cases, it is important that your cover letter be addressed to a specific contact ("Dear Sir or Madam" is impersonal).

There are three sections to a cover letter:

1. **Introduction**: The opening paragraph should immediately attract attention. This can be done by using the name of a person who either referred you, referring to a specific job listing or by identifying a unique talking point about the particular organization.

For example, you may decide to get attention by referencing an article or fact a trade publication.

2. The **body** of the letter should point out your value and answer the employer's number one question, "Why should I hire you?" Use language that the employer is familiar with from their website, brochures, manuals, job descriptions and your own personal work experiences. Highlight and focus on the most relevant qualifications listed in your resume.

3. The **closing paragraph** is the action stage. Take the initiative and suggest arrangements for a specific interview time and date. You may want to suggest two or three dates. Your suggested meet date should never be more than ten business days from the date of your letter. Close by thanking the employer for considering your letter and resume. You may want to type in the word "Enclosure" in the lower left-hand corner to indicate that your resume is included.

The cover letter should always be sent to the individual who has the authority to hire you or influence the decision. It should always be addressed to the person by first and last name. In your cover letter, tell your employer about yourself, who you are, what you have done, what job you would like, what you have to offer, and discuss your potential and why you want to work for that organization.

Get The Employer's Attention

1. Keep it to one page.
2. Demonstrate your interest in a specific employer.
3. Demonstrate your interest in a particular position.
4. Reference any individuals who recommended the contact (get approval first).
5. Address it to the specific person and include their title.

Stimulate the Employer's Interest

1. Relate your abilities to the employer's requirements.
2. Emphasize your talents, skills, and interest.
3. Describe why the employer should have an interest in you.
4. Emphasize your strengths and downplay your weaknesses.
5. Elaborate on the relevant qualifications in your resume.

Ask for an Interview!

1. Always ask for the interview.
2. Indicate that an interview will provide a better picture of your abilities.
3. Provide your availability (date and times).
4. Restate that you will contact the employer for an appointment.
5. Include your telephone number, address, and email address.

Hint: The better you do your homework on companies, the easier this will be.

Sample Cover Letter

Date
Mr. Ray Green
Vice President
XYZ Enterprises, Incorporated
16 Glen Road
City ST 01234

Dear Mr. Green:
I am writing to introduce myself and to request your consideration for the position of _____. Enclosed, please find a copy of my resume.

Having studied the development of employers in your field, I believe I can help your organization meet its goals. My education and experience make me a positive contributor to your team.

If convenient, I would appreciate a personal appointment to present my qualifications and review my resume. I am available on [date] at [time] and on [date] at [time] and can be reached at [telephone number].

Sincerely,
Signature
Your Name
Address
City, State, Zip
Email
Enclosure or attachment if emailed

According to current research, the average professional position has about 300 applicants. Therefore, it is critical that you grab the employer's attention in your cover letter. The following technique begins with a powerful opening and focuses on filling the employer's needs. There is no need to restate where you saw the position posted. Name the position you are interested in applying for since the company may have many positions currently available. Remember, the cover letter does not get you the job. It is simply a vehicle meant to compel the employer want to look at your resume and contact you for an interview.

Cover Letter Template

Contact Information
[Should look exactly the way it does on your résumé]

[Date]

[Contact Name]
[Company Name]
[Company Address]
[Company Phone Number] You do not need to list this if you do not know.

Re: [Name of the position you are seeking]
(ex. Re: Internship or Re: Marketing Coordinator Position, etc.)

Dear [Name of Hiring Person]: Never use "To Whom It May Concern."

With over [# of years] years of experience as a/n [include current/former title/position], in/with [field/industry/company], my strengths are in [first strength], [second strength], and [third strength]. Therefore, I'd bring [quality employer seeks] to the [job title] position at [company name].

Highlights of my professional experience include:
- [First highlight or accomplishment]
- [Second highlight or accomplishment]
- [Third highlight or accomplishment]

The opportunity at [company name] sounds very exciting to me and I am impressed with how [company name] [list comments about the company's website, LinkedIn profile, or relevant information publically known].

I feel there is a great deal I can bring to [company name] because I have [first skill], [second skill], and [third skill]. I would love to meet with you to discuss the valuable contributions I could make to your team. I can be reached at [preferred method of communication] and I look forward to your call. Thank you for your time.

Sincerely,

[Include Your Signature]

[Your Name Typed]

My Cover Letter

Now it's your turn, write a letter to a prospective employer. Keep in mind all that you have just read and be sure to include the following in your letter:

- Begin by doing a little research; choose your field of interest and research your dream job!

- Find out who has the authority to hire you or influence the decision and address the person by first and last name.

- Now that you know whom you are writing to, follow the model and be sure to use a proper business letter format and language. Remember, you want to make a good first impression!

- Your letter should be no longer than one page.

- Your letter should include three sections; **introduction, body** and **conclusion/closing.**

- Do not use abbreviates that are not universally known except for ones such as Ph.D., CPR, states, PO Box, etc.

- The introduction paragraph should:
  - Be one paragraph in length
  - Engage/make a connection with the reader
  - State the position you are applying for
  - Include the skills that you have that are relevant to the position you are applying for

- The body paragraph should:
  - Sell yourself as the unique solution to the challenges that company faces
  - Link your skills, experience, and education to the needs of the company
  - Focus on two or three strong selling points as evidence of your impact
  - Be no more than two paragraphs

- The conclusion/closing paragraph should:
  - Include a statement of how you would welcome a meeting to discuss your contributions as a team player
  - Close the letter by asking for an interview or face-to-face meeting
  - Provide your preferred method of communication
  - Thank them for their time

- End letter formally with "Sincerely".

- Sign your name in addition to typing it.

- When submitting your cover letter electronically, the same rules apply as with the résumé.

Important!

You are at a crucial time in your life, make sure your ring back tone and/or voice mail message is appropriate and professional!

Use an e-mail address that is also professional. A professional email should include only your name and no other descriptive words or things that reference anything other than business.

Cover Letter Template

Following the model, use the template below to write a cover letter to a potential employer.

_____   _____

_____   _____

_____   _____

_____

_____

_____

_____

_____

_____

_____

_____

_____

_____

_____

_____

Dressing for Success

Tip!

When going to an interview, you may want to dress similar to the person who is hiring you because every company or organization or employer has a culture, whether it is conservative or flashy. If you have the opportunity to conduct an information interview prior to an actual interview, get the chance to walk into the building, go into their cafeteria, or just stand outside and see how people dress when they come out of work, do so. This investment in preparation will provide a competitive edge over the competition interviewing for the same position.

First impressions are extremely important. The interviewer or employer is going to see you before you have had an opportunity to open your mouth and discuss your qualifications. Many studies show that an opinion is formulated about candidates in the first 12 to 30 seconds. And in the first 12 or 30 seconds of a meeting, what happens? You walk in, maybe you shake hands, sit down. You probably haven't even had a chance to say "Hello" or "What a nice office you have here."

Here are three Rules . . .

Rule #1:

You will never get a second chance to make a good first impression.
- Remember, the first impressions are lasting impressions.
- Target the type and style of dress your potential employer utilizes.
- Dress for the job you want and not for the job you currently have or recently had.

Rule #2:

Hiring Authorities state that a first impression is often formulated in the first 12–30 seconds of an interview!
- Prior to the actual interview, practice feeling comfortable with your chosen interview attire by going out to dinner or wearing it in a public setting.
- Don't be stiff or uncomfortable or it will negatively impact your chances of getting hired.

Rule #3:

If it comes down to spending a little less or a little more to look your best, spend the extra money; it will be worth it in the long run!

A Basic Outline

Tips: Dress in your best, most coordinated, and conservative attire.

1. Your outfit, suit or dress, should be a dark color, clean and pressed.
2. Be neat, clean, trimmed, and well groomed.
3. Jewelry, scents, and makeup should be on the conservative side.
4. Practice wearing new outfits before the actual interview.
5. Avoid fashion fads.
6. Dress for work, not to go out on the town.
7. Do not smoke for at least an hour before an interview, and NEVER smoke in your car on the way to the interview.

Remember . . . Inspect yourself before you leave for the interview and attend each session with a smile and enthusiasm.

1. Your first impressions are critical (opinions are formed in 12–30 seconds).
2. The interviewer will see you before you have an opportunity to discuss your qualifications. Look sharp.
3. Remember, if your appearance is not appreciated, you will not get the position!
4. Dress for the job you want, not the job you have or have had.
5. Look professional even as you park your car for the interview; you never know whose office you are parked in front of.

If you look good, you will feel good!

The Essential Wardrobe

Often, questions are raised as to how to dress for the job search process and, more specifically, what to wear to impress a potential employer. Of course, every person has individual style and may be sensitive to advice concerning professional attire or even what constitutes professional. However, be advised that impressions are often formulated by decision makers in the first 30 seconds of any meeting or interview. Do not take any chances! If you are unsure, the best suggestion is to visit the employer's location before your interview, observe what current employees are wearing and mirror their actions. Ideally, find out from an information interview.

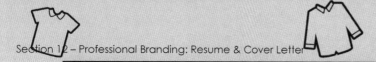

SUGGESTIONS FOR MEN:

- Have 1 suit in a dark tone but not black (try to avoid polyester)
- Have 1 jacket in a dark tone (try to avoid the color black and polyester)
- Have at least 3 shirts (long sleeve): white, light blue, or a conservative stripe
- Have at least 2 ties: 1 multi-colored, 1 striped (try to avoid polyester)
- Have 1 pair of polished shoes, black is recommended, no scuff marks
- Avoid wrinkled clothing!

Note: If your interviewer does not require you to wear a shirt, tie, jacket or suit, it is still important to look neat clean and professional.

SUGGESTIONS FOR WOMEN:

- Have a jacket or blazer in preferably a dark color such as navy, black, or gray
- Have 1 jacket or blazer (medium tones) such as deep tan, brownish, or plaid
- Have 2 skirts (solid): black, small printed and beige tone
- Have 3 blouses: off white, floral, and navy
- Have 2 pairs of shoes, preferably black pumps, brownish or beige, no scuff marks
- Have 1 scarf (multi-colors)
- Have several pairs of hosiery in flesh tones or off black. Bring an extra pair with you in case of a run

Note: If you have to substitute with a dress, consider wearing a jacket!

MY APPEARANCE

Take a good hard look at yourself. Be your own worst critic. Look past the things you can't change within a day or so, like weight or other physical characteristics.

- **Finger Nails.** If you are a female, how long are your nails? "Saturday Night Nails" may look great at a party, but will they give a different impression to a potential employer when you say that you are a hard worker?
- **Jewelry.** An easy rule of thumb regarding jewelry (and this is true for a male or female) is that it should not be the focus of attention. That means one ring on each hand, with the exception of a wedding and engagement band. One earring in each ear is surely acceptable, but no more, and earrings should be discreet. Facial jewelry of any kind is taboo, because it is distracting.
- **Clothing.** How about your choice of clothing? For men, a tie dresses up any attire, and shows professionalism, regardless of what sort of employment you are seeking. Both men and women must keep in mind the message that clothing sends. If your clothes are baggy, you will appear to be slouching, which sends a message of laziness. If colors are too bright, your attire will take center stage and your message will be lost. Very short skirts are unacceptable for interviews, as well as, when working, as are very tight or low cut clothing. Denim, in any form, is not to be worn. For women, wearing pantyhose and heels is essential. Neutral colors don't need to be boring. An interesting scarf can spice up a gray suit and white shirt or blouse.

Take a few minutes to put together a "mock wardrobe." What would you need? What can you do to acquire the items that you will need?

_____

_____

_____

_____

_____

_____

"You never get a second chance to make a first impression."

Section 13:

BEST JOB SEARCH STRATEGIES

LEARNING OBJECTIVES

1. Understand the difference between the hidden and published job markets.

2. Review the most effective strategies for finding your career.

3. Create your brand and learn how to stand out.

4. Formulate a job application.

Strategies for Marketing Your Unique Talents

Where the Opportunities Are

Even when you determine your passion and purpose and focus on a specific career, there is no single strategy that works 100% of the time to obtain the position. Here are some effective strategies for finding a career:

1. Build your network of influential contacts who can alert you to an opportunity

2. Respond to published opportunities

3. Research and attending job fairs for leads

Today, almost ⅔ of all new opportunities are created by small businesses: those with 20 or fewer employees.

HOW PEOPLE FIND JOBS
- 63.4% Informal job-seeking methods, direct contact with employers, networking
- 13.9% Agencies
- 12.2% Staffing Agencies
- 10.5% Other

MY IDEAL BUSINESS CARD

Focusing on a specific career involves targeting two critical factors:

1. Your ability to identify a specific organization or company, which will be your ultimate work location.

Hint: Target companies, not jobs.

2. Your ability to identify the specific job title you want. Also, you should be able to write a paragraph of your ideal job description.

Design your ideal business card:

Name:

_____

Job Title:

_____

Company:

_____

Duties:

_____

_____

_____

Skills and knowledge you must possess:

_____

_____

_____

Where People Work

Hint: Many small businesses do not even have a Human Resources Department. Candidates should be targeting the highest ranking person, often the owner!

Hint: Learn the techniques to target small businesses!

Why Traditional Methods Are Often Obsolete

Many people complete preschool, elementary school, and junior high school and, in many cases, graduate from high school. At that point in time, we have a decision to make. We either enter the working world or we decide to continue our education through vocational school (where we learn a specific trade or craft), community college, four-year university and possibly graduate school. Incredibly, the skills of determining interest and then self-promotion (marketing oneself) are often not prioritized throughout the educational process.

The vast majority of career seekers feel unprepared to get any job, much less seek a career calling. They create a resume, post their accomplishments on multiple job boards, and hope for the best. You may find yourself frustrated when you learn that less than 5% of all mass-mailed resume postings result in employment. The "hit" rate for internet-based job boards is just as dismal.

To improve my knowledge of how hiring authorities think and operate, I serve as a Director for one of the chapters of the Society for Human Resources Management (SHRM). This experience has given me tremendous insight into the challenges faced by folks whose job it is to seek and procure talent. You may be surprised to hear that hiring authorities are frustrated with the lack of initiative and creativity exhibited by most candidates and constantly challenged by their company to become the "employer of choice."

Your Two Options: The Hidden vs. the Published Market

To begin, there are two types of job markets. One is called the **hidden job market** and the other is called the **published job market**.

Let us begin with a review of the *published job market*. This source is comprised of Internet job boards, want ads, newspaper ads, and radio advertisements; these are media sources where employers will proactively seek employees. The published job market accounts for approximately 20% of all the jobs or one out of every five jobs.

Regardless of method, follow-up is the same: Obtain the name of a contact person and call or email a few days later to express your sincere interest and offer a concise statement indicating your qualifications. Find this contact name by visiting the company website and then play detective with the receptionist to determine whom to contact.

The goal is to put your credentials in one screen's worth of content. This means including the essential data you need to attract attention at the beginning of your message. Your subject line has to motivate the recruiter to open your email he or she may get hundreds of such messages daily, so yours needs to stand out

Be clever but still highly professional; present something that is intriguing and creative. Make sure that your email screen name is a variation of your name and not the handle you use for Internet dating or to correspond with cyber pals.

The main thing for you to remember when hunting online is that you follow recruiter directions, create a properly formatted resume, do your own follow-up and are relentless in pursuing your dream. The likelihood of you actually getting a job offer as a result of an Internet job board posting is still less than 5%, whereas we know for sure that about 80% of all new hires result from personal networking So where do you think you should devote most of your time and efforts given these statistics? *Not* to the Internet job sites, but *to building personal relationships* You can use the Internet for this purpose as well.

You can read headlines and scout out trade publications, follow the news, visit company websites, join and become familiar with the proceedings of various professional organizations and then contact the individuals mentioned. Tell them that you would like to speak with them

FOR INFORMATIONAL PURPOSES (do not ever ask for a job). In this way, you will expand your scope and increase your chances to hear of career opportunities that are not advertised. Stay in touch by phone or email; send the person you met a relevant article or clever idea; connect them to someone else that they might be interested in knowing. And make sure to connect with them on LinkedIn!

The Hidden Job Market

This is your key to entry into the hidden job market—to learn about new listings and changes within a company before the recruiters publicize their needs for new hires. You can gain a competitive edge, and be on the inside track so you can act on this information and suggest you are the person they need to meet even before they have advertised it!

80% of all the opportunities are found in the hidden job market. It takes inside information to hear about these jobs. The trick is to learn where those hidden jobs exist. I found that almost 80% of the people who are looking for a job will target those 20% published jobs, while only 20% or two out of every ten people looking for a job are smart enough to penetrate the hidden job market and discover where the best leads exist.

If an employer has to advertise, it signals that they can't find a viable candidate from word of mouth or internal candidates and likely there is something questionable about that job. The key is to gain inclusion in that 20% elite group, those who target the hidden job market. The reason why it's so challenging is because most people avoid critical reflection and don't know what really provides them with the greatest sense of happiness.

Connecting Your Past to Your Future

Getting the job you want is a matter of connecting your past to your future. If the links between then and now are not clear to a potential employer, you must make them so. If your experiences do not match what the employer has asked for, then point out how your experience will work for this position and be specific.

Once you get started working, choose your experiences carefully to learn what you need to get to where you are going. Volunteer for assignments, request transfers, fill in for a co-worker in the job you want while he/she is on vacation, go to school at night, or join a community action group! Take on these "extras" with a purpose: To get the experience you need for the next successful move up the career ladder you are building for yourself!

List your most important marketable skills as they relate to the position you want.

_____

_____

List prior employment skills and how they relate to your chosen job.

_____

_____

List your job-related education or technical training.

_____

_____

List non-related training that may be helpful or transferable to this job.

_____

_____

List activities or accomplishments that might improve your chances of getting this job.

_____

_____

Hopefully you're mature enough to realize that no one position is perfect. No career will provide you with pleasure every single minute. You dictate your pleasure. *B.C. Forbes stated,*

"Whether we find pleasure in our work or whether we find it a bore depends entirely upon our *mental attitude* towards it, *not* upon the task itself."

Volunteer!

Be willing to volunteer your time to a particular industry in order to get your foot in the door. You may not be able to get paid for it, but in the long run it may pay off for you in the form of a position on the path to your true calling.

How a Vacancy is Created

Companies fall into 1 of 4 hiring states:

1. **Necessity state:** Employer must hire; most competition for positions is here.
2. **Growth state:** Employer should hire or risk productivity loss.
3. **Luxury state:** No advertised jobs but good workers always wanted.
4. **Freeze state:** Not hiring; watch for turnaround and be first in line!

If they are actively hiring, an employment manager or business needs more staff. For the purposes of this example, let's call the employer *Mr. Jones.* Mr. Jones decides that he needs to add someone to the organization. So Mr. Jones develops a job description outlining the roles and responsibilities of the position. Then Mr. Jones seeks internal approval that "Yes, we do need to fill and create a job with these particular roles and responsibilities" and approval is obtained. The company will then put in their budget the money to pay the salary and benefits. Often, the Personnel Department has the responsibility for filling the position. The first place Personnel will look is within their own company, either by advertising in the company newspaper or by recruiting or broadcasting there is an opening. If no candidates emerge, Mr. Jones will then consider friends, family, or other contacts.

If this process doesn't produce a worthy candidate, Mr. Jones will then broaden the search outside the organization to include an executive search firm or employment agency. The search firm will utilize their own internal methodology, check their database, make cold calls to other related industries or companies and try to recruit a qualified person. The other tactic Mr. Jones can utilize is to advertise. Mr. Jones will discuss with the company Personnel Manager the particular characteristics sought. It is this discussion that serves as the basis for the Personnel Manager's advertising. Personnel will then write an advertisement, sometimes with the aid of an outside advertising agency.

The objective is to recruit a qualified candidate to fulfill the vacancy quickly, because, in the meantime, either the work is not getting done or the other co-workers are taking on more than their normal responsibilities. And that can lead to a morale problem. So, the pressure is not only on the Personnel Manager but also on Mr. Jones to fill the vacancy quickly.

I think it's important for you to understand how the process works because your focus will then be to convince them that you have the capabilities to solve that problem, to step in immediately and start assisting the organization and to take the burden off the other co-workers who have been doing double the work.

How the Personnel Department Works

Only about one to 5% of the people who contact the employer through the Personnel Department will gain an interview. Here is what happens to a response when it is received by the Personnel Department:

Mr. Jones wants no part of reviewing the hundreds and sometimes thousands of resumes that come in for the vacancy. They don't want the responsibility of screening resumes or trying to differentiate one from another. That's the job of Personnel. For example, a front line (for example, sales) manager who is responsible for generating significant television advertising revenues cannot afford to review a hundred resumes. That's the job of Personnel. That's what they get paid to do. Only in rare occasions will a front line manager bypass Personnel completely.

After reviewing candidates, the process is reduced to a workable number of applicants. Personnel will then begin screening process before recommending the top candidates for an interview with Mr. Jones; who will ultimately make the final decision.

It is important to realize that there are certain levels, most notably, Personnel, where they will look at your appearance, general attitude and qualifications and try to match up your accomplishments and credentials with the job description that Mr. Jones and the Personnel Manager collaborated on. The candidate who best fulfills that description typically is offered the position.

If you are answering an advertisement in a trade journal or industry publication, it's important that you *mirror the wording of the advertisement.* Remember, the only purpose in responding to an advertisement is to get in the door, to get an interview. Your response, whether via telephone call or letter, should incorporate the wording that the advertisement cites. For example, if they're looking for a person who can type 50 words a minute, who is independent or has leadership capabilities and has three to five years of experience, it is important when you document you have fulfilled all of those specific requirements. *The more, the better!*

REFLECTION: ONLINE PRESENCE

Your online presence matters to employers. Before you start job searching it's important that you clean up all of the information, photos, and profiles you can control.

Did you know? One in five hiring managers conduct background checks using social networks.

Why is it important to create a professional online presence?

Building a professional brand is necessary in this competitive job market. Job seekers need to have a professional online presence that can easily be found by hiring managers, recruiters, and career contacts. This can include creating a LinkedIn profile or a professional Twitter account where you post information about the industry in which you are trying to get a job.

To learn more about these websites and how they can help you with your job search, visit your online portal for tutorials and up-to-date best practices.

Don't Forget to Google Yourself!

There's a lot of information about you online that employers can find in a matter of seconds, including: your photos, address, age, relatives, and other information that you thought was completely private! Because of this, it's important to create professional profiles and add more professional photos to the Internet so that those links rank higher on search results.

Privacy Settings

We all use the Internet for our own personal lives, but it's important to always check your privacy settings on your social media accounts to make sure that your posts and photos are not public for the world to see. Limit your personal information, comments, posts, and photos only to your immediate friends and family to make sure the information can't be shared or copied for the world to see.

Pretend that everything you post online could be headline news!

My Personal Brand

Constantly think about your brand and how you are presenting it whether you are in person or online. You will be surprised that people will begin to buy, because of YOU!

What one thing will be the most compelling about your personal brand/social media profiles?

_____

_____

_____

Why will your audience want to read your profile?

_____

_____

_____

How will you "humanize" your online profiles?

_____

_____

_____

How will you measure your social networking success?

_____

_____

_____

Executive Recruiters and Search Firms

Executive recruiters, or, as they're known to some people, *headhunters* can help you in a job search campaign. If you'd like to learn more, I recommend that you consult the *Directory of Executive Recruiters*, which lists all of the firms currently employed in that field. I also recommend that if you're going to utilize a reputable search firm to help you obtain your career calling, you may want to put together an email that sounds something like this:

Always remember

that it's important for you to present your desired salary level. If you're willing to relocate or you have any other special skills, also mention that in your cover letter.

Close the letter and list your telephone number and address. It's important that your correspondence tells them if you're willing to relocate and your salary requirements.

Dear Mr. or Mrs. Recruiter,

Please review the attached resume with regards to any potential opportunities in the field (name the field that you have an interest in).

My expertise is . . . (cite your value . . . accounting, data entry, mergers & acquisitions, sales & marketing, systems integration, etc.)

My salary range is . . . (be honest and respectful)

Attached is my resume for review and consideration . . .

The Employment Application

So why do you have to fill out a job application? For starters, when you are accepted for a position, your employment application will remain in your personnel file forever. Employers keep records on everything that you do, starting with your acceptance into their organization, followed by your promotion scale, your medical history, your salary increases and any other important bits of information.

It is important that you be accurate and factual. There are horror stories about people who have included erroneous or untrue information. For example, when being considered for a promotion the employer found a falsified date or credential (somebody said they went to college and really didn't). Please, be honest because you never know when lies or untruths can come back to haunt you.

Hiring authorities place a great deal of importance on the job application. Some of them, quite frankly, have taken the time as part of their job description to design it. They take great pride in the document. Perhaps they spent money with an advertising agency to help them formulate it and typeset it. So, take the time to fill it out correctly.

Job applications are more important to those of you who are just starting out in a career, returning to the work force, coming out of college or just starting in a career because you really don't have a track record or list of references that an employer can turn to for questioning or assistance on making a decision. So, oftentimes, an individual will be hired solely on the basis of their employment application and credentials, especially in entry-level or blue-collar type jobs.

Four Sections of the Employment Application

1. Number one is *personal data*. Employers will ask you for your name, how to get in touch with you, your address, phone number and if you're a citizen of the United States.

2. Secondly, an employer will solicit *employment information*— what you desire from the prospective employer. They may question ask you what position you seek, how soon you can start, if there is a shift choice, if you're interested in working part-time or full-time.

They may also ask about your salary. If you're unclear on a salary level, put the initials TBD, which stands for "to be determined."

3. The next section is the *education and training* section. Here an employer will seek your track record from grammar school to high school to college education or post-college education, to any business, correspondence, or trade schools that you have attended.

They may seek special achievements, whether it is academic, special talents, skills, tools or projects. If the position is of a technical nature, this information becomes all the more important.

4. The fourth section is *employment history*, which will require you to list current or previous employers and contact information. Applications can get quite specific in asking your previous supervisor's name and title if they seek a reference. They may even request your salary, when you started, if you were promoted, why you left, what responsibilities you held. They may ask you for three or four previous employers as references.

List those employers that you feel strongly or positively about and that are applicable to the position sought. Be accurate and factual.

The final portion of the application will ask you to sign your name and confirm that all statements or claims made in the application or resume are truthful and complete. You may be asked to approve authorization to conduct any investigation in respect to examining your previous criminal or police record, if that's applicable, as well as any references that you may have cited.

Please review the application carefully, it may list specific contractual arrangements regarding employment benefits, additional compensation or at-will status. Employer websites are getting more sophisticated every day. The use of screening tools, key word searches and other technology based pre-employment assessments are evolving as of this writing. Some of these tools are effective but my advice is to get to a decision maker and state your reasons for wanting to work with them. The employment application is a very important document and you should take proper care and attention and detail when filling it out.

There are three basic rules to consider when filling out an application for your ideal career:

1. Make sure you are in a location that allows you to have the proper frame of mind to fill out the application; be clear of any nervous thoughts, people looking over your shoulder and ensure you're in a comfortable writing position.

2. Make the employment application legible and pleasing to the reader. Employers like something they can understand and don't have to struggle to read.

3. Be accurate and factual. Include specific experience, credentials and qualifications and make them up-to-date.

Tips for Filling Out Job Application Forms

Be prepared.

Take a "help sheet," your résumé, and two pens with you.

Follow all directions carefully.

Read the entire form carefully before you start filling it out. Don't be afraid to ask questions if you don't understand something. Proof read the application before you turn it in to make sure it presents you in a positive way. If you can, get someone to look over your application for errors.

Use your best printing and be neat.

Take your time when filling out the application. If it is a paper application, don't fold, tear, or smudge the application form. If possible, get a couple of applications, so you can use one for practice. If you can only get one, make a copy of it before you start filling it out.

Be honest and positive.

Tell the truth and be positive about yourself. However, don't confess everything on your application. If your written answer won't explain things thoroughly enough, write "Will Explain in Interview" on your application form, then be prepared to answer and discuss these questions in an interview. (i.e., Have you ever been convicted?)

Be thorough. Don't leave any blanks.

Leaving part of the application blank indicates that you have overlooked or ignored a space. Write "N/A" (not applicable) or draw a slash instead. You may want to put "open" in the spaces for desired salary and willingness to relocate. Remember to sign (if it is a paper application) and date the application.

Use positive terms for leaving past employers.

Instead of "quit," try "left to seek new challenges," "seeking increased responsibility," "seeking opportunity to use creativity," "pursuing education," or another positive reason that suits your situation. Instead of "laid off," try "reduction in force" or "plant closure," if that is the case. State a reason in words that are less personal. Instead of "got fired," try "let go" or "prefer to discuss at interview."

Be detailed and specific.

Avoid writing "anything" for the position desired. Be specific about the position or positions you are applying for in the company. Be detailed about your work description. Don't assume the employer knows what you did. Write down the skills, tools, and equipment you used, plus any achievements that you consider important. Describe the previous job duties that you have held, especially if they apply toward the job you are trying to get. Attach an additional page, if you need more room to write down your work history.

Check your references before you mention them.

Call your references before filling out the application to ensure that they can and will give you a good recommendation. Also, make sure that the contact information you provide for each reference (e.g. title, phone number, etc.) is current. If you have any question about someone's ability to be a good reference, do not list him or her. If you know that your direct supervisor will not give you a good reference, you can try to get someone else in the organization to provide one for you. Try a co-worker, your supervisor's boss, or a former supervisor.

Attach your resume.

If you are filling out a paper resume, staple your resume to the front of the application unless the employer says otherwise.

THE ONLINE APPLICATION

If you're directed to apply online, give the process the same amount of time and effort as you would to put together an effective resume. The same rules that govern your development of an attention-grabbing resume apply to your online application, but there are a few tips that can help you increase your chances of getting called for an interview:

1. Follow directions! Take care to enter the correct data in the correct fields.

2. Ask for advice on completing the application from a company recruiter or an alumnus who may work at the company.

3. Complete all fields- even those that aren't required. (Be sure to include a cover letter, even if it's not required.)

4. Use keywords from the job description; employers search for keywords when looking to fill specific positions.

5. If the company offers an optional assessment test online, take it.

6. Use "comments" fields to demonstrate that you have researched the company and/or to provide additional information about specific skills you have.

7. If you are asked to attach a resume or paste it into the application, make sure the format is compatible: Special characters, bold and italics, and fancy fonts, for example, won't convert in some electronic applications. It's best to use the universal PDF format.

8. Proofread your application before submitting it. If possible, run a spell check and a grammar check.

My Application

Complete the following application:

Personal Information	
Name (Last, First, MI)	
Street address	
City, State, Zip	
Home phone number	Work phone number
E-mail address	
LinkedIn URL or Professional Profile	

My Application

Education

	Name and Address of School	Course of Study	Total Years of Study	Degree/Diploma
High School/GED				
Post HS/College				
Other (specify)				

Have you ever been arrested? If yes, please explain:

Have you ever been convicted of a felony or misdemeanor? If yes, please explain:

Employment History

Fill out information for your most recent employer. You must complete this section even if attaching a resume. May we contact your current employer? ☐ YES ☐ NO

Employer (current ☐ Yes ☐ No)	Start Date	End Date	Fax number
Address			Job position(s)
City, State, Zip	Starting Salary	Ending Salary	Supervisor(s)
Phone number			E-mail address of supervisor
Reason(s) for leaving			

Section 14:

PREPARING FOR THE INTERVIEW

LEARNING OBJECTIVES

1. Review the stages of the interview process.

2. Demonstrate successful interviewing strategies.

3. Visualize interview success by putting yourself in a positive frame of mind.

What is the purpose of the interview?

The three purposes of the interview are:

    1. To provide the employer with information about you not already contained in your application, resume, or cover letter.

    2. To enable the interviewer to evaluate your personality, attitude, values, communication skills, motivations, and interests in terms of the demands of the vacancy and their organization.

    3. To enable you to obtain information about that particular employer.

Remember, you are there to gather as much information as you can about the employer, just as they are there to gather as much information as they can about you. It is a mutually beneficial process.

Regardless of outcome, view every interview as an information-gathering session, a chance to learn and an opportunity to demonstrate your abilities. When confident in their abilities, successful athletes, actors and interviewers can hardly wait to get in that spotlight. You should have the same attitude.

Five Objectives of Any Interview

Remember, the interview process is a buyer/seller scenario. The interviewer has a problem and you are potential solution to that problem. Smart candidates obtain a definition of the ideal candidate for the open position and then do their best to convince the interviewer that you *are* that ideal candidate.

More specifically, successful candidates should have these 5 objectives for any interview:

1. Create a favorable first impression.

2. Obtain a description of the ideal candidate sought by the employer.

3. Present yourself as the ideal candidate.

4. Overcome and neutralize any objections.

5. Get a second interview or ideally, a formal job offer.

The *Real* Deal
(What Employers Are Thinking)

- Can this candidate do the job?

- Does this candidate fit into our culture?

- What is the risk of hiring this candidate?

- Can we agree on compensation?

Three Areas That You Will Be Evaluated On:

Before you will be considered for a position, you must convince the person of your talents in the following 3 ways:

1. Yourself and your personality

2. Your abilities and your credentials

3. Your potential worth to the company *(What do you bring to the table?)*

Keys to Interview Success

• First, you need to plan and do research before pursuing an employer.

• Become an industry specialist. Become knowledgeable about the employer's competitors. Learn the buzzwords for that particular industry or organization. It may sound obvious, but know what specific position is for hire, title, and job description. Consider the interview forum itself. Is it going to be informal or formal; is it in an office or over lunch?

• Strategize from the employer's point of view. Visualize yourself on the other side of the desk. Would you be impressed? What type of physical appearance do you think they're expecting or looking for? Is it a conservative employer or business casual atmosphere? Will they be impressed with your level of education and research effort?

Emphasize your employment strengths and downplay your weaknesses. *Remember, you are screened in because of your strengths and screened out because of your weaknesses.* Discuss your positive attributes and how it will benefit the employer. Remember to demonstrate your versatility. Through proper preparation, be in a position to answer any question, no matter how obscure. And that will impress the interviewer.

Befriend the Receptionist!

Make pleasant conversation with the receptionist and data-gather. It's always a good idea to research the individual who will be making a decision. If you are chatting with the receptionist as you're waiting in the lobby, you may mention the fact that you have an interview and cite the name. Maybe they will provide a clue about the interviewer. Can you tactfully inquire or come up with a comment or question that may provide you with some insight into the interviewer, such as, "How long has this person been with the company?" Or "Does he or she have a busy schedule today?" Or if you're clever, you can target questions designed to help you find out the employer's personal interests. Be creative. On the way out the door, thank the receptionist for their courtesy and maybe even send a follow-up letter. You will be surprised how receptionists influence a decision (I always ask mine for their opinion!). Maybe they will add, "You know, that was such a nice man or woman who was in here. We could use a few more like them." That kind of endorsement can leave a very positive impression in the mind of any interviewer. It's the little things that make the difference.

Mastering the Interview: Step 1

Every interview is a buyer/seller relationship. You have a service to sell, which is your value to the employer, and like a good salesperson, you need to know how to use techniques to help you make the sale. Let's examine what a top-notch salesperson does.

Step 1: Establish Rapport

"Rapport is a "connection" between you and another individual. Establishing that connection creates a comfortable, friendly atmosphere. This is a crucial first step, and will contribute to the first impression that you make. You will always want to maintain your most professional demeanor. Attempting to go directly to selling yourself, without addressing the issue of rapport, will result in a colder meeting, and probably a shorter one. Remember, employers hire people they like.

What are some ways to establish rapport?

_____

_____

_____

_____

_____

_____

An Outline of the Interview Process

As an outline, consider the following steps to a successful interview:

1. Interview preparation (do your homework) Research the employer

    a. Review the website, obtain articles, annual reports, etc.

    b. Identify potential problems you can solve

    c. Formulate key questions/areas to discuss

2. Approach (strategy)

a. The telephone approach

State your credentials (if you are currently employed, state your position)

- State the reason for your call
- Qualify the employer (are they the decision maker?)
- Cite the benefits gained by hiring you

b. The written approach

- Cite the purpose of your letter (I want the offer!)
- Review the benefits gained by the employer
- Describe your method of contact
  (I was referred by . . .)
- Transition to information gathering (ask for an information interview)

3. Learning the employer needs (long and short-term)

a. Data gathering

- Ask open and closed ended questions
- Listen carefully to employer responses to your questions
- Obtain operational and financial data (for example, organization (chart)
- Verify hiring criteria (what kind of person are they looking for?)
- Determine future opportunities
- Determine what would prevent you from being hired
- Determine how you would fit in

b.   Assessment stage- Organize the information you have obtained

- Evaluate the information
- Formulate your hiring strategy (if not already hired)

321

4. Your ultimate outcome (hire me please!)

a. The process
- Restate employer objectives/goals as you understand them
- Obtain employer agreement to specific job objectives required
- Review the current condition/operations of the employer
- Obtain employer agreement that these conditions exist and are causing a problem (describe how you can solve this problem . . .)
- Describe the general benefits to hiring you
- Describe the positive results gained by hiring you

b. Close (confirm a response!)

c. Action stage
- Summarize the reasons why the employer should hire you
- Restate the benefits of selecting you as an employee
- Summarize and restate your credentials/potential
- Demonstrate the monetary benefits to your being hired ($ saved, $ gained)
- Use effective closing techniques
- Overcome objections (if any)
- Ask for the position!

5. Post-interview (evaluate your performance)

a. Etiquette and follow-up strategy
b. Letter form/telephone (thank you letter and/or resignation techniques from current position)
c. Neutralize problem areas

Interview Checklist

Here is a checklist to test if you are ready:

✓ *Have you mastered the ability to articulate your skills, researched the employer (including company websites or published information) and obtained a position description?*

✓ *Have you conducted an information interview with one or more employees in the company or in a similar industry?*

✓ *Do you know the major competitors of that particular company?*

Mastering the Interview: Step 2

Step 2: Discover the Employer's Needs

Once again, think about the "salesperson". Before he or she can begin to sell, your needs and wants must be uncovered. "What color do you like?" "Do you need a sedan or a coupe?" "What is your price range?" Woe to the salesperson who tries really hard to sell you that little red convertible, only to find out that you have your heart set on blue, and you have four children, so you need a roomy sedan.

Employment seekers also need to discover the needs and wants of the employers before selling themselves.

What are some of the needs and wants of most employers? What needs and wants might be specific to certain employers? What can you do to uncover those needs and wants?

_____

_____

_____

_____

_____

_____

_____

The interview has two objectives:

1. To give the applicant a clear understanding of the position and responsibilities

2. To provide the interviewer an opportunity to develop information about the candidate's qualifications or credentials.

This is best obtained by the use of open-ended questions in a conversational setting. An open-ended question versus a closed-ended question differs in the following respect. *"Do you want to work in marketing?"* is a close-ended question. It prompts a single response. *"How do you feel about working in marketing?"* is an open-ended question, which invite additional conversation. Be prepared for both types of questions.

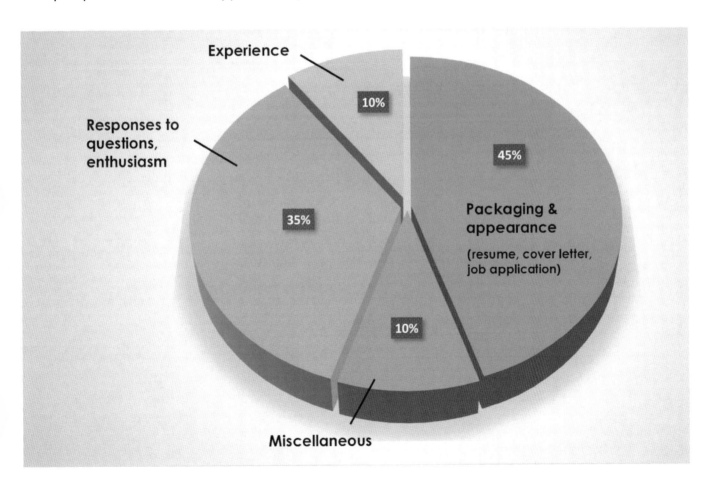

Mastering the Interview: Step 3

Step 3: Relate the Benefits of Hiring You!

Once you know what the employer needs and wants, you can zero in on the qualities that you can use to fill those needs and wants. If, for instance, the employer has informed you that he or she needs someone who is reliable, you will want to stress your punctuality, using examples from your past. If the employer mentions experience that you do not have, you will want to talk about how quickly you learn, or the experience you have had that relates to the job.

Using the needs and wants list from Step 2, write a statement about the benefits of hiring you:

_____

_____

_____

_____

_____

_____

_____

Here are the traits or qualifications most frequently sought in potential candidates:

First of all is a candidate's ability to communicate. Can they organize their thoughts, their ideas and beliefs effectively and do they express those beliefs, thoughts and feelings clearly?

Key traits include a willingness to accept responsibility, initiative, leadership skills, energy level, flexibility and versatility. Can you confront tough issues and deal with problems that may not have typical or normal solutions? Are you innovative? Can you present those thoughts or ideas in a persuasive way? Do you know your own strengths and weaknesses? Can you handle competition? Do you have the capacity to compete with other people and not be afraid to have your performance measured? A recurring theme was how important it was for an individual to have goal-setting capabilities. That is why it's important that you articulate your long- and short-term career goals. It will give you a competitive edge.

Consider these:

- Research the employer.
- Know the business of the firm interviewing you and their recent performance.
- Arrive 1 hour ahead of schedule (in the event you have to fill out an application). If not, 15 minutes should suffice.
- Bring an extra copy of your resume and references sheet.
- Make pleasant conversation with the hostess or receptionist (if applicable).
- If you must wait for the interviewer, be patient and review materials.

- Remember the name of the interviewer(s) (ask for a business card).
- Give a strong handshake and smile when meeting the interviewer.
- Be natural and try to relax by taking deep breaths.
- Bring a pen, notebook or briefcase.
- Speak slowly and quietly.
- Write down important points or topics.
- If asked to fill out an application, do so completely.
- Bring 2 pens of the same colored ink.
- Let the interviewer begin the conversation.
- Never interrupt or argue with the interviewer.
- Allow the interviewer to end the conversation before asking your prepared questions.
- Record what happened as quickly as possible following an interview.
- If applicable, thank the receptionist for his/her courtesy (by name).
- Send a thank you letter to the interviewer(s).

Dos and Don'ts of the Interview Process

- Prepare prior to the interview
- Be on time
- Be enthusiastic about the opportunity
- Dress in appropriate attire
- Establish a rapport with the interviewer
- Cite your accomplishments
- Take notes on important issues
- Send a thank you note

- Be late to the interview
- Put down other people and previous employers
- Be dishonest or lie
- Discuss specific salary figures
- Be pessimistic
- Let the interviewer do all the talking
- Leave without an understanding of your chances
- Forget to send a thank you note

Applicant Responsibilities

It is important to make sure that you take charge and direct the interview. Most people arri at an interview with no plan, wait for the interviewer to direct the conversation and passive or nervously respond to the questions in a rehearsed fashion. Don't!

The successful career seeker takes control of the interview. If you're going to be successful, don't wait around to be asked what to do, rather you look for the opportunity to demonstrate your marketability and ability to contribute. Confidence will go a long way to helping you get an offer. Don't be indecisive. Both you and the employer have a list of responsibilities that an interview session is designed to showcase.

As an applicant, your responsibilities are to:

1. *Highlight* your background and capabilities, to demonstrate your achievements, to demonstrate a keen and sincere interest in the job
2. Reach a firm and complete understanding of what specifically the job responsibilities entail
3. Negotiate a successful benefit and salary package
4. Find out how interested that employer is in you by asking good questions
5. Convince the employer that you are the best candidate for the job

Interviewer Responsibilities

Interviewer responsibilities are to:

1. Make you feel comfortable so that they get a true sense of the person they're interviewing
2. Evaluate your credentials, your appearance, and personality
3. Target a match between your qualifications and the opening
4. Obtain a firm and complete understanding of your goals and objectives
5. Make sure you understand specifically what responsibilities the job entails and what the benefits, salary, and vacation policies are
6. Let you know of a time frame for a decision and determine your interest
7. Negotiate a fair salary package and determine if you are the best candidate

Mastering the Interview: Step 4

Step 4: Uncover and Overcome Objections

If you leave the interview without learning about any reservations the employer may have, you will probably not get another chance to do so, and your ability to overcome those objections will be lost forever. Also, it may affect your chances of securing the position. In some cases, the employer may send you some nonverbal signs that indicate a lack of hiring intentions. For example, if the employer is not smiling, or constantly checks his/her watch, he or she might be sending a message indicating a lack of interest. More often though, no signals will be sent, so it will be up to you to dig for possible objections.

What are some objections that you may hear from a potential employer?

_____

_____

_____

_____

_____

Visualize Success

Win over the employer and get them on your side. Propose, if you will, a partnership and try not to alienate yourself from the employer. Try to make them feel like you're already part of their team. You both have a similar or mutual interest. Establish a sense of camaraderie with the interviewer.

As Abraham Lincoln said, "If you would win a man to your cause, first convince him that you are his sincere friend."

I like to think of an interview like a first date, where both parties are trying to impress each other. In relationships, the sooner you can break down those superficial barriers of trying to impress someone and get to your true essence, only then will you really know if you'll be comfortable with someone.

It's the same process in an interview. Try not to present an image of something you're not because if you successfully mislead the interviewer and get hired for a role that doesn't fit your true character, you and the company may both end up disappointed. Interviewers as professionals will do their best to break down those barriers. Let an interviewer know that you're at ease and you can be yourself so your interview is a comfortable setting and not like an uncomfortable first date.

What you do in the first 12 to 30 seconds of an interview will have a bearing on whether you're hired or given a, *"Thank you, but we'll keep you in mind."*

If the first impression that you give to an employer is negative regarding attire, attitude, or your personality, you run the risk of being eliminated before you have a chance to demonstrate your credentials.

The sad fact is that employers are busy people and have a number of candidates to interview, so they like to screen people out as quickly as possible. Be enthusiastic and look the interviewer directly in the eye. Studies show that if you don't look someone in the eye, it may suggest you are sneaky or less than honest. Don't be too cocky, conceited, or abrasive. Don't be too egotistical or overly aggressive. Politely greet the secretary or clerical support who often will assess you before the interviewer.

Your resume, cover letter, phone conversations or information interview have resulted in an actual interview. Your potential employer first will want to know that you have done your homework and have an understanding of the company and the position. They will test that knowledge by asking specific questions such as, "What do you know about our company or organization?"

Demonstrate to the interviewer that you have done your homework on them as a person, their personality style, how long they have been with the organization, and the company itself. There's nothing more impressive to help your own cause than to show an interviewer that you took the time to find out something about *their* interests.

I remember one candidate who found out that the person who would be interviewing him had just celebrated a birthday the day before the actual interview. You can imagine how impressed the interviewer was when the applicant walked in, looked him right in the eye with a firm handshake and said,

"Happy belated birthday."

Please review each interview situation carefully. But in a situation where you have found out that the person doing the interviewing has a particular hobby or interest, by all means try to take advantage of that in a clever but not phony way.

I'm going to take a moment here to talk about visualization. I'm a firm believer that if you visualize something in a positive sense prior to doing it, it can provide a competitive edge.

As a former marketing executive, I remember listening to a variety of self-help tapes that taught me to go into every sales call visualizing that I was going to get the sale and that the person was eager to meet me. Anticipate a positive outcome. Use the same strategy in your interviews. Before your interview, close your eyes. Breathe deeply. Picture a successful interview. See yourself getting up in the morning professionally dressed, riding the train, bus, or driving your car to an interview. Imagine what the building looks like. Imagine yourself being greeted by the receptionist and indicating that your interview is about to take place.

Visualize a firm, strong handshake, and following them confidently into their office. Visualize yourself sitting down, having a positive first 12 or 30 seconds with strong eye contact, a nice smile, confident and enthusiastic. Visualize your professional posture as you sit in your chair. Picture the interviewer asking the very same questions you anticipated. Observe yourself answering those questions professionally without fault. Visualize the interview ending on a positive note with your being hired.

How does that feel?

Overcoming Nervousness!

Many of you are probably thinking, "Well, that sounds great, but I'm petrified to go on an interview. Visualization can help me, but I'm still nervous!"

How do you overcome nervousness? Let me ask you a question. If you were going into an interview situation and you knew in your heart you were 100% confident that you were the best candidate for the job, the most prepared, the most knowledgeable and you knew that the interviewer was going to offer you the position before you even went in the door, what would your attitude be while you were walking in? Would you be nervous? Not likely.

Perception can be reality. If you visualize a positive experience, chances are, more likely than not, you're going to have a positive interview. If you see yourself as nervous, getting nauseous, having a headache, sweating, botching the interview, stammering over your words, you're probably going to experience that. You will become what you dream about and think about. In this case, focus on a positive interview and tell yourself that you're a great candidate.

Self-talk is important! Before you walk in the door, give yourself a little pep talk before walking into the interview, and tell yourself, "I'm the best candidate for the position. This is a step in attaining my career calling. I'm a great employee. I'm a great worker. I am knowledgeable about the company, I know exactly what position is for hire and I know that my credentials and background will be unmatched by any of the competition." Gear yourself up so that when you walk in the door and shake the interviewer's hand and look them right in the eye, they'll know right from the beginning that you are the right candidate for the position!

INTERVIEWING IS A SELLING PROPOSITION

"Whatever you say to a prospect about your product or service, imagine that he is looking at you and saying. . . *"so what?"*

—Brian Tracy
the psychology of selling

"Did you need a break or do you want to continue the interview process?"

Many people think that *sales* is a dirty word. Often, a salesperson conjures up the image of a pushy, sleazy person who will say anything to get you to part with your hard earned money. Although there are certainly "less than honest" salespeople who give the profession a bad name, there are an equal number of honorable individuals who understand that the essence of selling can be summarized by this: *Selling is a transference of feelings and emotions between two interested parties who seek a mutual gain.* Interviewing is selling. When on an interview, you are simply sharing your enthusiasm for your ability to solve the challenges resulting from their vacancy.

Success Tip: The key is to get the interviewer emotionally involved in the process and to perceive your skills, values, and abilities as a favorable solution to their challenge.

You and the interviewer are merely strategizing on the best way to solve the problems, (lost revenues, overworked staff, etc.) caused by the current vacancy or employees who are not as competent as you are. You are the consultant in possession of the experience, work ethic and a set of solution-oriented skills, which will make everybody's life easier.

Get it? Got it? Good!

It is not enough to simply introduce the interviewer to your credentials (education, experience, accomplishments); you must clearly demonstrate *how* these valuable attributes will benefit the employer. The use of word stories and citing specific cost savings or revenue increases resulting from your contribution is the ideal method to win over an interviewer.

Earlier, I stressed the importance of starting any activity with the end in mind. Before any interview, have a plan for exactly what you want to occur.

You should be asking yourself these two questions before every interview: "What would have to happen for you to make me a formal offer?" "What would you have to be convinced of to hire me today?"

Here is an important fact to help you realize that interviewing is a selling opportunity for you. *Interviewers buy benefits and solutions!* Features may arouse interest, but benefits arouse buying desire. Make sure that you demonstrate to every interviewer solutions you bring to the table. People do not buy products; they buy solutions to their problems. They invest in ways to satisfy their current or future needs.

Here are five recommended questions for you to ask the interviewer:

1. *"Who currently occupies this position or function?"*
2. *"What are you currently doing now in this area?"*
3. *"How is that working for you?"*
4. *"What are your plans for the future in this area?"*
5. *"What would you have to be convinced of to offer me the position?"*

In a way, you are like a detective.

You are seeking clues that will result in a formal job offer. As you can appreciate, your body language is important in interviewing. According to Albert Mehrabian of UCLA, the message you convey in a negotiation is "55% body language, 38% tone of voice, and only 7% in the words that you use."

Reasons for Hiring or Not Hiring

The *Ultimate* Questions: *What is your competitive advantage?*
Why are you the ideal candidate for the position?

In every interview (sale!), there is a *primary benefit* that the Interviewer is seeking. This is the one thing that the person who can hire you must be convinced of before they offer you a position. Your responsibility is to uncover this primary benefit and then to convince the interviewer that they will enjoy this benefit if they hire you.

At the same time, there is a *primary objection* to every sale, the major reason that the customer will hesitate or decide not to buy. It is absolutely essential that you uncover this key objection and find a way to answer it to the customer's satisfaction.

If you discover several reasons why the company is looking for candidates such as yourself, focus your attention on the top 20% of the benefits that your prospect will enjoy, and convince him or her in a professional manner that they will obtain these benefits by hiring you. If you can successfully demonstrate that hiring you will help them realize these benefits faster than from any other candidate, the interview becomes much easier (and the position is yours!)

"We will be in touch," "we will let you know" and "let me think it over," are common put-offs. You want an answer now! If you have truly done your job of articulating your unique and compelling skills and contributions in a passionate and purposeful manner, there should be nothing to think over, unless the interviewer does not have the authority to make you a formal offer. If this does occur, you can immediately reply by saying, "Mr. Interviewer, at this moment you know *a great deal* about me as a candidate. From our discussion and your reasons for needing to fill this position, I am a perfect match for you. When can I start?" *More on asking for the position later in this chapter . . .*

When conducting seminars, I always make it a point to ask my audience, "What percentage of an interviewer's decision is based on emotion, and what percentage is based on logic?" Almost everyone will say that interviewers are 50% emotional and 50% logical. But the correct answer is that hiring authorities are 100% emotional.

Remember this: Interviewers decide emotionally and then justify logically.

Mastering the Interview: Step 5

Step 5: Ask for the Positon!

Let's use the salesperson as an example once again. When someone purchases a big-ticket item, it's a major investment. The buyer wants to be absolutely certain that he or she is making the correct choice, and is unlikely to say, "Okay, I'll take it" without some bargaining and a lot of thought. If a car buyer leaves the dealership without making a commitment to purchase, he or she just might go elsewhere, be offered a slightly better price, and make the purchase. Or, the buyer might have second thoughts about the whole idea of buying. In either case, regardless of how great a job the original salesperson did, the sale has been lost, and the salesperson does not earn a commission. That is why salespeople are trained to "ask for the order", not just once, but several times during the sales process.

What are three ways that you can ask for the position?

1. _____

_____

2. _____

_____

3. _____

_____

Three Keys to Strategic Interviewing

1. Present yourself as a unique and compelling candidate. Identify your unique value proposition (UVP).

2. Differentiate yourself from other candidates who seek the same position through the "Prove it" technique (Don't just say it . . . prove it with a fact or example to make your statement real!)
If you are in sales, document your sales record. If you drive a truck, cite your delivery record. If you are a teacher, quantify your ability to empower students. If you are a social worker, recount stories of self-sufficiency or helping clients overcome barriers. If you are have an IT background, detail how you saved your previous employer money or improved revenues through your unique contributions.

3. *What is it that makes you superior to the other candidates? (Why you? Just being a "hard worker" or "team player" isn't enough!)* Many average candidates when confronted with the question, "Why should I hire you?" blurt out some rehearsed, uninspiring answer that derails the interview and results in a rejection. You need to inspire the person across the desk with a passionate, purposeful response that confirms you are a person in possession of the essential competitive edge . . . attitude! If you are not excited about describing your credentials and unique capabilities, thenyou are most likely confused, uncertain, and lack the confidence to be an A-list player.

How to Research Your Career Calling

Success Tip: In most instances, your primary major competitor is not another career seeker. It is ignorance. Employers simply do not know your services are available.

Here is a short list of five things you should consider and analyze:

1. What are the trends in your targeted industry?
2. Who exactly is your ideal employer partner? (Make a list of all the qualities and characteristics that your ideal employer would have).
3. Who will be your future employers? Project ahead 1, 3, 5 and 10 years. (Will you be working for a company or start your own firm?)
4. What other opportunities might there be for your skills? (Consultant, sub-contractor, part time employee)
5. Who or what is your primary competition? What benefits could the interviewer see in hiring another candidate? What are your shortcomings or weaknesses?

My Qualities

The following chart identifies the importance employers place on key qualities of potential candidates for hire.

Rate yourself on a scale of 1 - 5 by circling the number, 1 being the weakest and 5 being the strongest.

QUALITY (Highest to lowest)

Communication skills (verbal/written):	1	2	3	4	5
Honestly/Integrity:	1	2	3	4	5
Teamwork skills (works well with others):	1	2	3	4	5
Interpersonal skills (relates well to others):	1	2	3	4	5
Motivation/Initiative:	1	2	3	4	5
Strong work ethic:	1	2	3	4	5
Analytical skills:	1	2	3	4	5
Flexibility/adaptability:	1	2	3	4	5
Computer skills:	1	2	3	4	5
Self-confidence:	1	2	3	4	5
Leadership skills:	1	2	3	4	5
Organized:	1	2	3	4	5
Detail oriented:	1	2	3	4	5
Friendly/Outgoing Personality:	1	2	3	4	5
Tactfulness:	1	2	3	4	5
Well-mannered/polite:	1	2	3	4	5
Creative:	1	2	3	4	5

HIRING AUTHORITY FEARS...

Understanding a hiring authority's fears can provide you with good insight on what he or she is looking for when choosing a candidate. Here are a few things the hiring authority will be looking for during the hiring process, and surely does *not* want to see:

• If you were hired, you would be incompetent, or would need too much time to get your feet on the ground, become unproductive, and not pull your own weight.

• If you were hired, you wouldn't put in an honest day's work. You might be sloppy and constantly need someone to check your work.

• If you were hired, you would be lazy, give only the minimum effort, and would need be told what and when to do everything.

• If you were hired, you would frequently call in sick, arrive late, leave early, refuse overtime, and constantly ask for raises.

• If you were hired, you would be a chronic complainer, a braggart, or someone who blames others for your mistakes, blunders, sloppy work, or forgetfulness.

• If you were hired, you would say or do something to disgrace the company, the department, the manager, or your fellow workers.

• If you were hired, you would show no pride in your work, your office or work area, or your appearance.

• You could be arrogant, conceited, rude, pushy, antagonistic, or moody.

When you look at these concerns, you can clearly see that the hiring manager is looking for someone who is:

- **Aware of the company mission & brand**
- **A team player**
- **Has a strong work ethic**
- **Independent**
- **Dependable**
- **Responsible**
- **Positive**

343

CHOOSE A JOB YOU LOVE, AND YOU WILL NEVER HAVE TO WORK A DAY IN YOUR LIFE.

- Confucius

THE

INTERVIEW

PROCESS

LEARNING OBJECTIVES

1. Understand the three interview types.

2. Describe proper interviewing etiquette.

3. Practice developing rapport and emotional connections with hiring authorities.

4. Articulate your personal value.

The Five Interviewer Personality Types

There are five basic personality profiles that interviewers possess. For consistency's sake:

1. Laid Back Linda

Approximately 10% of interviewers have this profile.

Traits include apathy, negativity, cynical attitude, distracted, and sometime pre-occupied with their own challenges. By all means, do not get caught up in their toxicity, but rather focus on getting them excited about you joining their team.

2. For Certain Cindy

Approximately 10% of interviewers have this profile.

Traits include having a clear understanding of what they want from an applicant, a keen knowledge of skills and abilities needed to fill the position and an inflexible approach to compensation and salary negotiation.

"Take it or leave it" could be their motto.

3. Analytical Arnold

Approximately 25% of interviewers have this profile. Traits include a focus on quantifying value, detail, accuracy, and being concise. If you cite an accomplishment on your resume or verbally communicate an achievement, document via statistics or numbers or else. These folks will catch your mistakes and hate typos! When thinking of this profile, think accountant, attorney, bean counter, engineer, banker, etc.

4. Friendly Frank

Approximately 25% of interviewers have this profile. Traits include a deep need to be liked and respected. Friendly and outgoing, these folks like to build a relationship with candidates because they believe that is the key to effective interviewing. They use personal stories vs. inundating them with facts and figures and are complimentary about their office and location. This style may procrastinate on a final decision, which can be frustrating.

5. Bottom Line Betty

Approximately 30% of interviewers have this profile. Traits include a very direct, almost impersonal approach to the interview process, where the outcome is more important than the person seeking the position. You may be viewed as a "resource" responsible for measurable tasks and duties vs. a human being with feelings and emotions. I advise you to be concise and don't mince words, get to the point and be respectful of their time, which they value tremendously. Think of them as a radio station . . . WIIFM (what's in it for me?) should be their motto.

GREAT LISTENING = GREAT INTERVIEWING!

"You have two ears and one mouth so listen twice as much as you talk"   — Sign on a Career TEAM door

If there is one skill that I would personally like to improve upon, it is the art of being a great listener. My problem is that I like to talk and when engaged in a conversation, often I am thinking about what I want to say next vs. truly hearing what the other person is really saying. While I have made significant progress, I still have a long way to go before I would categorize myself as an attentive listener.

You must become proficient at the art of listening to the interviewer and hearing the direct and subtle references or clues in their dialogue. Failure to do so will jeopardize your chances of success and create the impression that you are incapable of active listening or, in some cases, following direction.

Listening is one of the most important competencies. Here are five keys to effective listening:

1. *Listen attentively, respond actively:* Be respectful to every interviewer you interact with; it is a privilege to be there. Let them begin the line of questioning. Listen without any attempt to interrupt, change the direction of the dialogue or dictate your own ideas. Understand before you attempt to be understood.

2. *Always remain patient in your responses:* When the interviewer concludes a point or line of questioning, make sure they are completely finished with their point. Before you respond, the strategy is to pause, wait a few seconds, and then carefully articulate your answer.

When you stop to think before you speak, you accomplish the following:

- You ensure clarity in what the interviewer truly means and minimize the potentially embarrassing risk of interrupting the interviewer, who may simply be looking for the right word or organizing their thoughts.

- You follow the old adage that, communicating takes places with the words, but acceptance of the candidate occurs during the silence.

- By pausing, you communicate (non-verbally) that you are seriously contemplating their point before reacting. In so doing, you are demonstrating a respect for their opinion by carefully absorbing the impact of their thoughts.

3. *The person asking the questions is in control:* You should never be merely responding to questions, but rather engaged in an *active* dialogue with the interviewer. Ask questions if you do not understand! Never assume that you know what the interviewer means or is thinking; this can be a fatal flaw. Rather, I suggest you tactfully ask, "How or what do you mean?" This question will force the interviewer to elaborate on the issue at hand and provide clarification. When you are talking at 100 to 150 words per minute, an interviewer can process words at the rate of 600 words per minute. This means that the interviewer has of his or her time available to contemplate other thoughts while you are responding. Conversely, when you ask a question, 100% of the interviewer's attention will be focused on answering you. This is why you both should be asking questions, not just the interviewer.

4. *Repeat key information to the interviewer:* Using your own vocabulary, repeat back what the interviewer has said to you in your own words. When you can repeat what an interviewer has said or may be thinking, you demonstrate that you were really paying attention.

5. *Use both open-ended and closed-ended questions:* Whenever you ask a question beginning with *who, what, where, when, how, why, which,* you encourage the prospect to talk and give you more information. Examples include: "What is a typical day like? How do you feel about the direction of this organization?" Incorporate closed-ended questions to bring the conversation to a conclusion. These are questions that can be answered by a yes or no. Examples include: "Are you ready to make a decision today? What two skills are most important to have for this job? When could I start?"

THE THREE TYPES OF JOB INTERVIEWS

"How well we communicate is determined not by how well we say things but by how well we are understood."

—Andrew S. Grove

1. The first type of interview is the *basic question-and-answer session*. Here, an interviewer will conduct your session in a very methodical, detailed, and structured manner. They seek specific information about your wants, objectives, skills, experience, education, capabilities, and future potential. Make the interview more of a conversation than a one-sided question session conducted by the employer.

2. The next kind of interview, and the most common, is the *free flowing interview*, where the interviewer usually begins with a question like "Tell me about yourself," and uses open-ended questions to gain insight.

Depending upon the position, you may have multiple interviewers or successive interviews, where you'll meet a number of different people from that organization in the same day, usually in succession. You may be required to impress a Personnel Manager, then a front line manager, then maybe one of your future co-workers before acceptance. Maintain a high level of enthusiasm and energy for every session.

3. Some employers conduct a *group interview*, which sometimes is the most difficult and most stressful. My experience shows that only about 10 to 20% of all applicants will have to go through a group interview. But they can occur regardless the position sought, from entry level to CEO.

Group interviews usually occur when a person will have to give presentations to a number of people and an employer wants to see how the candidate responds to multiple opinions. Questions are asked from two or three directions. It's important to maintain eye contact with each person. Sometimes employers will create a good guy/bad guy situation where one or two of the members will seemingly be on your side while the third member will be put in there as a plant to try to distract you, disrupt you, throw you off, or try to see if you get flustered easily. ID the enemy! Determine what specific credentials are required and transfer your enthusiasm!

Online Webcam Interview Tips

You may be asked to interview via webcam for a position. Since this type of interview is likely to take place in your house, there are many things to take into consideration:

- **Background.** Use a very plain or simple background. Make sure there is nothing distracting behind you such as other people or a window. If the interviewer can see part of your desk or your room, make sure it is perfectly clean and organized.
- **Technology check.** Not all laptop computers have webcams, not all desktop computers have a webcam or built-in microphones. For this reason, you should practice your interview days in advanced. The best way to do this is with a friend on another computer in a different location.
- **Lighting.** Make sure there is sufficient light so that the interviewers can clearly see you.
- **Wardrobe.** Treat an online webcam interview just as you would a face-to-face interview. Dress professionally; make sure you are clean, tidy, and presentable.
- **Background noise.** There should be absolutely no noise in the background. Do *not* consider doing a webcam interview in a public place.
- **Audio.** Will you talk through your computer's microphone or via a phone line? Regardless, make sure you test this out prior to your interview. If you will be using a cellular phone, make sure you have a strong wifi or cellular signal.
- **Personality.** Most important, let your personality shine. It is difficult to see your energy and your personality through a small video. Because of this, you may want to try overemphasizing things like your smile and enthusiasm.

Regardless of format, the interviewer has a lot to lose if they select the wrong candidate. A great tip is at the end of your presentation, ask, "What is it about my particular credentials or qualities that would make you hire me?" The question will impress them, believe me, because they'll have to answer you and focus on your best attributes. You want them to verbalize your strengths; this question ensures that will occur. At the end of any interview, the employer really has only three options: one is to hire you, two is to hire somebody else, and three is to do nothing or keep on interviewing. Try to find out at the end of your interview which one of the three choices the interviewer has made. If you're not sure, try to reinforce your competitive edge; that is, what separates you from the other applicants. Help them make a decision in your favor!

15 Most Cited Reasons for Rejecting Applicants

1. **Poor personal appearance**
2. **No career purpose or goal**
3. **Lack of enthusiasm**
4. **Lack of confidence**
5. **Overemphasis on money**
6. **Failure to ask questions about the job**
7. **Lack of courtesy**
8. **Failure to look the interviewer in the eye**
9. **Limp handshake**
10. **Failure to research the employer**
11. **Indefinite response to questions**
12. **Sloppy resume**
13. **Cynical attitude**
14. **Inability to take criticism**
15. **Failure to express appreciation for interviewer's time**

When talking with a number of professional recruiters, personnel managers, and interviewers, I've found that:

- When an employer says no to you as far as a job opportunity is concerned, what he or she is really saying is "know" that is, "I don't know enough about your potential" or "I am not convinced to the degree that I need to be about your potential."

- Preparation is critical. You've heard many athletes, celebrities, actresses, and actors talk about the importance of dress rehearsal or practice. Remember one thing: The excitement of the successful interview and career achievement in general is always preceded by un-sensational job search preparation or practice.

- Create an enthusiasm within your interviewer. Be a spark in their life and don't be afraid to communicate a bit of humor within an interview. But be careful because humor is a sensitive issue; it can backfire if misused. I remember one interviewer was telling me a story where he was in an interview, and the woman interviewing him asked, "Well, how much money do you feel you need?" The candidate tried to be funny and responded, "Well, how much do you have?" In this case, that type of humor did not work because the interviewer was an analytical, bottom line type of personality who didn't find it funny and didn't warm up to that type of response.

"At Career TEAM, we hire individuals who are seeking an outlet to demonstrate their passions. Ideally, they are on the cusp of finding it for the first time in their life, that is, where their heart and soul meets. When I personally interview them, I can immediately see this passion in their eyes, the spark surrounding their being is unmistakable. I can observe in these candidates a need to prove it to me. Why is this important? Because success is fleeting while greatness derived from a deep sense of calling endures over time. At Career TEAM, we ideally seek candidates who are about to experience a career defining moment . . . This is one of the secrets to our incredible success.

—Chris Kuselias

Ten Great Tips

1. Punctuality, smile, eye contact, firm handshake, and proper introductory greeting

2. A quality application, resume, and cover letter that cites relevant information

3. The inclusion of a clearly defined career objective

4. The Big Five: Attitude, enthusiasm, energy, confidence, and dependability

5. The critical four: listening skills, research, use of industry "buzz" words, persistence

6. An ability to communicate ideas clearly and effectively

7. The ability to organize and sell key points

8. Overall presentation and appearance

9. Desire to win the position and ability to ask for it

10. Closing techniques and comments

Employer Concerns

Remember that an interviewers fear of making a poor decision exceeds their desire of being applauded for hiring a good candidate. They are scared to make a bad hiring decision, make their life easy! Target a game plan to overcome some of their possible concerns, which are: *If I hire this candidate and it doesn't work out, I'll be looked upon as a person who can't make the correct decision or evaluate talent.*

- They are concerned that maybe you won't be able to do the job because your skills or experience level is deficient, yet they felt that you did such a good job interviewing that you could overcome that lack of experience.

- Interviewers also have a hidden fear that if you're accepted, you may take too long to become comfortable with your responsibilities and that the company will not profit from hiring you.

- They may have a concern that you won't get along with other people or that you'll be a loner or your personality, even though you have talent or experience, may conflict with your potential supervisors or co-workers.

- They may have a concern that you are a person who gets by doing just the minimum rather than striving to achieve maximum potential. They may fear that you won't put in a full day, or that you may be out sick a lot.

- They may be concerned about your commitment. They fear you may accept the position, but leave shortly thereafter because you have been being lured by another company, organization, or recruiter.

- They fear you're a person who will always be looking for more money, that you'll constantly be pestering people for a raise, and that people will point to the interviewer as the person who hired you.

- They are concerned that you're the kind of person who doesn't take initiative and needs to be given constant orders, one who constantly needs a kick in the rear end.

Tell Me about Yourself...

Let's practice answering a question that you will undoubtedly be asked. Interviewers may be word questions in a way to trick you. Everyone has negatives and it is essential that you tell the truth. So, the trick is to answer truthfully but in a way that minimizes the negatives and explains how the situation actually proved beneficial in the long run.

When you are on an interview, don't be surprised if you don't hear exactly the words used here. What is important is that you be prepared to explain yourself no matter how the question is posed. It is also important that you speak in a conversational manner, using complete sentences. One or two word answers are dull and don't "flesh out" your meaning.

"Tell me about yourself."

In one form or another, you are going to hear this. There are three parts to your answer. They are your professional history, your education and your personal background. Zero in on the issues that will be relevant to employment. Do not merely restate what is on your resume.

_____

_____

_____

_____

MY SKILLS AND ABILITIES

The following is a list of the most marketable employment skills in the workforce today. These are the types of qualities and attributes that employers are looking for.

First, place a checkmark in the last column, for each of the skills you feel you possess. Then, give an example of how your ability(s) relate to that type of skill.

TYPE OF SKILL	EXAMPLE	X
Administrative		
Compiling Data		
Computer Skills		
Imagination/Creativity		
Managing People		
Organization Skills		
Persuasive Skills		
Presentation Skills		
Public Relations Skills		
Ability to Work with Numbers		
Research and Analysis		
Teaching/Training Skills		
Writing Skills		
Sales and Marketing		

20 AREAS YOU WILL BE EVALUATED ON IN AN INTERVIEW

- Ability to Communicate
- Flexibility
- Interpersonal skills
- Appearance
- High Energy
- Leadership
- Competitiveness
- Honesty
- Maturity
- Confidence
- Imagination
- Optimism
- Creativity
- Initiative
- Personality
- Enthusiasm
- Integrity
- Punctuality
- Experience
- Interests

Hint: Consider how you will be positively evaluated in each area.

MY STRENGTHS

List five strengths that your parents/family/significant other/friends see in you:
HINT: Now is not the time to be modest. Brag away!

1. _____

2. _____

3. _____

4. _____

5. _____

Now list five strengths that your former/current (or potential) employer sees in you, or, if you have never been employed, list five of your strengths that you believe would make you attractive to an employer.

1. _____

2. _____

3. _____

4. _____

5. _____

Do others see you the way you see yourself? If not, why not? This exercise will help you see things from another perspective.

_____

_____

MY WEAKNESSES

Everyone has weaknesses; sometimes, unfortunately, they are even easier for you to list than your strengths. In this exercise, you will zero in on how you are going to improve. So, go ahead and list your weaknesses, but don't dwell on them. Put all your energy instead into finding solutions, improving what needs improving, and turning those weaknesses into strengths (in fact, the act of working to overcome a weakness is a strength!).

List three weaknesses that your parents/family/friends see in you:

1. _____

2. _____

3. _____

List one thing you can do right away to improve each of the weaknesses:

1. _____

2. _____

3. _____

Now, list three weaknesses that an employer might see in you:

1. _____

2. _____

3. _____

List one thing you can do right away to improve each of the weaknesses:

1. _____

2. _____

3. _____

Five Stages of the Interview

First Impression—Stage 1

Building Rapport (5–10 Minutes)

Usually this dialogue is "small talk" on the traffic, weather, local sports team, current events. This stage is designed to put both parties at ease. Remember, first impressions are extremely important!

Track Record—Stage 2

Question And Answer Session (20–30 Minutes)

Usually, the interviewer will ask 10–15 questions, which can be either open or closed ended. This stage is designed to determine your ability to handle the job and your future potential. Prepare for this stage by reviewing all possible questions and by practicing your responses. Remember to "prove it" and support your answers with documented examples.

Career Goals—Stage 3

Your Questions (10–20 Minutes)

Here is your chance to obtain any information not already covered. Remember, some employers state that it is the questions you ask and not your answers that provide best insight to your true potential. Prepare 3–5 questions for this stage.

Company Match—Stage 4

Evaluation (5–10 Minutes)

Does the position further your career calling? Can you see yourself working with this employer? Do you think they are excited about you working for them?

Summary—Stage 5

The Close (5–10 Minutes)

Use this stage to review your credentials, restate your interest and, ask for the position! One suggestion is to ask the interviewer, "How do we proceed?"

Five Essential Things Interviewers Look For

Here is a behind the scenes view of what the interviewer looks for:

1. In the first *impression* stage is the introduction, greeting, some small talk about traffic conditions, location, the weather, or maybe a sporting event. The interviewer is evaluating handshake, eye contact, appearance, wardrobe, and your poise and ease in an unfamiliar social situation.

2. The second stage is *track record*. At issue is your education, grades, work experience, and level of responsibility. The interviewer will evaluate your intellectual abilities, special or general interests, reaction to authority, sensibility in terms of resources, time, energy, vitality, enthusiasm, willingness to follow directions, and ability to motivate yourself and make things happen. An employer will consider your relationships, interests, extracurricular activities and hobbies, positive attitude, and social awareness. Are you a good person and a good citizen?

3. The third stage in the interviewer's perception is review of your *career goals*. The interviewer's targeted questions will lead you to disclose your immediate objectives, long-term objectives and interest in the company. It will also showcase your attitude about topics like relocation and other factors that may affect your performance. Here the interviewer seeks a realistic knowledge of your strengths and weaknesses, how prepared you are for this particular opportunity and your seriousness of purpose. Do you have a calling? Are you, in fact, career-oriented rather than just specific job-oriented? There's a big difference. Career-oriented people think long-term where job-oriented people think specific job only. Interviewers will target your knowledge of the company and whether your contributions are in line with your talents. Are you a dreamer or achiever? Most importantly, what are his or her company's chances to hire you at this stage?

4. The fourth stage is called the *company match*. Here you will discuss opportunities and how to fit in on both current and future projects. The interviewer will discuss the major issues and departments, the training programs, and the educational or other benefits offered. The interviewer is specifically looking for informed and relevant questions that you ask, indications of your interest in the answers, and an appropriate interest in the salary or benefits offered.

5. The fifth and final stage of the perception portion is called the *summary*. During the final stages of an interview, you may be asked to provide further information on the application. Finally, the interviewer will tell you when you will be notified of a decision.

Assessing Your Interview Performance

During the course of an interview, there are certain aspects that require you have a complete and thorough understanding of.

1. *Do you fully understand the duties?* Understand completely what the particular vacancy or opportunity involves. You've researched the employer, maybe done an information interview or two, and talked to people who do the job. Use the interview process to gain a clear understanding of the opportunity so that you can make a well-informed decision about whether you want to pursue your calling there.

2. *Can you see yourself pursuing your calling with this organization?* After doing your homework, information interview, meeting people in the lobby, and meeting the interviewer, is this where you want to pursue your calling. You have options. Are these the kind of people that you see yourself becoming socially active with? Do they share your values? Or are your goals or skills different to the point that you won't be comfortable?

3. *Is there a match?* Do you understand the role well enough to make a decision? The interview process should confirm that match. Use the interview as an opportunity to sell yourself and market your potential and capabilities. But also use it as an information-gathering session.

4. *What does the interviewer care about?* Remember to make the interviewer like you. Be interested in what they have to say. Have a smile on your face. Be enthusiastic. Remember their name. Listen intently when they're talking. Don't be afraid to take notes. Talk highly about other people or past employers. Don't talk negatively about your former employers or your former boss. Don't make excuses about your shortcomings. Talk in terms of *their* interest.

5. *Did you establish an emotional bond?* Be sincere and make the other person feel important, establishing a camaraderie and common bond. If they can see you as a cost effective value and they like you personally, that will go a long way to your acceptance.

Consider these questions:

1. Did I make a good first impression?
2. Did I talk enough?
3. Did I justify my statements with factual statements?
4. Which questions did I handle well?
5. Which questions did I handle poorly?
6. Was I confident?
7. How was my appearance?
8. Was I enthusiastic?
9. Would I have been impressed with me?
10. What will I do to improve my next interview?

It is important to evaluate your performance and reflect on how you could improve your next opportunity. Here are five questions to reflect on:

1. How well did the interview go?
2. How do you feel that you did in regards to some of the decisions you made during the interview and did you take any risks to distinguish yourself?
3. How well did you handle the interviewer's questions and did you ask and get answers to your most important questions?
4. What could you have done differently?
5. Did you accomplish all of your objectives?

Warning! Make Sure You Heard Right . . .

One of the biggest frustrations career seekers endure is to accept a position based on a series of perceived promises only to find out that what they thought they heard the interviewer say or agree to is, in fact, much different once they start working.

Before you accept any position, do your best to make certain that the following issues are clearly understood by both parties (even to the extent of getting them in writing). This may include a written job description and duties, a clearly defined compensation plan, an organization chart depicting your role on the team and authority to make decisions.

Keep in mind that while you can never guarantee that your duties, title, function, or compensation won't change or be modified in the best interest of your employer (things move fast these days!); requesting clarification in the interview process will present you as a serious and professional candidate.

Here are the three biggest issues that, if not addressed, often result in stress and anxiety:

1. Salary and compensation do not equate to what was promised in the interview; career objectives tied to commissions or bonuses are modified (increased) making them more difficult to attain.

2. The job title or duties are radically different from what you understood: you wind up wearing more than one hat and your job responsibilities are much more involved than you were led to believe.

3. Your decision-making capabilities are less than you were led to believe; you have less authority than you thought.

Mock Interview Rating Form

Name: _____

Date: _____

Part 1 Meeting and Greeting 5 Points
1. Smile   _____ /1point
2. Eye contact   _____ /1point
3. Shake hands firmly   _____ /1point
4. Introduce yourself using the interviewer's name   _____ /1point
5. Indicate what you are there for   _____ /1point

Subtotal _____ /5points

Part 2 Poise 30 Points
1. Leans slightly forward   _____ /5points
2. Appropriate hand gestures   _____ /5points
3. Eye contact   _____ /10points
4. Faces interviewer   _____ /10points

Subtotal _____ /30points

Part 3 Answering Questions 30 Points
1. No mumbling   _____ /6points
2. Complete answers   _____ /6points
3. No slang   _____ /6points
4. Professional demeanor   _____ /6points
5. No tangents   _____ /6points

Subtotal _____ /30points

Part 4 Asking Questions 30 Points
1. No mumbling   _____ /5points
2. No slang   _____ /5points
3. Complete sentences   _____ /10points
4. Show interest in what you can contribute   _____ /10points

Subtotal _____ /30points

Part 5 Closing the Interview 5 Points
1. Shake hands   _____ /1point
2. Thank the interviewer using his or her name   _____ /1point
3. Restate your strengths   _____ /1point
4. Ask for the job   _____ /1point
5. Next step: ask when you will hear back   _____ /1point

Subtotal _____ /30points

Grand total _____ /100points

Thank you Letter

Sending a thank you letter is not only proper etiquette, but it is also your chance to shine. This not just an opportunity to thank the person for his or her time; this is the moment to remind him or her why they should hire you! When writing a thank you letter, keep the following in mind:

Rule #1: Type it, if you can. It is perfectly fine to send e-mail. Handwritten is also a very good option if you have excellent penmanship.

Rule #2: Be relatively formal. You should use last names in your written correspondence. Avoid "Dear Mary"; rather, use "Dear Ms. Smith."

Rule #3: Mention the position. For example, you can say, "If you recall, the position I was applying for was..."

Rule #4: Make a reference to something that was discussed in the interview. Remind the employer of one of your qualities that impressed him or her.

Rule #5: Send your letter right after the interview. You want your letter to be received while you are still fresh in the mind of the employer.

Rule #6: Keep it short. Include your main points, but don't ramble. Too long a letter will not keep the reader's attention.

Rule #7: Sound excited about working for the employer. Remind him or her that you really want the position, and of what you can do for the employer.

Sample Thank You for Interview Letter

Date
Interviewer's Name
Title
Company
Address

Dear : _____

I appreciated the opportunity to meet with you on (date). The information you shared with me about (company name) was excellent, and I am excited about the possibility of applying my education and experience to the position.

During our discussion, you indicated that you were looking for a candidate who (restate qualities sought by employer). I believe that I have the skills and confidence needed to make an immediate contribution.

If I can provide you with any additional information concerning my qualifications, please let me know. I look forward to hearing from you soon.

Sincerely,
Signature

My Thank-You Letter

Now it's your turn. Imagine that you have just had an interview with an employer in your field of interest. Imagine how that interview went. Refer back to the section on "Assessing Your Interview Performance" before beginning your letter.

Now, begin to write your letter and be sure to include the following:

- Follow the model and be sure to use a proper business letter format and language. Remember, you want to make a great impression!
- Refer to your previous accomplishments/experience
- Demonstrate that you are a viable candidate
- Reinforce your interest in the position
- Offer references and request a second interview (if applicable)

Important! You are at a crucial time in your life, make sure your ring back tone and/or voice mail message is appropriate and professional! Use an e-mail address that is also professional.

Remember, this is your moment to shine, so make sure you shine like a diamond!

Thank-You Letter Template

Following the model, use the template below to write a thank-you letter.

_____   _____

_____   _____

_____   _____

_____

_____

_____

_____

_____

_____

_____

STEP-BY-STEP GUIDE TO INTERVIEWING

One of the most important events in your life is an interview. After all, a party on the weekend is over in just a few hours, and rarely has any lasting effects other than some fun memories. On the other hand, a 30-minute interview can shape the direction of your career and determine your future lifestyle, and yet people rarely do enough planning for this important event. A poorly organized approach will cause confusion during the interview.

Let's discuss some of the things that should be included in your planning.

1. Do your homework.
Your chances of employment will increase dramatically if you can talk intelligently about the employer's organization, so DO YOUR HOMEWORK!

2. Get your directions straight.
Call the company or check directions on a map. If you are unfamiliar with the employer's location, make a practice run. Check the public transportation schedule to make sure you know what buses to take. *Arriving late for an interview can be a fatal error.*

3. Assemble what you need to take with you.
Always carry extra copies of your resume, and include your list of references. Carry two pencils and two identical pens, so if one runs out of ink (Murphy's Law) you can still complete the paperwork neatly. If possible, carry a briefcase or portfolio, and make sure you write down the full name of the person you are going to meet. "I have an appointment at 11:00, but I don't remember who I have to see," just won't cut it.

4. Avoid smoking before the interview.
Many people are offended by the odor of smoke, and even if you could clear your breath, the odor will still be on your clothing.

5. Arrive early.
Even if you have already filled out an application, plan for more paperwork. Don't assume that your application will be on hand. Allow an extra fifteen minutes, at least. If you end up with time to kill, use it to check yourself in a mirror, review your qualifications, or learn more about the company.

6. Greet the receptionist.
The first person you will encounter will most likely be the receptionist or hostess. This individual can help you – or hurt you! It is important to make a favorable and memorable impression.

7. Smile!
Keep a happy, energetic attitude even before you actually sit down with the employer. You never know who is watching you.

8. Shake hands.
At least once with everyone you meet, and twice with the interviewer (at the beginning and at the end of the interview). Offer your hand even if the other party does not. Your handshake needs to be firm and dry. What does a weak handshake say about you?

9. Use the interviewer's name.

10. Offer the interviewer a copy of your resume even if he or she already has one.

11. Don't sit until the interviewer sits; doing so shows respect.

12. Watch your body language.
At least 70% of the messages you send/impression you make, comes from your body language.

13. Sit up straight.
If you are asked to sit on a soft sofa, test it out before settling in. You'll feel awkward trying to get out of those "sink to the springs" sofas.

14. Don't touch the interviewer's desk.
Don't touch anything on the desk or in the interviewer's office without asking for permission first. Individuals do not like invasions of their "personal space".

15. Don't cross your legs.
Doing so causes your upper body to slump. Cross your ankles and keep your feet together on the floor.

16. Keep your hands still.
Hold on to your notebook if you need a prop. Fluttering hands distract from the message and make you appear nervous. *Keep your arms at your sides*.

17. Maintain friendly eye contact without staring.
Practice with a mirror if this is difficult for you. What message do you send if you fail to make good eye contact?

18. Treat the interview the same way you would treat a conversation with any new friend.

In other words, don't allow it to be one-sided.

19. Take notes.
Unless you have a memory like a computer, you won't remember everything that is said. Taking notes also displays interest and serves as a reminder to ask questions about things the interviewer has said. What are some things that would prompt you to take notes?

20. Ask questions.
If the interviewer fails to offer you an opportunity to ask questions, ask for the chance.

21. Let the interviewer broach the subject of wages and benefits.
If it doesn't come up in the first interview, it will later on.

22. Leave the interviewer with the impression that you are enthusiastic about the position.
A good closing remark such as, "I'm really looking forward to working here" works!

23. Ask for the position.
Leave the interview with a firm idea of what comes next, including when the next contact will be made.

24. Always ask for a business card. Always send a thank you note.

25. Let that be your edge!

Evaluating A New Offer

Accepting or rejecting an offer is part emotion, part intellectual, and part gut feeling. To assist you in the process of determining if an offer fits into your big picture plan for attaining your career calling, here is a list of questions:

- Can I fulfill these duties?
- Will I fit into this new culture?
- Is the commute reasonable?
- Is the organization stable?
- Is there an opportunity for growth?
- Is the compensation fair?
- What adjustments will I have to make?
- Does it fit into my overall career-calling plan?

These factors influence their decision with regard to how generous they are concerning the salary and benefits package. Here is a summation of what you should evaluate before making a commitment. To begin, there are three primary categories typically associated with compensation, which include:

1. Salary (base, bonus, commissions, profit sharing, equity)
2. Benefits (medical, dental, disability insurance)
3. Savings Plan (401K, matching funds, stock options, equity positions)

Other Considerations:
(Should not be minimized, as they add up!)

- Advancement potential
- Cell phone reimbursement
- Child or day care
- Company car or vehicle
- Computer allowance
- Counseling services
- Expense account
- Job location
- Memberships/associations
- Overtime
- Parking privileges
- Performance appraisal
- Relocation reimbursement or allowance
- Training
- Travel requirements
- Tuition reimbursement
- Union or non-union
- Vacation time

Criteria to Evaluate Before Taking a Job

As far as salary is concerned, avoid any mention of a specific figure. Let the interviewer be the first to name a salary figure. Be reasonable in terms of your demands. Research what people in that industry or organization earn.

Remain open and flexible in regards to compensation. If unsure, say, "I'm looking for a salary and benefit package commensurate with what a person of my experience, background, capabilities and potential would normally obtain" or "What would you normally pay somebody with my skills and background?" That way, they are forced to answer the question and you can decide if it's in your acceptable range.

In the course of your answers, the interviewer will determine your maturity level, initiative, if you work well as a team member, how flexible and adaptable you are, how conscientious you are and if you're a hard worker. They'll be looking at your honesty, sincerity, how disciplined a candidate you are, any emotional adjustment and, finally, your professionalism.

Section 16:

ANSWERING DIFFICULT QUESTIONS

LEARNING OBJECTIVES

1. Apply the PROVE IT principle when answering difficult questions.

2. Formulate answers for a multitude of interview questions.

3. Compose questions you can ask at the end of your interview.

The purpose of this section is to provide strategies for answering the difficult questions. Depending upon the type of job, level of job, or title of the interviewer, the actual questions may vary or be tailored toward a particular industry or occupation. The following should provide you with a solid foundation on which to build exceptional responses.

Because the interview process can create anxiety, it's always a good idea to practice these answers prior to attending an interview. By doing so, you'll establish a greater level of self-confidence, improve your performance in the interview, and give yourself a better chance of getting a yes. These selected interview answers will provide you with a competitive edge.

Articulate your strengths in these areas:

1. Your personal background
2. Your achievements and accomplishments
3. Your employment history

Communicate to the interviewer that you are:

A hard worker who likes to start early, and looks to do more than just the minimum required.

- Your interview answers should demonstrate that this new opportunity will provide you with a strong sense of purpose, motivation, and accomplishment.
- If you are unsure about a question, ask for clarification!
- Always speak positively about former employers.
- Be completely honest with all of your answers.
- Turn questions about your weaknesses into answers of strengths.
- Be prepared to answer questions about your long-term goals.
- Demonstrate flexibility and give examples of your ability to work with all types of people.
- Demonstrate that you are a person who is organized and disciplined.
- Use anecdotes or examples to illustrate your statements whenever possible.
- Be poised, confident, and incorporate your personal experiences in your answers.

20 Most Frequently Asked Interview Questions

1. Tell me about yourself.
2. Have you ever done this type of work before?
3. Why have you chosen this particular industry?
4. Why do you want to leave your present job? Why did you leave your previous job?
5. Why are you interested in this particular organization?
6. Why should we hire you?
7. What interests you the most about this particular job?
8. Are you willing to relocate?
9. Who has had the greatest influence on your life?
10. What is your greatest strength?
11. What is your greatest weakness?
12. What would you like to be doing five years from now?
13. How would you describe your personality? How would others describe you?
14. What aspect of this job would interest you the least?
15. How do you feel about having a boss that is younger than you?
16. What type of people do you not like to work with?
17. Why have you changed jobs so frequently?
18. Why have you been out of work for so long?
19. Do you have plans to continue your education?
20. How do you tolerate coworkers with different goals, interests, or ambitions?

After writing your answers to these questions, you should practice saying them aloud!

Many career seekers are terrified by the prospect of interviewing. The key to mastering anything new is preparation and familiarizing yourself with what will occur. Regarding the interview, this means reviewing the proper procedures. So, what are the most frequently asked questions in a typical interview session?

1. Tell me about yourself...

In the majority of interviews, the first question is *"Tell me about yourself."* This question is what I call a "convince me" question.

Begin the answer by expressing your interest and desire to contribute to the employer. Offer to share your credentials and your prior research. In your answer, you have three basic options:

    1. To discuss your personal background
    2. To discuss your educational accomplishments
    3. To discuss your professional experience or work history

Begin with the most impressive and relevant aspect of your credentials. By doing so, you will establish an all-important first impression! If you choose, for example, work history, express your interest and desire to work for the employer and demonstrate your knowledge of their operations. Share how this contribution is your calling! State that you are a hard worker, that you come in early, are often the last to leave, and are looking to do more than just the bare minimum required for the position. Tie in your previous experience to the position. If you do not have a strong work history, focus on your education. The key is to tie your strength to the position you are interviewing for.

1. Tell me about yourself...

Now it's your turn to talk about yourself. Make sure to touch on the suggestions mentioned in the last paragraph.

Answer:

_____

_____

_____

_____

_____

_____

_____

_____

_____

_____

_____

_____

_____

2. Have you ever done this type of work before?

In this case, the employer needs to feel confident that you possess the necessary experience. Your response should include the fact that you are a flexible and versatile individual. Be sure to demonstrate from your background or credentials that you can adapt quickly to new challenges. Document examples that confirm your assertions. Don't just say it, *prove it*!

Now it's your turn to answer. Make sure to touch on the suggestions mentioned in the last paragraph.

Answer:

_____

_____

_____

_____

_____

_____

_____

_____

_____

3. Why have you chosen this particular industry?

In this instance, you have a perfect opportunity to share with the interviewer a true interest in the job, to demonstrate knowledge of the field or industry and then convince them of your capability to perform successfully. Convince the interviewer how this type of work will provide you with a strong sense of purpose, motivation, and accomplishment. Another tip is to mention the specific functions of the role and industry that you are passionate about.

Now it's your turn to answer. Make sure to touch on the suggestions mentioned in the last paragraph.

Answer:

_____

_____

_____

_____

_____

_____

4. Why do you want to leave your current job or why did you leave your previous job?

Emphasize the fact that you decided on a career change because you realized that your previous job was not providing you with every benefit that you felt could be derived from your career. Also, mention that you want a position in which you can grow and demonstrate your potential talents. For example, "I would be more effective in a position like this one where my computer skills, team player mentality, and customer service experience could be utilized." Provide specific examples of how these skills will be of particular benefit to the employer. Successful candidates always support claims of talent or skills with specific examples from prior experiences. By doing so, you develop credibility with an interviewer. Never speak negatively about your previous job or employer.

Now it's your turn to answer. Make sure to touch on the suggestions mentioned in the last paragraph.

Answer:

_____

_____

_____

_____

_____

5. Why are you interested in working for this particular organization?

Be specific and remember, "Because I need a job" is *not an unacceptable answer!* It is important to emphasize the fact that you are interested in working for this employer and that you have not only done your homework, but also, you have researched the industry and its competitors. This is your calling! It would be helpful to point out specific reasons why this particular employer is superior to some of the others. For example, "Your organization has introduced 14 new products in the last three years, while your competition has only introduced two new products" or "I prefer a more dynamic organization with a reputation for quality." The key is to support your reasons with facts and not just generic mumbo jumbo.

Now it's your turn to answer. Make sure to touch on the suggestions mentioned in the last paragraph.

Answer:

_____

_____

_____

_____

_____

_____

_____

6. Tell me, why should we hire you?

"Why should we hire you?" is one of the most important questions any interviewer can ask you. This question is a direct opportunity for you to present your credentials, qualities, experiences, and educational background. Make a statement like, "I have the capabilities to successfully do the job and my previous record of experience and education demonstrate that." Or, if you are just coming out of school or re-entering the job market, you may want to say something like, "I'm a quick study, a fast learner, for example." Or you may want to say something like, "I've done a great deal of preparation and planning to make sure that this is a field which matches all of my job requirements. I know that this particular organization and job function will provide me with all that I am looking for to be my most successful self. Since I am passionate about the duties, you as the employer will benefit."

Note: More experienced candidates should focus on their maturity and judgment.

Now it's your turn to answer. Make sure to touch on the suggestions mentioned in the last paragraph.

Answer:

_____

_____

_____

_____

_____

7. What interests you most about this particular job?

Or another way of saying it is, what is important to you in a job? These two questions are a perfect opportunity to present to the interviewer what it is that you view as most interesting about the position. Is it the competitive nature that you possess? Is it the outlook that the website, company information, or a particular article that you reference seemed to indicate? Is it the challenge of the position or the fact that a new division or product line has been introduced and you would like to help make that a success? Is it a team environment? The interviewer wants to make sure that your personal aptitudes and qualities are in sync with those that contribute to the progress of the employer's objectives. If they are, great, if not, you may become bored or discouraged and ultimately leave the job. Downplay the importance of salary or fringe benefits unless, of course, you're interviewing for a commission-based position and you want to show that you are motivated by accomplishment. For example, the more revenue you help to generate, the more the employer will benefit.

Now it's your turn to answer. Make sure to touch on the suggestions mentioned in the last paragraph.

Answer:

_____

_____

_____

_____

_____

8. Are you willing to relocate?

This question is asked because the potential exists to move you to a different geographic location, if not immediately, then maybe in the future. If you say "No" to the question of relocation, there's a very good chance that you are diminishing your chances to be hired because they're probably looking for flexibility. The best answer is, "Yes, for the right opportunity." Inquire as to potential duties, locations, and type of programs or incentives for people who do relocate.

Keep in mind that you might not be willing to relocate for entry-level but for a promotion to management, maybe yes.

Now it's your turn to answer. Make sure to touch on the suggestions mentioned in the last paragraph.

Answer:

_____

_____

_____

_____

_____

9. Who has had the greatest influence on your life?

In this answer, only give one person's name. Try to have that individual be a person with authority, whether it is a former teacher, professor, a former boss or author of an article or book that you've read that was influential on your life. *Here they are looking for the qualities you relate to in a mentor.* The person you select often provides valuable insight into your character and also provides a reflection of your exposure to studying successful individuals in your chosen field. Employers are impressed with candidates who have the ambition to study the top minds or performers in their profession. Follow your selection with a short explanation as to why you feel they have been the most influential person, whether they taught you how to take risks, to live every day to its fullest, or to focus and pursue your calling in life.

Now it's your turn to answer. Make sure to touch on the suggestions mentioned in the last paragraph.

Answer:

_____

_____

_____

_____

_____

_____

_____

10. What is your greatest strength?

Or what have been your greatest accomplishments or achievements thus far? In any interview there are a few questions designed for you to sell yourself, and this is one of them. Interviewers categorize this as a "convince me" question. Before the interview, prepare one or two key qualities that you possess that you know from prior research to be the greatest demand for that particular job. Through questions, find out what traits are most sought after and tailor your presentation to those qualities. In other words, relate your greatest strength to the qualities needed to satisfy that position.

If the employer is known for innovation, demonstrate that you are innovative. If they have a reputation for being conservative, follow suit. If they pride themselves on teamwork, discuss your ability to function within a group.

State the quality or strength and then support your claim with your previous accomplishments. Be ready to cite one or two what I call "hero stories" that will make you attractive to your employer and be sure to make them as interesting as possible. Interviewers hate to be bored! If leadership is a sought after trait, consider people you have hired or led, an academic experience, training course or a committee you served on which demonstrates leadership.

Now it's your turn to answer. Make sure to touch on the suggestions mentioned in the last paragraph.

Answer:

_____

_____

_____

_____

_____

11. What is your greatest weakness?

This is a trick question that has eliminated many qualified but unprepared applicants. The rule is to focus on the positive. Stay away from the negative. And never answer, "Well, I'm constantly late" or "I lack attention to detail" or "I'm afraid to be a leader."

Common sense dictates everyone has his or her positives and negatives. Remember this golden rule: You are screened in because of your strengths and screened out because of your weaknesses. In your reply, substitute the word weakness for challenge and consider, "Well, it's true that everybody has their strengths and challenges. However, I feel that if I had to identify my biggest challenge, it would be an inability to tolerate other workers around me who are not as dedicated to the achievement of the organization's objectives.

I am a dedicated team player who goes above and beyond the call and I expect the same from my co-workers." Then supplement with a word story. For example, in the past maybe you've coached a fellow employee to become more focused, to be motivated or be in sync with the organization's objectives. Try, "In my previous job, I came across an individual who was unfocused and didn't seem particularly excited about working. And as a result, his or her performance was lacking. I immediately noticed it (thereby showing sensitivity and a keen awareness of your co-workers), but rather than tattle to management or chastise my fellow co-worker, (here you're showing your maturity), I called him or her aside quietly and tried to find out if it was a personal distraction and offered my assistance." (There you are demonstrating loyalty and good judgment). This strategy will go a long way to your being hired.

Now it's your turn to answer. Make sure to touch on the suggestions mentioned in the last paragraph.

Answer:

_____

_____

_____

_____

_____

_____

_____

_____

_____

_____

_____

_____

12. What would you like to be doing five years from now?

This question provides the interviewer with useful information on your future objectives. Their exact thought process: Should we make an investment in this person or are they here for a pit stop? Remember, the employer may be investing thousands of dollars in your training, so they want to be certain of a return on their investment! Many an unprepared candidate has no idea where their career will lead them. They haven't done their homework with regard to upward mobility and have no clue about the progression schedule for outstanding talent. Interviewers want to know that you have a plan! Regardless of the job title for which you are applying, you should know what the next job title and duties would be if you were promoted. Know the career path! Highlight your plans to acquire the necessary skills for long-term growth within that organization. By doing so, you will demonstrate maturity, good preparation skills, and a true knowledge of yourself and the company and its career path. That will go a long way to being accepted.

Now it's your turn to answer. Make sure to touch on the suggestions mentioned in the last paragraph.

Answer:

_____

_____

_____

_____

_____

_____

_____

_____

_____

_____

_____

_____

_____

_____

_____

_____

_____

13. How would other people describe you?

In this case, the interviewer is looking for clues to your personality. Inform the interviewer that you get along with co-workers, have achieved the respect of your subordinates, previous instructors or supervisors, and articulate that you work well with other people. Create a picture of positive self-esteem and an active social participant so that the employer senses that outside the confines of the job, your co-workers will respect you.

Now it's your turn to answer. Make sure to touch on the suggestions mentioned in the last paragraph.
Answer:

_____

_____

_____

_____

_____

14. What particular aspect of this job do you think will interest you the least or you think you'll have the most problem with?

The strategy is to convert the question into an opportunity to sell yourself. Describe your passion for the field or industry and why you chose the occupation. Tell the interviewer that you recognize that some aspects are more exciting than others, but that you're not afraid of detailed type of work. Add that the positives totally outweigh the negatives. It is a good practice to never admit any negative feelings about the job, no matter how much the interviewer coaxes you into doing so. If the interviewer tries to throw you or sway you by saying, "Well, you realize that this is a very difficult work schedule and sometimes there's a lot of overtime involved " or "Some of our customers are very difficult to handle" or "Sometimes the organization is very cutthroat," reply in a positive but honest manner. They may be just testing you.

Now it's your turn to answer. Make sure to touch on the suggestions mentioned in the last paragraph.

Answer:

_____

_____

_____

_____

_____

15. How do you feel about having a boss that is younger than you?

Many times an interviewer will ask you about having a boss who is younger than you are. Cite the fact that you get along well with younger and older co-workers, subordinates, and supervisors and cite specific references to support that statement. Tell the interviewer that you are not a person who discriminates and that you have had pleasant relationships with both younger and older co-workers in the past.

Now it's your turn to answer. Make sure to touch on the suggestions mentioned in the last paragraph.

Answer:

_____

_____

_____

16. What kind of people irritate you or do you not like to work with?

Answer this question by citing that you do not tolerate irresponsible people, that you take your career seriously and prefer people with clear focus. Be very firm with this answer.

Now it's your turn to answer. Make sure to touch on the suggestions mentioned in the last paragraph.

Answer:

_____

_____

_____

_____

17. Why have you changed jobs so frequently?

If your resume indicates that you're a "job-hopper," it's important that you tailor your resume to exclude unrelated positions to help you appear more stable. One of the major reasons why applicants are rejected is because interviewers fear that the person is unfocused. Share why you are passionate about this field. The interviewer will appreciate your honesty and candor.

Now it's your turn to answer. Make sure to touch on the suggestions mentioned in the last paragraph.

Answer:

_____

_____

_____

_____

18. Why have you been out of work so long?

Take the offensive and address this concern before it becomes a negative issue. If you have gone back to school, raised a family, or you took the time to change your career path completely and needed a training course or apprenticeship program, these are acceptable answers. If you have no acceptable answer or went through a tough time in your life, try this: 'Well, quite frankly, I used this time period to really sit down and reexamine my personal goals and lifelong objectives. I have reached the conclusion that this particular job function and your particular company fit my goals and objectives for these reasons," and then list those reasons.

Now it's your turn to answer. Make sure to touch on the suggestions mentioned in the last paragraph.

Answer:

_____

_____

_____

19. Do you have plans to continue your education?

Many employers, especially large corporate employers, have education or tuition reimbursement programs. If you decide to go on for additional training and it relates to the job at hand, the employer may pay for a percentage of your tuition. A common concern is: "Will that help me or will they feel that if I go back for more education it will distract me from my performance during the working hours?" The rule here is to do your homework and find out if it's a prerequisite to having the job. If you're already continuing your education, be honest and tell the employer that you don't feel that your class time will be a detriment to your job. Restate that you are a person who is organized and disciplined and your schooling definitely will not detract from your performance on the job. If you are taking continued education, stress to the employer or interviewer that this knowledge will help you because it will make you a more valuable asset to their organization.

Now it's your turn to answer. Make sure to touch on the suggestions mentioned in the last paragraph.

Answer:

_____

_____

_____

_____

_____

_____

_____

_____

_____

_____

20. Is it difficult for you to tolerate or put up with other co-workers or individuals who have different interests, goals or are less ambitious than you are?

This question is a perfect opportunity for you to display the all-important flexibility and versatility that employers seek. Cite a specific word story or situation, which has demonstrated your diversity and ability to tolerate different interests. Interviewers recognize that you might not get along well with everybody in the organization. And that's okay as long as you can continue to do the job effectively. Consequently, you want to demonstrate an ability to persuade and influence others.

Now it's your turn to answer. Make sure to touch on the suggestions mentioned in the last paragraph.

Answer:

_____

_____

_____

_____

_____

_____

_____

_____

_____

Do you have any questions for me?

It is always regarded as professional to pull out a well-prepared sheet of three to four specific questions that were not covered during the course of your interview. Questions can help you and are an essential element of job-hunting etiquette. Regardless of how positively or negatively the interview itself may have gone, don't appear too lazy by not asking questions. The questions you ask will also demonstrate how intelligent you are. In fact, many hiring authorities believe it's not your answers that are important but the questions you ask that will really demonstrate how capable you are of doing the job. Intelligent questions convey to the interviewer preparation, seriousness of purpose, and a real sense of knowledge of the position.

Don't be afraid to ask about the incumbent, why the position is open, the training, how the career path will be changing in the future, new product lines or changes to the industry. Don't be afraid to ask the interviewer about their passion or how they got started within the company. In fact, if it's difficult to break the ice at the beginning of an interview, I counsel my clients to ask the person across from them, "Tell me, how did *you* get started with this organization? What's your background? What do you like most about the company?" Remember, the interview is a conversation, not an interrogation.

Now it's your turn to answer. Make sure to touch on the suggestions mentioned in the last paragraph.

Answer:

_____

_____

_____

_____

Many candidates report that when using my techniques, interviews sometimes ask, "Hey, who's conducting the interview here, me or you?" When that happens, I know you're on the offensive and showing passion for the role. At the end of the interview feel free to pull out your notes, sit back and fire away with your questions that clarify any open issues.

The Ten Best Questions to *Ask* Any Interviewer

1. How are employees evaluated and promoted?

2. Will I be able to see my specific work location?

3. How did you get started with this organization?

4. Can you describe your training program?

5. How did the opportunity become available?

6. What separates top performers from average employees?

7. What are the most important attributes that you look for when hiring?

8. What is the potential for advancement?

9. When will you be making a decision on this position?

10. How do we proceed from here or is there anything we have discussed that would prohibit you from hiring me?

Section 17:

ON THE JOB SUCCESS

LESSON OBJECTIVES

1. Understand the process of career calling.

2. Identify how to take initiative on the job.

3. Describe the qualities of a leader.

TAKING CONTROL OF YOUR FUTURE

Dictate the Game!

One of the essential points I would like to leave with you is the importance of taking control of your professional activities. Be proactive. Create; don't simply respond. Hopefully, I have provided you with a glimpse into my own life and what has worked for my family and the thousands of clients served through these principles.

Football is the most popular sport in America today. One of the sports innovators, Bill Walsh, best known as former coach of the multiple world champion San Francisco 49ers, actually scripted the first 20–25 plays of every game on his clip board. He was the first professional coach to do this. It was his philosophy and proactive mentality that instead of reacting to the game events, he would seize control of the contest by dictating what went on during the game. Today, every team in the National Football League scripts their plays in an attempt to control the events on the field.

The message:

Script your life and don't be dictated to when it comes to your career activities! Do not be directed by the economy or by industries in demand; instead, focus on exactly what you want and it will come to you. What is important is not that you have finished this book, but that you will actually apply what you have learned to pursue your God given greatness.

You now have a blueprint for exploring and finding your unique and compelling career calling. With these newfound principles and techniques, the change from working for a living to contributing to your calling, can be swift and powerful. Reading the words is important but taking action is the key! Recall one of my favorite Chinese proverbs:

I hear and I forget.
I see and I remember.
I do and I understand.

Please reflect carefully on the following five questions:

1. Will you have found your unique and compelling contribution or will you simply fade into mediocrity?

2. Will you have given more than you have received in your one shot at life?

3. What individuals or organizations will benefit from your professional talents?

4. Will you become a mentor; what person or entrepreneur can benefit from your expertise?

5. What will be your legacy and how do you want to be remembered?

"My purpose is to inspire and empower others to find their career calling and achieve a life filled with balance and happiness. I assist others to fulfill their dreams through my speeches, workshops, radio and television appearances, and practical personal growth books. I believe we are all born to do something extraordinary; my life's work is to make certain this occurs for every person or organization with whom I interface." –Chris Kuselias

top and take the time to write yours!

our career and everything you do should be an expression of your purpose. do not wish for you to end up like many, wandering generalities unsure of heir purpose or passion and working in a job without a clue as to why they are oing it. Be mindful of the "Is this all there is?" syndrome. As you have learned, is important, almost essential to have felt a yearning or a void, a sense of mptiness that will motivate you to pursue your rightful place in the world, a lace where you can exhibit your unique and compelling gifts and ontributions. Without a strong enough motivation, often we are complacent nd miss an opportunity for greatness.

our objective is not to accumulate "stuff" to validate your success. If you ant a possession, make sure your motives are because you truly want it and ot because you feel it will validate your accomplishments to others. Trust me, host people don't really care. Gradually people come to the realization that ollecting material things is not fulfilling.

t some level we all hunger for greater purpose and meaning in our lives. Ve need to feel in our heart and souls that we matter, that we are making difference to others, that we are leaving the world a better place. It is an mpty feeling to merely take, to exist; there is so much more to life. Adopting a elief system that puts passion and purpose first provides an opportunity to spire others, by leaving your mark and contributions in a positive, nforgettable way. Be memorable, be unforgettable!

"If a man is called to be
a street sweeper,
he should sweep streets
even as Michelangelo painted,
or Beethoven composed music,
or Shakespeare wrote poetry.
He should sweep streets so well
that all the host of heaven and
earth will pause and say:
'here lived a great street
sweeper who did his
job well.'"

—Dr. Martin Luther King

Challenging Tasks

1) Write one positive event that has happened at work during the past week. This can be something involving co-workers, supervisors and/or customers or guests.

_____

_____

2) Write an example of when you had to be a good team member and work together to accomplish a goal or task?

_____

_____

What was the task? _____

_____

Who was involved? _____

_____

SIX REASONS PEOPLE FAIL IN THEIR QUEST

Pride in a job well done is a key ingredient to career success and happiness. Regardless of where you are in the cycles of obtaining career passion and purpose (finding your calling), you MUST always give your best to the job at hand. Here are six reasons why many people fail in their quest . . . beware!

1. *Negative attitude:* Be careful of your negative self-talk and self-defeating beliefs about your potentia You have learned to control your thought process and expect success!

2. *Lack of persistence*: You have been exposed to countless examples of individuals who have overcor hardship and obstacles to achieve their calling; simply commit to avoiding excuses and see roadblocks as adventures to be conquered.

3. *No enthusiasm:* Get excited! Regardless of economic indicators, there has never been a better time i history to pursue your individual career calling. There are innovations and inventions creating incredible opportunities for great careers where you can contribute and demonstrate your unique and compelling ski and abilities.

4. *Disorganized approach:* Start with the end in mind and direct all of your energies, resources, and contacts to that objective. You have learned the systematic process of getting in touch with your authentic self and mastering the 5P's . . .

5. *An inability to handle objections:* You have learned to anticipate challenging questions and how effectively answer them with conviction and specific examples. Nobody obtains their career calling withou overcoming obstacles; expect them and use them as an opportunity to learn!

6. Failure to seek help or ask for the position: You have learned to expect success and more importantly, to deserve it! It is your destiny; do not let a little discomfort or shyness prevent you from asking for what you truly want and deserve!

Passion-Purpose-Power-Profit-Peace of Mind!

"IF THE RATE OF CHANGE ON THE OUTSIDE EXCEEDS TH RATE OF CHANGE ON THE INSIDE, THE END IS NEAR."

- Jack Welch
  former chairman and CEO of General Electric

Commit to Lifelong Learning

Success in life and the attainment of your career calling require you to behave and act in accordance with your authentic self, that is, your *true identity*. You have learned that incredibly, you can alter and control your own internal identity, which is a mirror of your belief systems and associations to events that have occurred throughout your life.

Your true identity should be unique and compelling and through your career calling, you should aspire to contribute your gifts to others for the betterment of society.

Seek out quality mentors and strive to become a quality mentor for others. Be a person others seek out for guidance and wisdom regarding mastering this increasingly complex and confusing game called life.

Be unconventional; that is, do not follow the path of least resistance or follow the crowd but rather carve out your own niche, your own special place in society. Work hard to rid yourself of fear, uncertainty, and doubt that restrict your progress and erode your confidence and self-esteem. Tap into that inner reservoir of talent, creativity, and contribution to solve problems and challenges of others. Create new systems, inspire your peers, develop new solutions, and invent new products and services that enrich lives.

Every day is an opportunity to further your purpose and enhance your passion. Be mindful of the 5 P's (passion, purpose, power, profit, and peace of mind), which are essential to achieving true balance and happiness.

Here are my suggestions for lifelong learning and living the life of your dreams:

See the Bigger Picture:

In the scheme of time, we are all here for but a brief moment. That does not mean we cannot strive to become significant. Come to grips with your place on earth, in your community, in your family, in your employment and in your own heart. Avoid the limiting beliefs of others who have fallen prey to the trappings of materialism or other external reward systems. Serve a higher power, whatever that higher power is for you. Push your own boundaries and you will find that you have a gift for others to expand their own horizons as well.

Be Accountable for Every Action You Take:

We are all imperfect beings on a journey of self-knowledge and contribution. You will make mistakes and bad decisions; if you are not you are most likely playing it safe and not testing your full capabilities. Convert each defeat or failure into a learning experience that results in progress. Push yourself! As indicated, we are only using about 10% of our mental capacity. Strive to achieve larger accomplishments to impact more people through your thoughts, words, and actions.

Be a Mentor and Role Model:

By pursuing your career calling, you become an automatic role model to others who are stuck in a negative cycle or repeating destructive patterns or behavior. Share your newfound knowledge of the process and educate others and their families on what it takes to achieve true balance and happiness. Share the secrets of your success! Make certain that each and every day, your presence raises the expectations and performance of those with whom you interact. Adopt the philosophy that you are a "success celebrity," and that meeting you is a privilege. People want to study you, mirror your actions, and achieve similar results.

You are a person of influence; use this gift wisely!

Live with Integrity:

Be a class act under all circumstances and eliminate pettiness, jealousy or envy from your life. Set standards based on your own personal thermostat and not by artificial measures or others' beliefs. Every champion record holder knows that to attain a state of grace and excellence, one must create their own targets in order to further their calling. Raising my standards has been a catalyst for massive change and success in both my personal and professional life.

If you adopt these belief systems and live by these standards, you will find more people want to be with you, do business with you, interact with you and seek your friendship. We can all use more quality friends! Select your associates and friends carefully; as you grow personally you will often find that your interests and dialogue may require a change in your relationships.

"DON'T GIVE THEM WHAT THEY WANT; GIVE THEM WHAT THEY NEVER BELIEVED WAS POSSIBLE."

—Orson Welles

Checklist for the 21st Century Superstar

With all the changes brought about by the emerging global economy, increasing frequency of career changes and mandate to control and manage one's own career, here are my thoughts regarding what makes a superstar in this new era:

1. *Smart, educated and informed* (21st century superstars understand you can have more degrees than a thermometer, but if you do not remain informed on your industry, employer, department or product/solutions)

2. *Technologically proficient* (21st century superstars save time by investing in their knowledge of technology and the incredible value provided by the Internet)

3. *Articulate* (21st century superstars practice or join groups, for example, Toastmasters, to master the ability to speak in public, or at least to large groups)

4. *The ability to be decisive and not afraid to make decisions* (21st century superstars can be wrong more often than they are right, but they learn from each decision and keep swinging!)

5. *A willingness to take risks* (21st century superstars understand and live by the concept of no risk, no reward!)

6. *Act on conviction* (21st century superstars establish moral and ethical principles and stick to them!)

7. *Hard working and driven* (there is no end game or finish line, 21st century superstars understand that continuous improvement is the critical competency!)

8. *An abundance of physical, mental and emotional energy* (21st century superstars schedule time each and every day to feed their body, mind, and spirit with beneficial exercise, wisdom, and enlightenment!)

9. *A sincere and caring interest in people* (technologies become obsolete, machinery breaks, patents expire, but 21st century superstars understand that people will always be the common element to all business)

10. *The ability to anticipate the future* (21st century superstars always remain a step ahead!)

Defining Initiative

Definition of Initiative

According to Webster's Dictionary – **initiative is the action of taking the first step or move.**

What is your definition of initiative? _____

_____

_____

What actions can be taken on the job to show you are taking the initiative?

1. _____

_____

_____

2. _____

_____

_____

3. _____

_____

HOW TO DICTATE THE GAME: A CHECKLIST FOR THE 21ST CENTURY SUPERSTAR

In Studs Terkel's book, *Working,* a phone receptionist from Chicago was quoted as saying, "I don't know what I'd like to do. That's what hurts the most. That's why I can't quit the job. I really don't know what talents I may have and I don't know where to go to find out."

Maybe you shared these feelings prior to reading this book. But if you gave your sincere attention and commitment to the text and corresponding exercises, I am quite confident that this will no longer be the case. So, congratulations! You have achieved your goal to finish what you started. And as the saying goes, "You've come a long way, baby." You have been an active participant, are educated on the process, and should be commended for sticking with it. Quoting Thomas Jefferson,

"What we learn to do we learn by doing."

This book was designed to help you obtain your unique career calling. After reading it, you are now familiar with the tools and have "learned by doing" the strategies that will be helpful for the rest of your career. These techniques are time tested and produce results. They can work for you if you will make the decision to dedicate yourself and follow through. Armed with a competitive edge and useful tools, it is time to get busy!

One of my favorite sayings is, "It's what you do after you know it all that counts." You now know what to do, so go do it! Because each of us is truly a unique and compelling being, formulating a career path is a do-it-yourself activity and will take a great deal of effort to solidify each job as you move closer to your ultimate destination. How much effort you put into careering will have a direct correlation to how successful you are in finding your ideal role.

415

THE QUALITY OF A PERSON'S LIFE IS IN DIRECT PROPORTION TO THEIR COMMITMENT TO EXCELLENCE REGARDLESS OF THEIR CHOSEN FIELD OF ENDEAVOR.

- Vince Lombardi

The level of the role that you target is also going to have an effect on the amount of time you need to land that position. The more prestigious the position, the more time it's going to take you to find and secure it. It is easier to find an entry-level job simply because there are more of them and the skills required are less demanding. So persevere. The swift do not always win the race; sometimes the winners are those individuals who keep on running.

You have learned that it is advisable not to quit your current position until you have discovered one more suited to your talents. It is easier to get hired if you are employed than if you are unemployed. The perception on the part of some employers is that if you don't have a job, there may be something wrong with you. So try to conduct your search while you're still working and have a steady means of income. It will make things easier and put less financial pressure on you.

TEN CAREER SUCCESS RULES TO LIVE BY

1. Remember that finding your career calling is a full time job.

2. Aim high but have reasonable expectations about your time frame.

3. You must enjoy your career or you will ultimately stop doing it.

4. If you don't have a career goal, you will most likely wind up working for someone who does.

5. Avoid fear and procrastination by identifying a specific career goal and reducing large job search activities to smaller tasks.

6. Start with the end in mind and have no regrets.

7. Your choices and actions, not fate, will determine your career destiny.

8. It is easier to find a new career while still employed; never quit until you've found a new career.

9. Spare no expense in your career search campaign. Remember: *Good things don't come cheap and cheap things are rarely good.*

10. To find your career calling be the most prepared; qualifications and intelligence are often secondary to preparation and dedication.

Five Career Axioms to Live By

1. Career success equals knowledge, desire, commitment, and dedication.

2. You should target the decision maker who has the ability to hire you and demonstrate that you have problem solving talents that will help their organization achieve their goals.

3. Great careers may come to those who wait, but only those careers not wanted by those who hustle.

4. Career seekers: It isn't lonely at the top . . . it is crowded at the bottom!

5. The road to career success is always under construction; keep the faith!

On the Job Initiative

Examples of Taking Initiative On the Job:

1. Come to work a half hour early every day.
2. Be at work every day.
3. Volunteer to work overtime.
4. Volunteer to work in another department.
5. Learn something new at work every day
6. Learn a new skill that you have not used before.
7. Offer to attend an optional training program.
8. Be willing to train a new employee.
9. Clean your workspace, even if others are responsible for it being disorganized.
10. Help a co-worker who needs assistance.
11. Make a suggestion for improving a procedure.
12. Think ahead so you will always be prepared.
13. Clean your workspace every day before leaving work.
14. Offer to set up a new display.
15. Offer to cover someone's shift.
16. Offer a suggestion for improving the appearance of the company.
17. Find something constructive to do when it is not busy.
18. Make it a personal challenge to have customers smile before leaving.
19. Do a task that no one likes to do.
20. Take customer's suggestions to your supervisor so improvements can be made.
21. If you see trash on the floor pick it up.
22. Make an effort to pick up the phone by the third ring.
23. Make suggestions for improving productivity.
24. Volunteer to work on the weekend.

What else can you do to take initiative at work?

_____

_____

_____

_____

There is never a perfect time, nor are circumstances ever ideal to obtain your ideal career;

sometimes you just have to start! There will be costs to finding your calling, including: technology costs, telephone costs, postage, traveling costs, and wardrobe costs. Be frugal, but not cheap! If you appear cheap or cut corners, that will show when you go to meet your employer. Don't sacrifice or be anything less than 100% professional because taking time to spend money
now will pay big dividends in the future. If you spend an extra dollar here or there or are concerned about funds, think about the millions you'll earn over the course of your career.

For example, if you start at age 20 and retire at 60 (work for 40 years) and average, say, $50,000 a year, that's $2 million dollars earned over the course of your lifetime! With that perspective, a few dollars here or there shouldn't matter to you. If you're going to buy that one suit or dress for the interview, make it count. You deserve a professional resume. If you need to make a long distance telephone call to a mentor or buy lunch for an employer, do it!

With the tools that you now have at your disposal, I know that with effort you can find your ideal career. It will be challenging, but as a long-term thinker seeker, you know that good things take effort. Quoting again the great Vince Lombardi, "The difference between a successful person and others is not a lack of strength, not a lack of knowledge, but, rather, a lack of will."

By finishing this book, you should be congratulated on achieving that goal. You are ahead of 90% of all career seekers who talk the talk, but do not walk the walk. You have a competitive EDGE; now use it! Many people say that they found a great career after having completed less than half the book because a word, example or exercise created a breakthrough in their thought process.

It truly is the little things that make the difference. In today's 21st century workplace, people will be forced to change jobs and industries at a record pace, while many will start their own venture. That is why it is essential to take action and plan for the long term. This is a marathon, not a sprint!

And please don't put the book on the bottom shelf or give it away because there will most likely is another day in the future when you may need to refresh your memory on the enclosed strategies.

I strongly recommend that you periodically go back to the "hot buttons" and refresh your memory, even after you have found what today you consider your career calling. Tomorrow your priorities could change.

Remember: change is inevitable; progress is not!

Strive to continually educate yourself and be open to new ideas. Malcolm Forbes, at one time one of the world's richest men, said, "Education's purpose is to replace an empty mind with an open one."

Maybe you read this book because a decision to find a better career was made by you or, for many of the individuals who are unfortunate out there, it was made for you. So many of you have in your mind that this will never happen again or it could never possibly happen to you. I recommend that you remain ever alert and keep your options open. Maintain contacts with these friends and former employers through social events, letters or what have you. Give them a call once in a while just to keep in touch. Keep your credentials updated at all times.

Build your network and expand your connections. If you attended an educational institution, stay active in your alumni association. Keep track of the people that you meet through trade organizations or committees because you never know when you're going to need these people for support and guidance.

As I have told you, there are many different ways to adopt these tools and incorporate these concepts. Ultimately ten people can get ten different ideas from these concepts. But remember one thing. If your particular plan is not working, simply change your approach. Modify your actions. That is why I have included so many different variations of strategies, because what works for one career seeker might not be as successful for another.

You should now be motivated to establish a long-term career plan and seek to derive incredible passion and energy from your chosen occupation. I want you to thoroughly enjoy the process of self-discovery. Do not achieve to be happy; happily achieve your objectives! And be confident that you now have the tools to achieve those goals.

Your *Career DNA* is unique!

Go back and review those particular components of the program that were confusing or you felt you might need more help on and use them as reinforcement. Use these materials before going into an information interview or an actual interview setting to assist you and to help build your confidence. Commit yourself to constantly being a lifetime achiever. As I mentioned earlier, be a personal growth stock and not a career seeker whose assets are on the decline. Become "Me, Inc.!"

Be able to articulate your unique and compelling strengths and learn to create a desire for your talents. Make your strength your knowledge of yourself and your thorough preparation. If you have an audio player in your car, invest in positive messages and training programs rather than listening to music or news.

Remember the old saying, "You have two ears and one mouth. So listen twice as much as you talk." When starting a new career, be reserved. Take in the sights. Learn the employer's culture. See who the people in power are. Find out which people you can trust. Look for those people in a position of authority whom you'll have to impress. Once you find out who the key players are in the organization, learn what their particular objectives are and tailor your performance to coincide with their objectives. In other words, mirror the goals of the people who make up the power structure. And, more importantly, through your own methodology, let them know that you are mirroring their goals, either by memo form or just by your day-to-day performance.

Careering isn't always fair. Be aware that at certain times in your career you may truly be the best person for a job or for a promotion but, because of politics, friends, or relatives of the people who are above you or who are your management, that may result in your not getting the position. You're not always going to win against the boss's son or daughter or son-in-law. My advice is to focus on your needs; there are always options. Use social activities like company picnics, sports, dining out or parties, to get to know your peers on a non-professional level.

Your outlook is now bright and you should feel energized by your newfound knowledge and potential. You have the competitive edge! Your dreams will become reality. Quoting Eleanor Roosevelt, "The future belongs to those who believe in the beauty of their dreams."

As mentioned earlier, most people change occupations several times during their lives. Job changes usually occur more frequently when career seekers are young. Generally, men tend to remain in occupations longer than women, college graduates longer than people with less education, full-time workers longer than people who are part-time workers, and self-employed people longer than individuals who collect wages or a salary.

If you do decide to change careers, always leave a job on positive terms. You never know when you will need a good reference or recommendation. Leaving a job can be emotionally difficult. But, again, focus on the positive aspects of your new status.

Go to work with a smile on your face. And remember to be loyal to your employer. That doesn't mean loyal to the degree that you can never leave if things aren't working out your way or you're unhappy. But whether you are in a position 1 day, 2 days, 10 years, 20 years, be loyal to your employer. They deserve your best until you leave!

If you have an entrepreneurial drive, be smart and surround yourself with quality mentors. Starting a new business is difficult, but if you have a passion for your product or service, you have the essential ingredient already. If you decide that a franchise is where your career calling lies, do your homework and obtain testimonials from other franchise owners. At the risk of sounding sappy or like I am preaching, be sure to act polite and decent to every person who assists you, coaches you or inspires you.

In most cases, you can get what you want by using these four expressions:

1 word: "**Please**"
2 words: "**Thank-you**"
3 words: "**I love you**"
4 words: "**How may I help?**"

Rewards and Benefits

The rewards of taking initiative on the job include some of the following:

- Getting a raise is a clear indication that you are doing your work in an acceptable and timely manner.
- Receiving an incentive bonus for special efforts is another way that an employer can show appreciation for a "job well done".
- Receiving a special award for attendance or for making a suggestion to improve productivity.
- Getting a promotion and moving up in the company benefits both you and the company.
- Receiving more respect from co-workers and supervisors as well as more self-respect.
- Getting better assignments can give you the job tasks you enjoy doing.
- Acquiring better hours may help you handle child care and family responsibilities.
- Improving self-esteem and motivation to do an even better job.

What can you do to get noticed as a good worker? _____

_____

_____

_____

What is the next position you want? _____

_____

_____

_____

My Fears

Taking initiative requires a number of qualities. In order to take initiative you need to be willing to take a risk. The risk may be an emotional risk because a co-worker or supervisor may not like your suggestion. A suggestion for improving procedures, may require your co-workers to learn new ways of doing things. This may not be met with great enthusiasm because some people may not want to change.

Taking initiative is not always popular. Standing out in the crowd is not always comfortable. However, taking initiative is required if you are going to be a leader. Leaders who accept a challenge and are willing to take risks do not always please everyone.

Taking initiative may initially result in failure. For example, you are learning to operate a new machine or computer and you hit the wrong button and lose the work that you spent hours creating. You may feel like a failure but you need to remember your goals. Learn from your mistakes and try again.

*Why is it hard for you to take initiative?*_____

_____

_____

_____

_____

What can you do to overcome your fears about taking risks? _____

_____

_____

_____

_____

Who can help you? _____

_____

_____

_____

_____

What is your plan of action to start taking risks at work? _____

_____

_____

_____

If unclear on any aspect, I strongly urge you to review until you feel comfortable. Your career and life are that important. Do this until the career that you dream about becomes your daily reality. I am confident that you can find your career calling and, by doing so, will experience health, happiness and success in your life.

I will leave you with one of my favorite poems on the subject of contribution . . .

"For man must live his life on earth
Where hate and sin and wrong abound
Tis here the soul must prove its worth
Tis here the strength of it is found
And he has justified his birth
Who plants one rose on barren ground"
—Edgar Guest

Find your passion, achieve your purpose, yield your power, realize your profit and attain what we all seek . . .
peace of mind.

By following this *Career EDGE Program*, you will leave a positive legacy and know in your heart and soul that you mattered.

PLANNING FOR YOUR FUTURE

LEARNING OBJECTIVES

1. Establish a plan to create work – life balance.

2. Develop techniques to promote physical, mental, and spiritual well-being.

3. Review the steps to creating a sound budget.

4. Compare and contrast options for saving for retirement.

Some people "live to work" while others "work to live."

These seemingly similar phrases could not be more different! Living to work implies that you put work ahead of everything else including your family, friends, outside interests, and even your health and well-being. Working to live implies that you work enough to satisfy your basic needs, as well as achieve some of your personal or career goals.

As with most things in life, the perfect balance lies between the two extremes. If during your entire career you live to work, chances are you will not have the opportunity to establish meaningful relationships, take vacations, or explore other hobbies. While you might be financially successful, the toll on your physical, mental, and spiritual well-being can be significant.

The other extreme is people who work to live. These people

may have a zest for life and work only to pay the bills. They find meaning and self-worth outside of their career and do not have a desire to climb the corporate ladder unless required to maintain their desired lifestyle. While this attitude may lead to fulfillment outside of the workplace, it can also limit your promote ability and earnings potential.

Successfully planning for your future can help you to find the perfect balance between work and family. I can also enable you to have both a fulfilling career and a rewarding life.

It may seem strange that we are talking about subjects such as saving for retirement and remaining current in your field when you have not even graduated. As they say – failing to plan is planning to fail! Decisions you make now, and the mindset you establish from your first day on the job, will impact the enjoyment your life can bring. Let's begin by assessing your goals and attitudes about work-life balance so we can establish a plan that you can carry with you through your career.

WORK – LIFE BALANCE

The term "work-life balance" is a misnomer because it is never a perfect balance. The amount of time you will dedicate to either facet of your life will vary over time and throughout your career. That's how it should be. There is no perfect, one-size-fits all balance to try and achieve. Success for you will depend on your attitude, goals, and definition of success.

During your time in college, you determined the definition of your success. For some people, success is passing the course. For others, it is achieving an A. Some students define success as graduating, while others place more value on the experience and relationships they developed. The same is true when establishing a healthy work-life balance. You get to define a successful breakdown of where you spend your time and energy. The key is being deliberate about your choice. Deliberate means that you are making a conscious choice about how you will manage your time and the decisions you make. For one person, a deliberate work-life balance means being home several nights per week. For another, it's about having enough emotional energy to connect with both family and co-workers. If you ask 100 people what deliberate work-life balance looks like, you will undoubtedly get 100 different responses.

An article in the Harvard Business Review titled "Manage your Work, Manage your Life" chronicled research conducted by the Harvard School of Business. This research included interviews with over 4,000 executives and yielded interesting perspectives related to establishing work-life balance.

Not surprisingly, the definitions of professional success, personal success, and acceptable work-life balance varied by gender. Females place greater emphasis on individual achievement when defining professional success and men focus more on financial achievement. Even in this day and age, the research found that men identify with the role of breadwinner, while women see their contribution as leaving a positive impression on their children. There was one attitude that was common between men and women and that is the guilt associated with professional success when it interferes with their close relationships. Both genders defined personal success as *not* having regrets about "missing out" on time with their loved ones.

The first step in establishing a deliberate work-life balance is to assess your attitude about success, happiness, priorities, and your goals. Once you have done that, there are several tools to assist you in maximizing your effectiveness with both areas of your life.

Manage your Technology

One of the greatest interferences away from work is actually the technology that keeps you connected to work. Reading your emails over dinner or taking conference calls at your daughter's dance recital sabotages the quality time you have set aside for your family. One executive that was interviewed stated, "Always being plugged in can erode performance. Certain cognitive processes happen when you step away from the frenetic responding to e-mails." Another executive suggested that expecting 24/7 availability could actually inhibit productivity in an organization, "If you have weak people who must ask your advice all the time, you feel important. But there is a difference between being truly important and just not letting anyone around you do anything without you." [1]

Rather than going cold turkey, wean yourself off the reliance of your devices by setting certain timeframes when you will not access the technology. Set an out of office notice so that people understand that you will reconnect in a few hours. Communication is key to deliberate work-life balance.

Find Support

Another strategy for successfully executing your work-life plan is to enlist the help of others. If extra time is required at work to complete a big project, consider hiring a housekeeper or somebody to run errands for you. This way, your time at home is spent connecting with your family and not catching up on chores. Can't afford that? Consider setting up a co-op with friends and take turns assisting one another in accomplishing these tasks.

Finally, make sure you and your family have a shared vision. If your spouse is working extra hours to save for a house, the strain on family time might be understandable for a while. Losing precious time with family in order to buy a plasma TV may cause resentment.

Understanding your attitudes about work-life balance is the first step to establishing a healthy and happy life-after-college! The years after finishing school can be tumultuous. Finding a job, establishing yourself within a career, making major purchases, and starting a family are on the minds of many college graduates. It is easy to see why these activities could take a toll on you – mentally, physically, and spiritually. Remembering to nourish all three areas ensures that you will be at your best and ready to conquer the exciting times that lie ahead.

Self-Care = Self-Love

The World Health Organization states that health is "complete physical, mental and social well-being and not merely the absence of disease or infirmity."

Characteristics of good mental health include:

- Being content with your life
- Having fun and enjoying life
- Having the ability to handle stressful situations and overcome adversity
- Having a love for learning and flexibility
- Having the ability to create and manage healthy relationships with loved ones and friends
- Being self-confident and demonstrating a positive self image
- Having a deliberate work-life balance

MY WORK-LIFE BALANCE PLAN

Did you know there are 168 hours in a week? Consider your attitudes about work, your goals, and your family situation and then complete the chart below. You will have to use your math skills, so get your calculator out! When you are finished completing the chart, answer the questions that follow.

Activity	Total hours per week	Percentage of time per week
Work		
Sleep		
Meals		
Commuting		
Leisure		
Chores		
TOTAL	**168**	**100%**

Are you satisfied with the percentage of hours spent on work-related activities? Why or why not?

_____

_____

What changes would you make to have your ideal work-life balance?

_____

_____

List two changes you could make to get closer to your ideal work-life balance?

_____

_____

While the majority of Americans do not suffer from serious mental health issues such as bi-polar disease or schizophrenia, almost all of us have experienced depression or anxiety at one time during our lives. A person that is mentally healthy understands how to cope with the normal stressors of life and functions more effectively and astutely than individuals experiencing depression or anxiety. According to the American Psychological Association (APA), having resiliency, the ability to bounce back after a trauma or setbacks, is the key to good mental health. The good news about resiliency is that it is not a trait that you have to be born with; you can develop it over time.

The APA suggests these ways to increase your resiliency:

- **Accept that life involves change.** By acknowledging this, you can free yourself to focus on things that you can control and develop strategies to manage adversity that may arise.
- **Connect with people.** Invest time to foster relationships with people that are important in your life. Real connections require giving and time. Be comfortable asking and accepting help if you need it, and be comfortable saying no if you are asked to help but just don't have the capability to do so.
- **Make Decisions.** Making and sticking to a decision, even during stressful or adverse situations, will go a long way in building your self-confidence and comfort in trusting your decisions in the future.
- **Be goal oriented.** Good self-care includes making progress towards your goals. A goal without a plan is just a dream. Therefore, in addition to creating realistic goals, you must create the steps and timeline to ensure you achieve them. Track your progress and reward your achievements.
- **Talk nice to yourself.** Do not let negative thoughts about yourself creep in.
- **Be kind to yourself.** You will be more prepared to deal resiliently if you are physically and emotionally healthy. Physical exercise reduces stress and increasing mental well-being.
- **Take a realistic perspective.** When dealing with adversity, take a deep breath. Ask yourself, "will this problem that I am stressing about today impact my life next month or next year?"
- **Strengthen your resilience.** Improving your resilience requires reflection about situations you have overcome. Try journaling, or meditation.

Even resilient people will experience a depressed mood or anxiety from time to time. If left untreated, depression and anxiety can be debilitating and should be treated by a physician. However, there are many things you can do to bolster your mental health. The Anxiety and Depression Association of America recommends these activities to help chase away the blues.

Staying in control when you are in the midst of a situation that makes you anxious or stressed is not easy. It is easy to feel overwhelmed. Try these strategies:

- **Relax.** Do an activity that helps you to relax. Maybe that is yoga, listening to music, getting a massage, or practicing deep breathing techniques. Stepping back from the problem can help to clear your head.
- **Reduce the intake of alcohol, caffeine, and tobacco. These substances raise your blood pressure and can result in increased anxiety. Get enough rest.** A body under stress requires additional rest to stay healthy. Set a time to go to bed and stick to it. Strive to get at least 7-8 hours of sleep per night.
- **Stay active.** Exercise releases endorphins, which naturally fights stress. Physical fitness is good for both the mind and body.
- **Forgive yourself.** It is important to remember that you can only do your best. Use positive self-talk and reward yourself for making progress towards your goals. Keep your anxiety in check by asking yourself, "Is it really as bad as you think?"
- **Have a positive attitude.** Stress is often caused by feeling helpless or out of control. Try and keep a positive attitude. Find the good in a difficult situation by looking at it from another perspective.
- **Give back.** Giving your time to a worthy cause can reduce stress. Volunteer or participate in activities in your community. New relationships create a support network and relieve everyday stress.
- **Listen to your body.** Learn what triggers your stress and anxiety and find ways to mitigate it. Keep a journal and look for patterns of situations that cause your anxiety. If caring for family causes stress, see if you can enlist others to help so you can get a well-deserved break. If it is work-related, set boundaries with your co-workers. Knowing what triggers your anxiety will help you to control these emotions.
- **Find a release.** Sometimes the best way to deal with your stress and anxiety is to hare your feelings with somebody. Talk to friends and family about what you are dealing with. Let them know you're feeling overwhelmed, and accept any help they offer. If you can't get your anxiety under control, talk to a physician or therapist. Your feelings are normal and seeking professional help is a smart alternative to risking your health.

My Mental Health

Think about your feelings over the last two weeks and select the answer that is closest to your experience. Use this form to discuss any concerns you may have regarding your level of anxiety or depression.

	Not at all	Several days	More than half the days	Nearly every day
1. Little interest or pleasure in doing things				
2. Feeling down, depressed, or hopeless				
3. Trouble falling or staying asleep, or sleeping too much				
4. Feeling tired or having little energy				
5. Poor appetite or overeating				
6. Feeling bad about yourself—or that you are a failure or have let yourself or your family down				
7. Trouble concentrating on things such as reading the newspaper or watching television				
8. Moving or speaking so slowly that other people could have noticed? Or the opposite—being so fidgety or restless that you have been moving around a lot more than usual				
9. Thoughts that you would be better off dead or of hurting yourself in some way				

If you checked off any problems above, how difficult have they made it for you to do your work, take care of things at home, or get along with other people?

Not difficult at all ☐   Somewhat difficult ☐   Very difficult ☐   Extremely difficult ☐

ence
d on Patient Health Questionnaire-9 (PHQ-9) Developed by Drs. Robert L. Spitzer, Janet B.W. Williams, Kurt Kroenke, and colleagues, with an educational grant from Pfizer Inc. No permission
ed to reproduce, translate, display, or distribute.

When building a successful life after college, having good physical health is just as important as having good mental health. This is often a challenge during times of change. Starting a new career can sometimes mean packing on the pounds, eating lunch daily with co-workers or picking up fast food on the way home because you are too exhausted to cook. Your mental release from the stress at work could be zoning out on the coach in front of the TV. Sometimes when life gets crazy taking the easy way out is easy to do!

Physical health refers to the body's ability to function without excess fatigue. It means you have enough energy stored in the body to accomplish all your daily activities. Typically, physical fitness is associated with endurance, strength, coordination, flexibility, and agility. There are many benefits to being physically fit, including a lower risk of cardiovascular disease and cancer, having more energy, living longer, and having a more positive outlook. For most people, the first step to physical fitness is monitoring their caloric intake and increasing their exercise.

Unfortunately, the terms diet and exercise have negative connotations for many people. Just as you have learned new skills and developed new attitudes in college that will enable to succeed on the job, changing any negative attitudes about diet and exercise will help you live a longer, healthier life.

439

According to WebMD the secret to healthy eating is portion control. Half of your plate should be filled with fruits and vegetables. Whole grains and lean protein should take up the other half of the plate. Don't deprive yourself of eating the foods you enjoy, but eat them in smaller quantities. Select a way of eating that you can maintain for life. In addition to using portion control, consider using a calorie counting application. There are many free apps that enable you to keep track of the calories you take in. When losing weight you must take in fewer calories than you expend. Think lifestyle – not fads.

As with all things, you will be more successful if you have a plan. It's easy to buy everything you want at the grocery store if you don't have a list, and it's easy to overspend if you don't have a budget. Eating healthy requires planning! If you know you are going out for a dinner, eat lighter for the rest of the day. Pack your lunch and avoid calorie-packed coffee drinks. When you get to dinner, order half your entrée as takeout. This saves calories and you won't feel guilty about leaving food on your plate. It also saves money and time because you will have lunch for the next day.

At home, take time to prepare food that you can use for a quick snack. According to nutritionists, there is a direct correlation between the amount of time spent on meal prep and healthy eating habits. You are more likely to grab carrots and hummus if they are cut up as opposed to the chips and dips. If you are not getting the required amount of fruits and vegetables, try to sneak them in. Add fruit to your morning cereal or use frozen berries to make a smoothie. The great thing about eating at home is that you have more control of the ingredients you choose. Purchase whole wheat bread instead of white bread. The calories may be the same but the nutritional value of wheat bread is significantly higher. The same is true for whole grain pasta, which tastes the same, but is much healthier for you. When purchasing salad dressing, look for a dressing that contains oil rich in alpha-linoleic acid (ALA). One study found that people who consume a minimum of 1g of ALA per day had half the number of fatal heart attacks. [1]

MY PLATE

Keeping in mind the healthy guidelines that we just discussed, fill each plate with the correct proportion of food. Use each food only once. Once you've done this, think about the last meal you ate, did your plate look like one of those below? If not, take small steps to rethink your meals. Even adding a few vegetables to each meal can make a big difference!

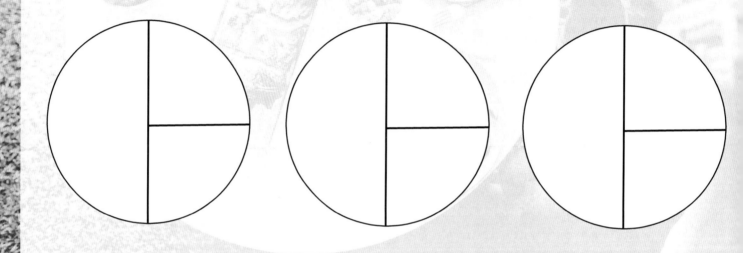

FOOD SELECTIONS

Protein	Grains	Fruits & Vegetables
Chicken	Hamburger bun	Salad
Shrimp	Spaghetti	Peas and Carrots
Hamburger Patty	Rice	Watermelon slices
		Oranges
		Broccoli
		Bananas

In addition to adopting healthy eating habits, exercising is essential for physical health. The most common reason for not exercising is lack of time. As a college student, you planned your day to ensure that you had time to study, work, and attend classes. As a graduate, you must still make important decisions about your time. A healthy work-life balance includes exercise.

EXERCISE

When beginning an exercise regimen, it is important to ditch the all-or-nothing attitude. Too often people overdo the exercise, which results in injury or burnout. You don't have to go to the gym seven days per week for hours on end to make a healthy change. A small amount of exercise is better than nothing. Try to park as far as possible from your office or at the mall. Bring your sneakers to work and take a short walk during your lunch hour.

Adding small amounts of physical activity to your weekly routine can have a tremendous impact on your overall well-being. Get creative! Choose activities that you enjoy and will want to do regularly. Even video games like Wii and Kinect are fun ways to start moving. They can also provide some quality time with the family. There are also smartphone apps that can keep your workouts fun and interesting. Collecting characters in Pokémon Go or running from zombies are fun and get your heart rate climbing! Each activity session should last for at least 10 minutes to get the maximum health benefits. You should strive for a minimum of 2.5 hours per week of aerobic exercise.

Aerobic exercise elevates the heart rate. Adding these types of activities is essential to losing weigh. Playing ball with the kids for 15-minutes, walking the dog, or taking the stairs at work several times per week, will help you quickly reach your weekly goal. In addition to aerobic exercise, add activities that strengthen your muscles and bones at least twice per week. Examples of muscle-strengthening activities include lifting weights, heavy yard work, or strength training at the gym. Examples of bone-strengthening activities include running, walking, and weight lifting.

Research shows that people that exercise with a friend or a team are more likely to stick to their exercise plan. Set goals and be accountable to one another. Schedule exercise when you are most likely to complete it. If you are not a morning person, scheduling 6:00am runs will most likely not last very long. For those who enjoy exercising with others but dislike competition, consider joining a mall walking club or joining group classes at the YMCA. Some people feel that a bit of competition keeps them motivated to workout. Find a golf league or join a co-ed softball team. The key is to set yourself up for success. You can always be ready to participate by keeping change of clothes and a pair of walking shoes in the car and at the office so you can respond when motivation calls!

Exercising does not need to be exhaustive to be effective. As we have learned, exercising in several 10-minute blocks per week is all that is needed. By the same token, eating healthy doesn't mean sacrificing the foods you love, just modifying the portions. Incorporating those small diet and exercise changes will go a long way to improving your physical health.

Below are some additional strategies you can easily incorporate into your daily routine that will pay big dividends when it comes to physical well-being.

Get enough rest. This is easier said than done for the recent graduate! Studies show that getting at least 6-8 hours of sleep can add up to 11 years on to your life.

Give your body a boost. Start taking a daily multivitamin. Vitamins come in gummy forms and powders that you can incorporate into other foods. Women should add a calcium supplement. Vitamin C & zinc support your immune system.

Stay hydrated. Drink at least 8 glasses of water per day. Water keeps you feeling full and aids in your digestion. Drink one full glass of water before each meal. In addition, don't wait until you feel thirsty, because at that point, your body is already feeling dehydrated. For people that don't like the taste of water, there are flavored spritzers that you can add to make it more palatable.

Make time for downtime. Mental and physical rest is essential to living healthy. Make time for some breathing exercises, meditation, or yoga everyday.

The third domain of personal well-being is spiritual health. Spiritual health should not be confused with religion. While we often associate organized religion and prayer with spiritual health, there are many other expressions to consider. Spiritual health is a universal concept, such as hope, purpose, and peace. Many people that consider themselves spiritual do not associate with one religious denomination or another. Some people prefer to call this domain "social health." Regardless of what you label it, identifying with or participating in something greater than yourself, characterizes this domain. For some people this means belonging to a church, praying, and living by the Ten Commandments. For others it means contributing to society, helping others with joy in your heart, or giving without expecting anything in return.

More and more research is pointing to the reality that participating in spiritual practices results in better health and well-being. Spiritual activities include many things such as prayer, meditation, and yoga. Information published by the University of Minnesota Center for Spirituality and healing found that prayer elicits the relaxation response, along with feelings of hope, gratitude, and compassion—which all have a tremendous impact on overall health. According to their research, prayer is rooted in the belief that a higher power exerts some level of influence in your life. Knowing this provides a sense of comfort and solace during rough times. Recent research determined that clinically depressed patients who believed their prayers were heard by a higher power, showed more progress in their treatment than patients who did not.

Similar to prayer, meditation can bring feelings of calm and peacefulness while increasing concentration. Brain researcher, Richard Davidson's research shows that meditation actually improves the brain's gray matter density. This can decrease sensitivity to pain, improve your immune system, and support you in managing difficult emotions, and reduce stress.

While meditation is becoming more common for individuals as a form of preventative care, it has proven helpful for people with both mental and physical illness such as depression, anxiety, various forms of cancer, fibromyalgia, chronic pain, rheumatoid arthritis, type two diabetes, chronic fatigue syndrome, and cardiovascular disease. Yoga, which practices meditation in many forms, has been found to provide similar health benefits.

In addition to the benefits of solitary activities like prayer and meditation, spiritual health is nourished by being with other spiritual people. Faith communities help people overcome tragedies. They provide a foundation and a support system. The ritual nature of many religions can be familiar and comforting.

Spiritual health usually gets the least attention by recent college graduates. You know how to make lifestyle changes to improve your physical health, but addressing your spiritual well-being feels much less tangible.

Try some of the following strategies to enhance your spiritual growth:

- **Quiet time.** When you are facing a big decision or are in the midst of big challenge, aha moments often come when you create stillness in your mind. By allowing the clutter of day-to-day life to take the backburner for a minute, you will be able to "listen" for clarity and direction; but you must create a moment of stillness to allow this to happen. Keep an open mind. Clarity comes when you least expect it. Try not to brush off or judge in these moments. If an idea pops into your head, especially more than once, listen up!
- **Accept painful situations and opportunities for breakthrough.** Sometimes contrast, or pain, is the best way to help us illuminate opportunities for breakthrough. Allow yourself to feel your pain fully, and then ask, "What is the lesson in this?"
- **Have fun!** Everyone has different outlets to recharge their batteries. Make time to play sports, do yoga, dance, sing, or anything else that fuels your soul.

Avoiding Burnout at Work

It seems silly to be talking about avoiding burnout at work before you may have even graduated! To the contrary, many techniques used to avoid burnout at work are the same as those used to keep you motivated to finish your college education. After all, this chapter is about planning. Learning to identify the warning signs of burnout now, and developing the strategies to avoid it, will help you refrain from getting into that vicious cycle to begin with.

So what is burnout? Herbert Freudenberger defines it as, "A state of fatigue or frustration brought about by devotion to a cause, way of like, or relationship that failed to produce the expected result." Although fatigue can be alleviated by rest, disillusionment is at the heart of burnout, and that is much more difficult to overcome. [2]

Specific symptoms of burnout include:

- Intense desire to avoid going to work or thinking about ways to leave early.
- Sleeping difficulties or insomnia.
- Finding excuses to be absent or late to work.
- Feeling lonely or misunderstood.
- Having increased physical ailments.
- Having negative perceptions about your contributions at work.
- Avoiding co-workers or customers.
- Being a poor colleague, by not completing your share of the work or blaming others for your shortcomings.
- Being preoccupied by looking for another job. [3]

Exactly what drives people to reach a burnout stage will vary. As we learned earlier, resiliency can counteract or delay these feelings. Even though some people will become burned out sooner than others, it is the same type of activities or situations that contribute to burn out. Common attributes include a lack of autonomy over your work or the feeling that you never have the time or resources to complete your tasks and projects to your standards. Sometimes the reason is that your ethics are not in line with the goals, actions, behaviors, or values of your organization, or of your role. Employees that do monotonous or low-stimulating work or who work on a dysfunctional team, report higher levels of burnout.

Many people do not understand that the consequences of burnout can be severe. It takes a toll on personal and professional relationships. Productivity suffers, creativity lags, and motivation can be non-existent during a burnout situation. Energy is spent finding excuses to miss work or take days off sick, rather than getting the job done. As previously mentioned, professional burnout can affect your personal life, negatively impacting your well-being and the relationships with your friends and family.

You can start planning now to avoid burnout in the future by identifying the types of positions you will be seeking after you graduate and the responsibilities you will have. If you abhor the idea of working behind a desk, start looking at opportunities where you can use your education in other ways. Get creative. For example, rather than working in an office, consider positions like insurance adjuster, park ranger, or direct sales, where your role would allow you to be mobile.

Other ideas to avoid burnout include the following:

- **Work with Purpose.** Find a way to give your job another purpose beyond the money. Not everybody can work for a non-profit organization that directly provides charity. However, if you work in the medical profession, you could suggest a day where you provide services to the disadvantaged for little or no money. If you work in the food industry, you could find ways to donate food that would otherwise be discarded. You can find a higher purpose in any job, and this can help you avoid burnout!

- **Lend a helping hand.** Similar to finding purpose at work, helping others, either on or off the job, helps keep burn out at bay. "Paying it forward" is a concept that encourages people to do a small act of kindness as a sign of appreciation for a kindness once done for them. It brings true joy – and joyful activity is not conducive to burnout.

- **Take Charge.** Burn out is often the result of not feeling challenged or in control of your destiny at work. You can overcome burnout by finding ways to create more autonomy in your role. Ask your boss for "stretch activities," which are activities just currently beyond your current scope of responsibility.

- **Get creative.** Burnout interferes with your ability to perform well and reduces your ability to think creatively. Find other ways to express your creativity, even if this creativity is outside of work. It will still help stave off the effect of burnout.

- **Get enough exercise.** We have already discussed the benefits of regular exercise. In addition to relieving stress, exercise can ward off signs of burnout by keeping you physically and mentally fit. Regular exercise also helps you sleep better, which is important for physical and mental health.

- **Manage Stress.** Stress exacerbates the intensity and frequency of burnout. Therefore, it is important to manage stress effectively. There are several strategies that we have already discussed to manage stress. Some other ideas include engaging in activities with others, writing down your feelings, exercising, and practicing positive self-talk.

Financial Health

Living a rewarding, healthy, and satisfying life is much more likely to become a reality if you also pay attention to your financial health. Financial stress can negatively impact your physical health. It can change your appetite and your sleep patterns, even prevent you from seeing a doctor. Recent graduates, who may not have a job and who may have student loans, are especially prone to financial stress.

Financial stress impacts people at all income levels. A 2014 survey from Financial Finesse Inc. found that just 11 percent of men and 7 percent of women earning less than $60,000 felt completely free of financial stress. But higher earners felt similar pressure, with 68 percent of men and women earning more than $100,000 admitting to "some financial stress" and 11 percent of men and 14 percent of women at this level reporting high financial stress levels.

The best way to avoid financial stress is not to live beyond your means. As a college graduate, you may be tempted to celebrate your accomplishment by purchasing a car or making a large purchase on your credit card. This is never a good idea. The enjoyment of "things" that you purchase on credit will be short-lived and lead to long-term financial instability. Instead, evaluate your financial health and then develop a plan for the future.

- **Evaluate your financial condition.** Determine what spending habits resulted in your current situation. Do not dwell on past mistakes; rather learn from your previous behaviors so that you can make more responsible choices in the future.

- **Honestly evaluate your relationship with money.** Buying things could satisfy your need for control, comfort, power, love, security or something else. Do you buy gifts as a way to garner love from your children? Perhaps you purchase items to fill a void in your life. Knowing the root causes of your spending and what triggers you to get off budget is the first step to having a healthy financial relationship.

- **Seek Guidance.** There is plenty of free help available online and in-person for people that want to learn how to set up and follow a budget. Many churches, community resource centers, and financial institutions have seminars or one-on-one sessions available. Don't be embarrassed if you don't know how to create a budget. The sooner you learn, the better off you will be!

- **Follow a budget.** Once you learn to make a budget, the next step is to follow it. Using a budget can feel both constraining and empowering. Think about budgeting as if it were a game. To win the game each month, you must come in within the budget. Reward yourself (within budget, of course), for a job well done)![4]

Creating a personal budget is as easy as determining your income and expenses, and then comparing the two. Even if you don't yet have a job or you are living with family members, understanding the process for creating a responsible budget will serve you well. There are several resources to help you make an educated guess at what your expenses will be.

- **Rent.** Look up current apartment listings on Zillow or Craigslist to determine the rent on studio or one-bedroom apartments or visit roommate sites to determine if that is an option in the area where your first job will be located.

- **Utilities.** Sites like Zillow or realtor.com include average utilities in various neighborhoods. The utility company websites also provide averages by month or by season, depending on the size of the dwelling and number of inhabitants.

- **Food.** The USDA website provides information about the average amount people spend on groceries weekly or monthly based on age and gender.

- **Transportation.** Look up the monthly cost of a transit pass in the town you plan on moving to. If you already own a car, you probably know your monthly repair and fuel costs. Be sure to factor in your own car insurance policy if you have been on your parent's policy.

- **Student Loans.** Talk to your financial aid officer or lending institution to find out what the monthly payment on your loan is going to be.   If the required payment seems high, and you have federal loans, look at enrolling in a different payment plan, such as the Pay as You Earn Plan or the Income-Based Repayment Plan. If you are unable to get a job within six months of graduation, putting your loans on deferment or asking for forbearance are options to remain in good standing.

- **Health Insurance.** Due to recent changes with the Affordable Care Act, you are eligible to remain on your parents' health insurance plan until you're 26, as long as they let you! If remaining on your parents plan is not an option, you can review plans on HealthCare.gov marketplace to determine what you might need to pay each month.

- **Savings.** It's hard to think about saving money when nothing is coming in! However, as a placeholder in your budget, set aside 10% of your anticipated income for emergencies as well as retirement savings.

- **Miscellaneous.** The miscellaneous category is the most difficult to budget for, since many of the items in it are discretionary. Discretionary means that they are more "wants" than "needs." If necessary, these are the first expenses to cut to make ends meet.

- **Anticipate your entry-level salary.** The Bureau of Labor Statistics provides information on median and average salaries for almost any occupation in the U.S. Sites like O*net, Careeronestop, and BLS.gov have plenty of data for the location where you want to work. When looking at income data, start by assuming you will earn on the low side. If you're a new college graduate without much field experience, you should expect to be at the bottom when it comes to earnings.

As a soon-to-be college graduate, it is easy to get carried away. Face it – you have been skimping for the last several years and putting your life on hold for the promise of a good career. It's easy to get carried away once you graduate and reward yourself with things you can't afford with the knowledge that "someday" you will have the resources to pay it off. Living off credit is a dangerous practice that you don't want to start. That's why getting used to living on a budget and spending less than you earn right out of college is so important! As your income increases, you can put that extra money towards paying off your debts, rather than increasing your spending in other areas. Making good financial decisions today will result in a less stressful, more rewarding, life.

A Budget Case Scenario

Paul and Kate are recently married. Paul's net pay per month is $2,000. Kate works part-time and has a net income of $800 per month. Kate also receives $200 per month from a trust fund set up by her family. The payments will end when Kate turns 30, which is in 3 years. Paul and Kate are eager to buy their first house and have been evaluating their financial situation. They have managed to save $6,000 but neither has begun saving for retirement. Their monthly bills are as follows:

$750	Rent	$180	Health Insurance
$120	Utilities	$500	Childcare
$80	Car Insurance	$120	Gas and automobile maintenance
$240	Food	$200	Student Loans
$65	Cell phone	$160	Credit cards
$40	Cable		

Using the income and expense information provided, populate the budget worksheet. Be sure to save at least 10% for savings. When finished, answer the questions that follow.

Income Source	Total
Income Grand Total	
Expense Source	**Total**
Expenses Grand Total	
Income Grand Total – Expenses Grand Total	

1. Based on the financial budget, should Paul and Kate buy the new house? Why or why not?

_____

_____

2. Looking at the expenses, what changes could the couple make to improve their financial health?

_____

_____

Generally speaking, making good financial decisions will result in a more rewarding life because good credit affords you more options. In general, people need good credit or large savings to accomplish four major goals. Those most common include saving for retirement, having money to overcome an emergency, make a major purchase (such as a vacation, home, or new car), and to pay down debt. These goals will vary based on your age and where you are in life. Usually, for new college graduates, the priority should be on saving for an emergency, saving for retirement, and repaying debts. Saving for life's extravagances, such as a fun vacation or your home, can come later, after you are more financially secure.

There are several strategies for managing debt. One strategy requires that you focus on paying off the loans with the highest interest rates first, such as credit cards or installment loans. While you are doing that, be sure to make the minimum payments on any other debts so you don't get saddled with late fees or other penalties. Hopefully, by using this strategy, you will have some money left over to establish an emergency fund. Experts say that you should have approximately six months of earning in your fund that you can use for things such as a medical bill, car trouble, or in case you lose your job. Don't get discouraged if you can't build your emergency fund as fast as you like. Just keep making progress!

Even though retirement seems like a long way off, starting to contribute when you are young is essential to your overall financial health. Start by participating in an employer-sponsored plan or set up an individual retirement account (IRA). Contribute something every month. The $10 a month you save now will be worth $100 a month in a few short years.

As your situation changes and you get older, your priorities will change. Eventually, your student loans will be paid and your credit card debt will be under control. At that time, you will be ready to establish new goals, like increasing your retirement savings or purchasing a home. Using credit responsibility and making sound financial decisions now will ensure that you have the ability to make bigger financial purchases down the road.

SAVING FOR RETIREMENT

Those financial commercials that show the millennials sitting in their lush homes planning for their retirement seem so fake and out of touch. Most new college graduates are still in an apartment, trying to find a job or learning to fit into a new corporation. Retirement planning seems futile. However, taking time to think about what you want your retirement years to look like is an important step to transition from college to career. Below is some information to help you navigate the different financial planning and retirement terms and opportunities that may be available to you as a new employee.

Start Now

At some point in your academic career, you learned about calculating compound interest. Just in case you forgot, there are financial calculators online that can do the calculation for you! The most important concept for you to know is that saving for retirement as soon as you get your first job will yield huge gains. Let's look at this example.

Two employees begin work at the same company at the same time. Pat chooses to contribute $100 every month. He begins this deduction from his very first paycheck. He starts this saving at the age of 25 and he wants to retire at 65, thus giving him 40 years to contribute to his savings before retiring. For the sake of the example, Pat's contribution will remain the same, at $100 a month, for forty years. His colleague, Julie, decides not to begin setting aside money for her retirement when she first starts working. Unlike Pat, Julie waits until five years later to start saving. At age 30, She contributes the same amount, $100 each month, but now she only has 35 years instead of 40 to save her money. Lets see what difference those five years will make when they retire.

At 65, Pat will have just over $310,000 while Julie will have only $206,000. Due to the impact of interest on the money they are saving, the five-year's difference, cost Julie over $100,000 in her retirement. Wow!

Employer Sponsored Retirement Programs

Offering an employer sponsored retirement program is a benefit that companies use to attract and retain good talent – like you! Keep in mind that not all plans are created equal. Find out if your company offers a matching program. If they do, this means that for every dollar you invest in retirement, your company will match up to a certain percentage. For example, many companies will match 100% of your contribution up to 3% of your salary. So if your salary is $50,000, and you invest $5,000 a year into your retirement plan, the company will match an additional 3%, or $1,500. This is essentially "free money," so it makes perfect sense to take advantage of it.

By far, the most popular employer sponsored retirement program is the 401K. A 401k plan is tax-deferred, so it comes with great tax benefits. The amount you choose to contribute is deducted from your paycheck pre-tax, which reduces your taxable income. This not only reduces the tax taken out of every paycheck, but also reduces your taxable income at the end of the year.

Money you contribute to your 401k will be invested in investment engines, such as stocks, bonds, mutual funds, and money market accounts. This is called your "portfolio." Your employer will have you meet with their advisor to determine if you want a high-risk, medium-risk or low risk portfolio. Typically, younger employees choose higher risk portfolios since they have a long time until retirement, whereas older workers are more conservative. Your financial representative will help you select a risk level that is appropriate for you. [4]

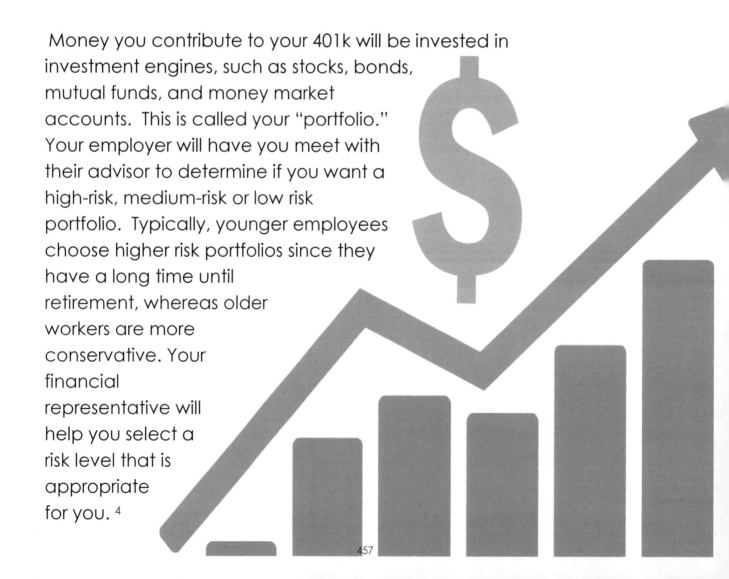

Another employer sponsored retirement option is called a pension. Pensions are expensive for companies to administer and are not as prevalent as they once were. Essentially, a pension is a plan where only the employer contributes on your behalf. Generally, these plans require that you worked for a minimum number of years in order to receive the complete package. For example, a postal worker may be required to work for twenty years. After twenty years of service, the employee will receive 75% of their salary each year until death.

Freelance Retirement Plans

Freelance plans are retirement plans available to any individual. A popular plan is called a Roth IRA, where IRA stands for Individual Retirement Account. Even if you have a 401k with a company, you can still open a Roth IRA. Unlike a 401K you pay into your Roth IRA with after-tax dollars. You can begin collecting this money beginning at age 59 and a half.

Another freelance plan is a deductible IRA. When you contribute to a deductible IRA, you use after-tax dollars just like the Roth IRA. However, unlike the Roth IRA, you can deduct your contribution from your taxes each year. Additionally, your money is put away tax-deferred until you start to withdraw it at which time you'll pay income tax.

In between the company sponsored 401K and the traditional IRA is the simple IRA. The simple IRA is great for those who are self-employed business owners with a small number of employees because you can to choose how you contribute to the plan at the beginning of each year.

Contributions made to a simple IRA are made with pre-tax dollars. This gives you the tax advantage other IRAs do not. Once you begin withdrawing your money, you pay income tax. Until then; however, your money grows in the account, tax-deferred.

Social Security

If you have ever received a paycheck, you noticed that some of your money is deducted for social security. The premise behind social security is that the government collects the money from your paycheck every month and holds it in an account so that it will be available to you when you retire. It provides you "security" for your retirement.

Unfortunately, as you have probably heard in the news, social security is in danger. This is because people have a much longer life expectancy. When the Social Security Program was first started, most people didn't live to be 70 years old. Even twenty years ago, most people only lived for five to seven years after retirement, which means they were only drawing social security benefits for 5-7 years. Now, people are living into their eighties and even their nineties. This means the government is issuing social security checks for twenty or twenty-five years when the program was originally budgeted to sustain someone for only five to seven years past retirement.

Because of concerns surrounding the viability of social security, it is a better strategy not to count on any money from the government as part of your retirement planning. Even though it might be unfair to be contributing to a system to which you will get no benefit, it is better to put yourself in a position where you are not dependent on it.

RETIREMENT PLANNING

Read the following scenarios and describe which retirement solution or solutions would be the best and why.

Scenario	Retirement plan options
Alison works for a small bridal company. They only have 12 employees but the company wants to offer a retirement plan for its employees.	
George is a recent graduate who just secured his first job with Motorola. He is anxious to begin saving for retirement while he is young.	
Matt is a cosmetology graduate. He plans on opening his own salon but wants the security of saving for retirement.	
Samantha already has a 401K plan but wants to save more for retirement.	

Savings

Saving for a rainy day does not come easy to some people, especially for younger employees that live hand to mouth. They spend every cent of their paycheck and scramble to survive until the next one. Keep in mind that saving isn't just about retirement – it should be a habit that is an integral part of everyday living. Some banks have a program where you can round up every purchase made on your debit card and the extra change is put in your savings account. Some people put a coin jar in their kitchen. When it is filled up, it goes into saving. Savings doesn't need to be a lot, but start now before you create your lifestyle on your full paycheck! It will save you a headache when an unexpected expense comes up. Retirement plans are just another type of savings account. The difference is that the savings you accumulate outside of retirement can be used at your discretion.

CAREER ADVANCEMENT

So far in this chapter we have discussed strategies to establish work-life balance; stay physically, mentally, and spiritually healthy; and have addressed your financial health. As you prepare to graduate from college, you are no doubt on the top of your game. You have acquired solid knowledge and skills in your field of study and are ready to show an employer what you can do.

Keep in mind that next year, and the year after that, and the year after that, there will be new crops of bright-eyed graduates from your field eager to enter the job market. While being in a career and having seniority at a company is a good thing, if you do not stay current and relevant with changes in your area, you will find yourself being replaced by somebody with comparable skills and a desire for lifelong learning.

While professional development is mandatory in some professions, like doctors, nurses, and teachers, in other fields, like business or the service industries, it is optional. Even if your employer does not require you to complete continuing education units (CEU), the smart employee will always stay informed. Staying informed might mean going back to college to obtain a higher degree or enrolling in a single course to learn a new software program or other knowledge. Besides formal classes, it is always a good idea to fill your bench with resources that can help you progress professionally. Besides formal classes, intelligent employees can find creative ways to stay on top. [5]

- **Develop a network.** Smart employees understand that they need a network of professionals to help them navigate life after college. Find a mentor within your organization that can help you position yourself within the organization. Choose a mentor that is successful and who has the time to spend with you. SCORE is an organization made up of retired executives who mentor up and coming employees at no cost.

- **Find a financial advisor.** Not everyone is an expert in investment programs. A financial advisor can show you the pros and cons of different investment strategies. They can also share the tradeoffs of focusing on retirement savings versus paying off any debt rapidly.

- **Join a trade organization.** Almost every job imaginable has a trade association. Google your profession and investigate your options. Sign up for free newsletters and industry alerts.

- **Conferences.** Trade shows and conferences are great for learning about competitors, new products, and industry trends; and they can provide ample networking opportunities.

- **Online networks and blogs.** Online networking sites and blogs are not for personal journaling anymore. Many bloggers are highly respected in their fields and have relevant information to share. Connecting with professionals within your industry on Twitter and LinkedIn can also point you in the right direction.

- **Custom search engines.** Google Alerts service notifies you when certain words you've "tagged" are indexed by Google's search engine. For instance, if you're a nurse, you might want to get notified about news in your field such as changes in scope of practice, or legislation that impacts the medical field. You set up the frequency of your notifications and can have the information sent as links via e-mail or an RSS feed.

As an impending graduate, life is your oyster. You have your entire life in front of you and you are ready to take advantage of your education and begin a new life. Transitions in life bring with them anxiety, uncertainty, and fear. You are going from the security of your classroom into the unknown. But you are prepared! In this section, you learned how to take care of yourself and plan for your future. You learned about the importance of communicating your needs and preparing for the unexpected. You are ready to conquer the world!

Congratulations! You've completed the Career EDGE workbook. You now have the tools, strategies and tips to help you succeed in school and at work. You can take these lessons with you for the rest of your life. Things may change in your life and in the world around you but topics like studying, anxiety, cultures, career, and finances will always be a part of our everyday.

Let that be your EDGE!

1 http://www.webmd.com
2 Freudenberger, Herbert. Burn-Out: The High Cost of High Achievement. Mass Market Paperback, 1989.
3 https://www.mindtools.com
4 http://www.betterinvesting.org/
5 http://www.verticalresponse.com/